# This Medical Life

# This Medical Life

by

James Owen
Drife

First published in collected form in the UK 2020

*A catalogue record for this book is available from the British Library*

ISBN: 978-1-85457-0970
This Medical Life James Owen Drife

Published by:
Clinical Press Ltd.
Redland Green Farm, Redland, Bristol, BS6 7HF

# *Foreword*

"Medical journals are dull; I don't think that there is any doubt about that," wrote Richard Asher, the doyen of medical writers of his era, in the *British Medical Journal* (renamed the *BMJ* when Britishness became suspect) in 1958. Asher condemned the wrapping, presentation, typeface, dreadful titles, lack of colour, and capacity to make the interesting boring, but he most condemned the way that doctors' journals are filled with *"pudder"* and *"gobbledygook"* or what Michael O'Donnell, editor of the much-missed World Medicine, called *"decorated municipal gothic."* Asher complained that doctors *"clog their meaning with muddy words and pompous prolixity."*

What then can medical editors do to make their journals less dull? Asher, a physician, is longer on diagnosis than cure, but he does end by advising that *"medical articles should, like after-dinner speeches, finish before the audience's interest starts to wane."* His article, which I suggest is a little too long, was based on a talk, and was clearly intended to be funny. It is amusing in places, but oddly he doesn't mention in his article the lack of humour as one of the worst failings of medical journals. A few funny articles, especially if short as Asher advised, can do marvels to lift the appeal of medical journals, which are prone to pomposity and taking themselves and the world too seriously. What's more, humour can often address deadly serious subjects with more impact and insight than straight writing—as Juvenal, Shakespeare, and Swift have shown.

Editors of the *BMJ*, of whom I was one, thought that a few funny articles would make the journal more attractive, but where could we find a doctor who could write funny articles? It is much harder to write funny than straight pieces, and many attempts at being funny fall flat; and even if you can write a few funny articles it's an art that is hard to sustain.

Some of us knew Jim Drife. I was at medical school with him, and we sat together on the Medical Students Committee in Edinburgh, insisting in minutes that Lyndon Johnson get out of Vietnam and debating for hours whether we should pay for a football for the medical school team. Jim was senior and I was junior, but I remembered his wit, beard, bounce, and bowtie. I remembered as well that he sang comic songs with Walter Nimmo, another doctor. Jim, we thought, could be just what we needed to lift the *BMJ*, and so began his series of columns in 1988.

I've had a marvelous time reading my way through this collection of Jim's columns. I regularly laughed out loud, which is something I rarely do. Jim manages to sustain the humour across more than a 100 columns, a considerable achievement. It may seem fanciful, but his writing reminds me of P G Wodehouse: Jim has not only the humour of Wodehouse but also his gentleness, lightness of touch, readability, self-deprecation, and gallery of fearsome aunts (politicians and senior managers in Jim's case). Jim is more Bertie Wooster than Jeeves but also with a touch of Lord Emsworth.

Some of Jim's columns have stayed with me for decades, and it was a great pleasure to reread them. I have never been able to see the acronym *BMA* without thinking that it means not only *British Medical Association* but, as christened by Jim, the *British Misery Association.* Jim mimics perfectly the tone, mixed metaphors, and clichés of a BMA letter to all doctors:

*"The BMA is seriously concerned that some doctors (very few, I grant you) are happy in their work, and it is my urgent task to stamp this out....Much as I prefer hewing at the bread and butter of clinical work, it has fallen to me to fight your corner against Whitehall mandarins, Westminster apparatchiks, and Brussels bureaucrats... Next, a stern word to all you consultants. On the train the other day I overheard a consultant saying that life wasn't too bad. Admittedly he had drunk half a bottle of Chateau Intercity Cote de l'Est Privee but I did have to change my seat and reason with him. Careless talk costs salary increases....*

*The BMA has successfully demonised every Health Secretary since Bevan and rubbished all their initiatives, well intentioned or otherwise. Nevertheless, we cannot rest on our laurels. The moment we relax our vigilance, contentment may break out and spread like some foul contagion from practice to practice. This must not happen. We at the BMA are the leaders of Britain's GPs and your morale is in our hands. If it ever rises, it will be over our dead body."*

Jim in his satire makes a serious point also made much more ponderously by Enoch Powell, who was once minister of health—that the only way to get more money into an NHS funded through taxation is to complain to the government that everything is dreadful.

Humour can, of course, get you into trouble, and another column of Jim's I have remembered for decades was entitled "*Are breasts redundant organs?*" It was a column where the seriousness was dialed up and the humour down, although comedy is always there with Jim:

*"Sometimes when I'm lecturing I point out how easy it would be to abolish breast cancer. My suggestion tends to outrage the men in the audience and I have to reassure them that my proposition is philosophical, not practical. Women listeners, however, usually react more thoughtfully.*

*Breast cancer becomes more common with age and will eventually affect at least one in 17 women in Britain. Screening may improve survival rates but does not aim at abolishing the disease altogether. The way to eradicate breast cancer is to remove the breasts before the cancer develops...*

*The audience eyes me warily, no doubt feeling there is something weird about a man who talks about removing normal breasts. They may be right. Perhaps all this is a distorted grief reaction to the deaths, over the years, of relatives, friends, and colleagues, killed painfully by glands they didn't need."*

Jim advanced this idea years before the discovery of the BRCA genes, which mark an increased risk of breast cancer and have led some women—like actor Angelina Jolie—to have both breasts prophylactically removed. The column created a media storm and provided material for a later column, in which Jim described touring media outlets and how *"a tabloid carried my sinister picture – lip curled, eyes shifty"* and another paper *"made me 'Wally of the Week.'"*

And on the rare occasions that I've worn a bowtie I always think of Jim's observation that *"Bowtie wearers are never left alone with other men's wives."* What, I always wondered, did that say about Jim, a man famous for his bowties? The same column on how doctors should dress advised on the tricky subject of blood stains:

*"Next, a word about bloodstains. It is all too easy to overdo these. The aim is to show that you still carry out practical procedures, but*

*you don't want people to think that you are clumsy. Bloodstains should therefore not be seen on the body area, collar, or spectacles and should never be more than 2 mm in diameter. The cuff is the ideal place for most doctors, though for obstetricians the socks are a possible alternative."*

A true satirist, Drife mocks widely—not only the BMA but the Committee on Safety of Medicines, the General Medical Council, royal colleges, NHS managers, evidence based medicine (using *Animal Farm* as his model), conference organisers, public relations companies, and, of course, editors *("I don't mean grandees like ED, BMJ, who I imagine spends most of his time in full evening dress being chauffeured from embassy cocktail party to college power dinner")*, and journals.

He satirises the questionnaires used in newspapers and increasingly medical journals to try and brighten them up:

*"How do you relax? I swim with a friend who happens to be a dolphin* [that line makes me laugh every time]

*What is your greatest fear? Losing my humility.*

*What are you currently reading? Nietzsche's Die Geburt der Tragödie, Unzeitgemässe Betrachtungen and Menschliches, Allzumenschliches.*

*What is your greatest regret? Not learning German."*

Or the award schemes that are money-spinners for journals:

*"Hospital cyclist of the year—Because cycling is healthy, exponents feel empowered to walk around the hospital dressed like extras from Star Trek, glaring at people they suspect of being motorists. The prize will go to the cycle parked in the most outrageous place within the hospital grounds. (Last year's winner: inside the MRI scanner.)"*

And inevitably obituaries, which were the bane of my life as editor of the BMJ in that they were the only submissions we couldn't reject, were written in code (*"he was a bon viveur"* meaning he was a drunk, and *"he was a true Celt"* meaning he was a Scottish drunk), and whereas all doctors had faults while alive they became saints at the moment of death:

*"For the first two decades, Drife's career was that of a conventional medical academic. At 48, however, he published the first of his racy Euronovels under his anagrammatic pseudonym, Jason de Merwife. His style, aimed unashamedly at the translators, was described by one critic as "like a dubbed film without the pictures." With plots drawn from his*

*experience on the editorial board of the European Journal of Obstetrics and Gynecology, Drife pioneered the "shopping and refereeing" style of fiction now familiar on bahnhof bucherstanden throughout the continent."*

If only any of our obituaries had had such swagger.

Jim touches on many serious subjects in his columns—maternal mortality, teenage pregnancies, pill scares, poverty, sectarianism, inequalities, complaints, the agony of phoning hospitals, and the tax on sanitary towels—but all are done with a light touch and humour, which you might think impossible if you have not read the columns.

Many of the subjects he touches on are bugbears of doctors, particularly hospital doctors, and the comedy lightens their load and—importantly for editors—makes the journals seem less remote and arrogant and more in touch with the concerns of their readers.

One subject guaranteed to irk many doctors is managers and their instructions, guidance, and pathways.

*"A colleague recently calculated that, as lead for obstetrics in his hospital, he had received 3825 pages of advice, guidelines, and reports about maternity care from various bodies. I should point out, in case anyone from top management is listening, that "recently" means a year or two ago. Rest assured that he is on target, and his total must be well over 5000 by now."*

*"Comedians mocked the news that it took 247 steps to change a light bulb in an NHS hospital, but I felt cheered. In these difficult times, the fact that somewhere in the NHS a light bulb has been successfully replaced is surely a cause for celebration. Doctors involved in management, however, were gobsmacked that this change was achieved in only 247 steps. We need to know more about this thrusting, no-nonsense hospital."*

This collection of columns might perhaps appeal most to doctors and others who work in health care, but I think that anybody will be able to find much that will bring them a smile and even, as with me, a belly laugh. I hope that Jim feels proud of what is not only funny but a magnificent body of work.

**Richard Smith**
*Assistant editor at the BMJ from 1979 to 1991 and editor in chief from 1991 to 2004*

# *Author's note*

I'd like to thank the BMJ's editors for their generosity over many years in giving me a space in the Journal and the freedom to write about whatever happened to be bugging me at the time.

Some of the early pieces appeared in now-defunct journals but without the BMJ's deadlines most of these articles would never have existed and my bonnet would still be buzzing with unreleased bees. I'm grateful to Stephen Lock for taking me on, to Richard Smith for his kind Foreword and occasional advice, and to Fiona Godlee for allowing the articles to be republished. I've resisted the temptation to tweak the wording or add footnotes and if I have any conflicts of interest to declare, I've forgotten what they are.

**James Owen Drife**
*Emeritus Professor of Obstetrics and Gynaecology, University of Leeds, February 2020*

*James Owen Drife performing at the Fringe in 1979*

# The collected articles: Part 1

## *British Medical Journal (BMJ)*

## *Personal view (1974)*

### *Louder and funnier*

Last spring three of us decided to produce a late-night revue in the Edinburgh Festival Fringe. We are all junior hospital doctors but we thought we should easily have enough spare time to mount an hour-long show of songs and comedy. We had been doing Christmas concerts for years for our colleagues in Edinburgh hospitals, and it seemed logical to try, just once, presenting a non-medical show for the public.

During those three or four years we had developed a system of putting our concerts together. We would start well in advance with the music, plagiarising the world's most popular tunes, and adding our own words. The cast would begin rehearsing these songs and finally scripts for the comedy sketches would be written, sometimes very much at the eleventh hour. Apart from composing half-a-dozen original tunes and tightening up the organization, we felt we could follow the same scheme this time.

* * *

By March we had found a suitable theatre. Most halls in town had been booked up months previously by last year's performers: appearing on the Fringe was, it seemed, addictive. Assured of premises, we joined the Fringe Society, which is a co-operative organization of the groups on the Fringe. It co-ordinates publicity and provides a central box-office and club at Festival time. In March, however, the society consisted of one man, issuing sensible advice, which was at that early stage deliberately discouraging: "An audience of zero is as traditional as the Fringe itself ... you will need money and hard work." He emphasised this with a request for a subscription of £17.60.

We were prepared to invest only moderate amounts of cash and effort but we went ahead and opened a communal bank account, convincing an obliging manager that our overdraft would be purely temporary. About this time we completed our company by obtaining the services of a (small) brass band that we knew, and of a talented nurse who had appeared with us once before.

Obviously the show needed a name. "Louder and Funnier" had suggested itself months earlier. We assumed it was an old stage joke, a phrase thrown by cruel audiences at a comedian who was visibly struggling. (We found out later the phrase was apparently first shouted by a director at the dress rehearsal of one of Noel Coward's less inspired plays.) Our group also had to be christened and we bore in mind that the Fringe Society's publicity material listed the groups in alphabetical order. We thought that "A-1 Productions" would be too obvious an attempt to top the bill, and we settled on "Abracadabarets".

The minutiae of producing a show proved time-consuming and expensive. Microphones and lighting had to be arranged, tickets printed, and a piano borrowed and tuned. Posters had to be designed: as we shrewdly guessed that our hospital colleagues might flock to the show, if only to jeer, we had our picture included in the poster to emphasize who was performing. A friend took flattering photos but processing them for screen printing made them quite unrecognisable and cost £20.

We heard that struggling companies sometimes sold a cyclostyled sheet as a programme at a large profit. We thought this immoral and had ours properly printed, with advertisements to recoup the cost. Nevertheless, by the time the show was ready we were well over £200 in debt and since our tickets were, we now realized, among the cheapest in town, we would have to half-fill the hall each night to break even. We over 100 other attractions sharing our opening night we needed some good publicity, if possible well in advance.

During the week before the festival, therefore, we held a preview in a local hospital for an audience of patients, mainly from the geriatric wards. We sent invitations to the drama critics of all the local and national newspapers and, rather to our surprise, two turned up. (One paper failed to send a reporter but printed a detailed review nonetheless.) The performance was a mixed success: there were no breakdowns in the production, but our elderly audience responded with complete silence to most of our efforts, and indeed some fell asleep.

This was not unexpected, as the show was designed for a rather different clientele, but we found the reception surprisingly demoralising. Our hopes were shaken even further when the more distinguished of the critics left, expressionless, pleading an urgent appointment. Up till that night our confidence had remained high, but then this was the first time we ourselves had heard a full performance, with musicians and lights and without pauses. In the best showbusiness tradition we waited apprehensively for the morning papers.

Fortunately the critics' verdict reassured us, though as it turned out the reviews were probably less important for publicity than a large picture in another local paper showing our leading lady sitting on top of the piano. By this time a steady demand for tickets had built up from our colleagues and in fact they formed the bulk of the audience on each of the six nights. Enough members of the public joined them to ensure full houses throughout the week and enthusiastic ones at that. With our finances secure we could relax and enjoy ourselves. Strangely, this proved difficult. Each night we faced an audience of friends with high expectations and we wondered if tonight we were going to let them down. Comedy is an unpredictable business and our performances as well as our audiences differed a little each night. Tension grew instead of waning during the week and by the last night there was, mixed with the nostalgia, a distinct feeling of relief that it was all over.

* * *

Now that the clearing up is finished we can look back with more objectivity. Our profit amounted to £200, not much when shared among a dozen people. The last night really was the end of the enterprise: nobody beat a path to the stage door offering to buy us or our material. Despite several promptings the television producers covering the festival stayed away in droves, selecting other (and, we were sure, vastly inferior) shows for broadcasting. We have remained unrecognised in the streets and, fortunately, in the outpatient departments. We have time now to ask ourselves, Was it worth all the bother?

We still think it was. We gained a clear idea of the limitations of our talents as well as some insight into the actors' world – a place of unsuspectedly hard work and ephemeral rewards. As with writing or operating, or anything else for that matter, trying a thing yourself makes you realize very quickly the skill required to do it well. We are now perhaps more appreciative of the stunning array of talent and technique to which the theatregoer and television viewer tends to become so blasé. "Louder and Funnier" was an interesting and valuable experience and, like many other valuable experiences, one that we are keen to avoid repeating for quite some time. 1974

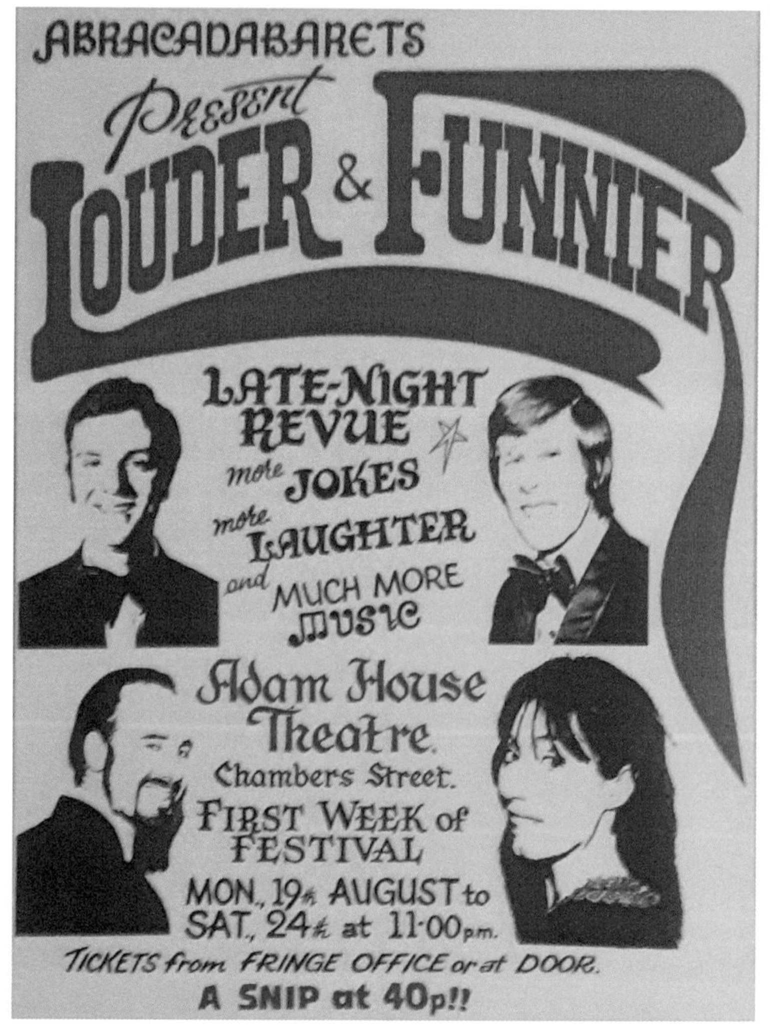

# *Materia Non Medica*

## *Away from it all?*

"Escapist literature," I cried as I headed for the paperback shelves, and an hour later I emerged armed to the teeth with the works of Margery Allingham, P G Wodehouse and, as a gesture towards self-improvement, Graham Greene.

On the beach, however, doctors started popping up out of the pages with frightening frequency. In the first Allingham detective story the otherwise far-fetched plot included a Suffolk GP with an interest in the occult, who treated his more intractable cases by witchcraft, and finally went off his rocker in the middle of a chalk circle trying to raise a demon. I moved on, shaken, to Greene. His hero turned out to be a young doctor in Argentina whose specialty was sleeping with his patients, or rather (being a Greene hero) lying awake beside them thinking. The mood of the novel grew more and more cynical (*"as exquisitely melancholy as a Mozart symphony"*, burbled the back cover) and for all I know the second half of the book might be as depressing as the first. Returning desperately to Miss Allingham, I found *The Fashion in Shrouds* one of the best crime novels ever, except that corpse number one was the son of an eminent physician with long sensitive fingers, and corpse number two was attended by a conceited Harley Street consultant, who didn't escape the lash of Miss Allingham's prose. *"His head was like a balloon which lifted him gently ... from exorbitant nursing home to fashionable funeral, with a grace and ease not afforded to any man with his feet set firmly on the ground"*.

My holiday half over, I groped for Wodehouse. Aunts, butlers, curates, cooks, and Aberdeen terriers milled helplessly between the covers, but, thank heavens, there wasn't a doctor in sight.

1975

## "The Beano" and I

When my wife dropped a teaspoon the other day, she said "Erk!" Our guests looked politely startled and I explained that she had picked up the expression from her husband. I didn't explain that her husband had picked it up from the Beano.

As a veteran Beano addict, I have an expletive for every occasion. The characters in that splendid periodical always choose *le mot juste*, but since at least part of their readership is made up of children, their vocabulary must be small and respectable.

*Erk* signifies surprise, or the sudden dawning of horrible truth. *Eek* introduces a note of fear, usually feminine, while *Yikes* involves an element of pain, as on sitting on a tack – a disaster that frequently strikes within the Beano's pages. Severe pain such as that associated with being felled by a sledgehammer or squashed by a double-decker bus (again, very much occupational hazards) is expressed by *Aaargh,* the depth of the emotion being indicated by the size of the letters and the number of "a"s.

The Beano, however, gives its readers more than just a vicar-proof vocabulary: it provides some enduring images. As a schoolboy I once read of my favourite characters, "The Bash Street Kids", having a biology lesson: on looking down a microscope they saw a Germ. I remember it well, with its twenty hairy legs, its maniacal grin, its striped jersey and, if I'm not mistaken, a steel helmet with a spike on it. A much more accurate picture, I was sure, than the version in my encyclopaedia, an anaemic illustration of something that looked like a loaf of bread.

I eventually managed to unlearn the Beano's contribution to bacteriology, but I fear my "Erk!"s are with me for ever.

1976

## Bing

How many impressions of a Bing Crosby concert can be squeezed into 400 words? The familiar inscrutable superiority of the box-office as we applied for tickets; the few empty seats on the night in the over-priced stalls and circle; the old ladies in the audience, plus a few elegant younger suntans. An unfamiliar excitement just before the opening, and the huge applause as the star appeared, unannounced, at the very start. His high-stepping, short-paced gait, lively in appearance but economical of effort; his raised chin and firmly closed mouth, an attitude elderly men tend to use for keeping old skin taut. His impeccable microphone technique; his voice as rich as ever, except for the high notes, which he avoided. His charm and, well, talent is the only word, I suppose, for an ability to command a stage for almost three hours without moving a wrong muscle.

The orchestra ranged behind him, strong on brass; their tubby director watching Bing over his shoulder as intently as a Western gunfighter. The musicians impassive as statues while the supporting comedian ran through his routine, pursued by applause and laughter; the same musicians leaning raptly to watch the jazz quartet improvising. The quartet becoming a quintet as Bing went into a remarkable medley of 20 to 30 songs; the rapport between him and the wiry little pianist crouched over the Steinway like a racing cyclist and wisecracking with the front row. Bing forgetting the words near the end of that long series but singing a nicely phrased apology instead of the missing line.

Bing's family; and the people behind me explaining to each other, loudly and wrongly, which was his younger son. The older son's musical ability, poise, and embarrassingly poor voice. The frequent entrances of Bing's wife and daughter, much more professional than we had feared. The old man's watery blue eyes as he sang *The Way We Were*. His self-possession during the applause at the end – doesn't he realise how rare standing ovations are in Edinburgh? – and his gentle send-up of our enthusiasm as he strutted off, hand on heart. Not a single note of *White Christmas* throughout.

The large crowd round the stage door. Applause. Bing in his golfing hat, looking surprised, old, tired. Five big policemen round him, squeezing him into his limousine. Bing's youngest son following unnoticed, looking just a bit awe-struck. And no wonder.

1976

## *Coffee Times*

My wife, who has literary inclinations, recently purchased a set of mugs from The Times. They look as if they may well kill the art of coffee drinking, decorated as they are with facsimiles of that newspaper's most arresting items from the last century or two. As one sips one can discover that the news of Waterloo broke on Printing House Square four days after the battle itself: the Duke of Wellington, stiffly describing the proceedings as "sanguinary", reported that the enemy had lost "One hundred and fifty pieces of cannon, two eagles, and a large part of Bonaparte's baggage". During the General Strike the paper announced calmly that few people were turning up for work, but the page has a typewritten appearance so lacking in authority compared with the normal dignified Monotype Times that one can sympathise with readers who failed to take the strike seriously.

The earliest reproduction, from New Year's Day 1806, holds strong opinions on medicine. "O Quackery! Where wilt thou end? O Physic, when are thy disgraces to terminate?" it thunders, apparently fulminating against a contemporary charlatan. However, my favourite is another medical – or rather, obstetrical – mug, announcing the birth of the future King Edward VII. With decorous rapture it proclaims "The Accouchement of Her Majesty ... We have the utmost pleasure in announcing that at 10 minutes to 11 o'clock this morning Her Majesty was safely delivered of a Prince". With some surprise we learn that the father was in attendance, and with downright amazement that "Her Royal Highness the Duchess of Kent, several Lords of Her Majesty's Most Hon Privy Council, and the Ladies of Her Majesty's Bedchamber" were also present. All pushing like mad, no doubt, and taking care to faint without turning their backs on the parturient monarch. I suppose that in reality the crowning of the princely vertex was achieved behind an arras, but none the less Victoria will never seem quite so aloof again. Still, perhaps one shouldn't believe all one reads on coffee mugs.

1977

# *World Medicine (1977-8)*

## *"My clinical hobby-horse"*

## *Blinded by science?*

Don't be put off by the bloom of youth in my portrait. As a mere registrar, out on my clinical hobby horse and off the leading rein for the first time, I don't want to pontificate on my experience of medicine. My hobby-horse is more of a hobby-mule, the product of two very different experiences, neither of them clinical.

Until recently I've been employed as a scientist, a perfectly respectable thing for a doctor to be, at least temporarily or part time. Perhaps even something to be proud of, unlike my second experience, which is my secret vice. I tend, you see, to become involved with amateur theatricals and (worse than that) with musicians. I sing songs in public, a pastime to which few professional men would admit in print. Why, I wonder, is this activity less reputable than my scientific bent (if that's the word I'm after)? I want to point out the importance of the arts to medicine and I'm afraid I must start by revealing the irrelevance of science.

Science, like draught beer, nostalgia and Kenneth Tynan, is not what it was. In the past most people were content with the idea that if God had created something it was eccentric, if not downright blasphemous, to ask how or why. Then, a century or so ago, intelligent men began asking obvious questions and getting some correct answers. People started listening and great sciences such as Physiology, Biology, and Zoology blossomed. Electricity, evolution, organic chemicals, bacteria and the atom were discovered and classified: all these had direct relevance to medicine and it was logical at that time for doctors to try to keep pace with the strides of science.

Nowadays things are different. Every schoolboy knows the vocabulary of science rather than that of Virgil, and science's concepts are household words. The modern researcher is a super-specialist examining minutiae. Electron microscopists, molecular biologists and other detailologists work at a submicroscopic level using higher maths and computers To say that a doctor need be acquainted with these disciplines is as sensible as saying that he needs a course in metallurgy to use a sigmoidoscope. Real science in 1977 is as impenetrable as nineteenth-century theology, and if you don't believe me try reading a letter to Nature.

Yet doctors still try to be scientists. Even the level-headed pipe-smoking readers of World Medicine are well verse in the concepts of double-blind-randomised-controlled-clinical-trials and values of P. Doctors who might otherwise be usefully employed administer placebos to trusting patients in order to discover whether *Buggicilin* cures marginally more UTIs than *Piddlebritin*. Our medical experiments often involve studying thousands of patients for several years: the cynic might ask if results so difficult to demonstrate have any bearing on clinical practice.

It is amusing to see the Nobel prize for medicine each year being awarded to a lab worker who wouldn't know a patient from a pork pie. It is less amusing to watch students of our healing profession wasting the prime of their lives memorising metabolic pathways and the principles of gas chromatography. No time for novels or learning about life in disreputable bars – by way of compensation they study behavioural science. We train students to be good scientists, but there's more to medicine than that. The good scientist is interested in his figures, not in individual cases. The good scientist categorises and counts: each patient must have a diagnosis, a treatment, and a result. Faced with ill-defined diagnosis, a blunderbuss treatment or an equivocal cure, the good scientist loses interest. Science deals in certainties, and subliminal clues and clinical impressions are alien to the scientific method.

Art, on the other hand, can cope with nuances: they are its stock-in-trade. The artist is not afraid of recognising things he cannot analyse. Literature, for example, involves the observation of people partly by intuition, as does medicine, and it is no coincidence that medical schools have produced so many authors. A short story by Chekhov or Maugham has more to tell me about people than a term of behavioural science. Yet we militate against literacy in our profession. Faced with a succession of multiple choice examinations over the years, a student may never have to express himself coherently on paper. He need write no prose even if he evennchooly bekumms an MRCP. The ability to write clearly is inseparable from the ability to think clearly, and has to be demonstrated by fledglings in the civil service or industry. But not, it seems, by doctors.

My favourite art, apart from books, is the theatre. This art is fundamental to medicine, and not only because doctors frequently have to lecture. Nor merely because the formal ward round, with its cast of thousands and its audience agog, is a "production number" of more magnificent impact than any in the theatre. Like an actor, a doctor has to be aware of his effects on a patient who is minutely examining his expression and interpreting his tone. Our manner is one of the tools of our trade: we have to act confident, act reassuring, or just act natural.

It's time to acknowledge that the diagnostician uses the intuitive eye of the artist as often as the analytical precision of the scientist, and that treatment is based on sensitivity and compassion as much as on statistical probabilities. A computer can't comfort an anxious mother.

I have always been the first to admit that arty types are more of a trial to be with than scientific types. Artists at their worst are voluble, extravagant, unreliable, and hopelessly biased – quite unlike doctors. But then scientists at their worst are cold, shy, and pedantic – equally unlike doctors. Really good artists and really good scientists are surprisingly similar types – they're rather like doctors, I've noticed. And with that observation – purely intuitive – you understand – let me climb off my hobby-horse and pour an old-fashioned unscientific remedy for my new syndrome of writer's cramp and saddle-sores.

*World Medicine 9th February 1977 p48-9*

## *Situation Vacant*

*ADVERTISEMENT: "Teaching is a good way of learning" – unusual opening for trainee in second Guy's teaching practice at Thamesmead. "Urban village" community served by experimental interdisciplinary team who attempt to provide a medical supermarket. Physically, intellectually, and emotionally demanding work with medical student teaching thrown in to make things really impossible. Stimulating supportive environment aided by extensive professional sub-culture. Details and questionnaire will be sent to selected candidates. Initial applications with curriculum vitae to Primary Health Care Team, Macaulay Way, London SE28.*

Dear Primary Health Care Team,

I'm really really interested in integrating myself among you. Your advertisement in this moment in time's BMJ struck me as a deeply relevant document and motivated me to synthesise this application.

As of now I am involved in a locum situation within the clinical chemistry laboratory of Professor Otto I. Moon here in Lambeth. The aims and objectives of Otto's strategy have always been the taking of clinical chemistry into the heart of the community to which, in which, and with which it belongs, together with the remedying of the outmoded "ivory tower" conceptualisation of the specialty – a conceptualisation which is becoming less and less meaningful to the last quarter of the twentieth century. My role, as both doctor and caring human being, has been an educative one: through the medium of workshops and seminars I have tried to make the autoanalyser more real and more relevant to the ordinary man and woman of Lambeth, and to help him/her develop an ongoing personal relationship to, for, and (most importantly) with his/her own urea and electrolyte profile.

In this I feel I have been only partially successful, though I fully accept that the parameters of "success" can perhaps never be completely quantitated in such experimental work. My decision to leave, however, is a positive rather than a negative one, and has been fully discussed with my peer-group, in the serum magnesium assayists' mutual support therapy sessions. Frankly, in spite of – or because of – the intellectual demands of my current position, the job does not leave me emotionally drained like it used to: I feel myself searching for something more physical and, ideally, more harrowing.

My co-workers and I think I am now ready to move into the environment on a grass-roots level. Previously my career (of which I enclose an overview) has been wide-ranging, involving both the urban villages of Stoke-on-Trent and the rural megalopolis of Ross and Cromarty: now I am keen to weave these various modalities into a cohesive whole by working at the interface of medicine and non-medicine (if indeed such a dichotomy can validly be made).

After all, is not health care a holistic entity?

I am anxious to look further into your unusual opening, because I think it could provide the structured framework necessary to the escalation of my experience. I am particularly attracted by the name of your team: I take "the second Guy's teaching practice" to be a paradigm of your emphasis in caring particularly for the underprivileged – the first Guy is usually well able to take care of himself.

I hope I can fit on the shelves of your medical supermarket: I see myself among neither the luxury items nor the bland convenience foods, but rather, if you like, among the wholesome, high-roughage biodegradables – between the courgettes and the King Edwards, in a sense! I should be proud to be one of your selected candidates, and I have applied for study leave in anticipation of receiving your questionnaire. I hope to be favoured with the honour of a dialogue, but successful or not I shall support your ideals, and I trust that your seminal approach will rapidly expand.

Earnestly yours,

*James Owen Drife*

# *"Doctors as Patients"*

## *Student health*

I have enjoyed disgustingly good health since my final year at medical school, but I'm blowed if that's going to prevent me from contributing to this series. Before graduation I had the grant-aided leisure to indulge a hypochondriasis fuelled by new-found knowledge, and enjoy it with none of the guilty introspection of the moribund medical man snatched back from death by colleagues he once despised.

How clearly I remember the consultations: the student health service GP, wearily cynical to begin with (*"How d'you know you've got a hernia?" – "Just done it in anatomy, please, sir."*) then visibly impressed; the elderly surgeon adding one more appendix to the list after I had stoically sat through a long outpatient session with him; and the Indian casualty registrar, searching vainly for a fracture in the scaphoid views but putting me in plaster just in case. Then there was the Scottish registrar telling our tutorial group, *"This is sometimes known as Jeep Disease, but as some of you know"* – fixed stare – *"you can also get it from riding around Edinburgh on a Honda."*

(Note the impeccably surgical nature of my complaints. My psychosomatic manifestations, if such they were, involved an awful lot of Plaster of Paris and Michel clips. Not for me the skin rashes and vague abdominal pains of the neurotic student – my alopecia was, and unfortunately still is, far from areata. However, readers of a psychiatric or astrological inclination may wonder why I should only fall off my scooter on the way to work as a casualty orderly.)

Of course, in my youth we didn't have the benefits of the advances that medical invalids enjoy nowadays. In particular we lacked "Doctors as Patients" series in the medical journals. In those days we were forced to suffer in relative silence, our suffering increased tenfold by the belief that the reading public would remain forever ignorant of the details of our preoperative suppositories, the relief afforded by post-operative analgesia, and our doomed infatuation with the night nurse.

Some would say this was no bad thing. Some would say that there are few subjects as boring as another person's operation, and that a doctor's recollections of hospitalisation are every bit as predictable and self-centred as anybody else's. Fired by their own eloquence some would go on to say that the possession of a medical degree and a Dictaphone is insufficient excuse for inflicting the minutiae of one's own disease on a world already full enough of shared misfortune.

Some, I'm glad to observe, had been triumphantly proved wrong. Acting as one man, medical editors have extended the frontiers of good taste to encompass not only lurid descriptions of *My First Bowel Movement After Heart Surgery*, but also *How I Faced My Terminal Illness, by the late Dr So-and-so.* Presumably these appalling pieces are supposed to give the living and unobstructed remainder of the profession a deeper understanding of the patient's lot. So here I come, a network of scars below the belt, to add to your education.

With which insight shall I begin? The *"I Was Scared Stiff in the Anaesthetic Room"?* The *"By Gum It's Sore When Your Plaster Comes Off"?* The *"I Didn't Half Feel Sick When the Houseman Smuggled Me Out to the Pub on the Second Day Post-op"?* Suddenly my hands, poised (via their still-intact carpal bones) over my Olivetti, are paralysed by the growing suspicion that nobody really wants to know. If I were Minister of Health the profession would clamour to read a blow-by-blow account of the application of collodion to my verruca; if I were dean of a medical school I could assemble five thousand saleable words on the excision of my ingrowing toenail: if I were a consultant geriatrician in Slagthorpe I could still hold a moderate readership with a mid-thigh amputation. But who wants to read about a registrar's appendicectomy, apart from the registrar and his mother? It might interest strangers if it had been performed halfway up the Andes with a rusty penknife and a llama giving the anaesthetic, but emergencies are so humdrum in the NHS. It's not as if I'd broken my neck hang-gliding, submitted to the creation of an artificial vagina, or survived cardiac arrest: the most exciting event during my career as a patient was when I finished the Times crossword for the very first time during the interval between arriving at the fracture clinic and seeing the orthopod.

To everyone but me, the victim, all the horrors I underwent were merely minor surgery – what the terribly confident housemen and theatre orderlies call "Mickey Mouse Operations": experiences, like coitus or one's driving test, to be lived through privately, not used for public reminiscence. But experiences of more than sentimental value – one emerged from them matured. The first time I saw a man cry was when I was flat on my face in a four-bedded side ward. He was a diabetic who had just had his second leg off, and he had coped by means of irritating extroversion until the night before he was to be discharged. I watched aghast as he broke into childlike sobs, to be comforted by the other two men in the room. Not by the nurses, and certainly not by the doctors – although that conscientious unit had twice-daily ward rounds, the doctors seemed miles away, controlling our fate unseen, like civil servants.

Looking back, I'd claim that my catalogue of small physical cataclysms contributed significantly to the amazing amount of insight I now have into my role as a member of the secondary health care team. My elective periods as a hospital inmate were much more valuable than some of the official modules in our curriculum. Perhaps I might suggest to medical school planners that what future generations of students need is more illness. Undergraduates should be encouraged to succumb to interesting pandemics, and those who obstinately insist on remaining healthy should be covered with impressive dressings and confined incognito to surgical wards, one student to thirty specimens of suffering humanity. By George, it would make men of them – and they could spend the vac writing it up for World Medicine.

*World Medicine 17th May 1978 p47*

# *BMJ: Personal View*
## *Obstetric Registrar*

*Personal View* is an unlikely name for a column in a medical journal. Doctors spend their working day viewing persons and listening to highly personal confessions, and for relaxation many of us shun people and their views. We go sailing or hill-walking, or we retreat into little workshops and make things. Accustomed to probing, we are suspicious of those who foist their opinions on us, wearing their inner selves too near the surface, like television personalities. Trained to be good listeners, we avoid indecent exposure of our own personalities, and prefer to write impersonal views, in the passive voice whenever possible. Only when goaded by strikers or administrators, or when facing retirement, emigration, imminent death, or a cut in salary, do we allow the professionally stiff upper lip to wobble a bit.

It is particularly difficult for an obstetric registrar to write about himself. He keeps falling asleep over his typewriter. His bleep goes off just before *le mot juste* appears on the page. Though the reading public is adequately supplied with the memoirs of medicine's leisured classes, like ship's doctors and medical officers at the South Pole, the 3am forceps has not yet found its place in the world of letters. This has led people to the conclusion that obstetricians are illiterate, but the truth is that they are merely preoccupied – just as the diaries that some of us used to keep would wax verbose when we had nothing else to do, and wane to blankness when our evenings were full.

* * *

There are two types of obstetric registrar, those in general hospitals and those in large maternity hospitals, and they have only a few things in common. Both, for example, are "resident when on duty." (So far as I am concerned, only those compulsorily resident qualify for the title of obstetric registrar: the rest are imposters, like "Cockneys" born out of earshot of Bow Bells.) The other shared attribute is that for both types the first flush of youth is beginning to fade. The man in the maternity hospital is the less conscious of his advancing years. For much of his time he still feels like an inkyfingered fourth-former, surrounded as he is by senior registrars – the prefects in the hard school of life. For every close shave he has in the delivery suite, one of them has escaped disaster by a shorter whisker, and every debacle he presides over can be matched by a more entertaining cataclysm from the mess fund of anecdotes. Though he may do more than his share of the firm's work, he remains the junior partner.

In a general hospital residency, however, the obstetric registrar is surrounded by beautiful young people, and feels more conspicuously aged every six months. The changeovers of the house officers occur with increasing frequency, and like policemen the other residents get younger every year. If the mess president is father of the mess, the obstetric registrar is its grandfather, as ectopic as Val Doonican on "Top of the Pops." He subsides over breakfast behind his Telegraph, harrumphing in agreement with editorial policy, while around him the residents converse brightly over their Guardians, describing their hangovers to one another and arranging to buzz off in their sports cars for impromptu skiing weekends. While he frets over changes in the mortgage interest rate, they make plans to hitch-hike to Katmandu as soon as they are fully registered practitioners.

In the maternity hospital, mess parties are genteel affairs with lots of gin. The so-called junior staff walk around slowly, with an occasional glint in their eyes, and end up dancing to Beatles' records, to which they know all the words. In a general hospital, however, residency parties are different. A mobile discotheque pounds out incomprehensible music with four-letter lyrics, shock-haired youths in vests jump up and down, and student nurses dance with each other. The beer runs out early, and gatecrashers threaten violence. The obstetric registrar also runs out early, after finding that the girls call him "sir," ask if he is examining in the hospital finals, and inquire pointedly after his wife's health.

* * *

George Orwell, who wrote his first novel when he was thirty, believed that "the great mass of human beings ... after the age of about thirty abandon individual ambition ... and live chiefly for others, or are simply smothered under drudgery." He exempted writers from his sweeping generalisation, stating without a blush that they belonged to a "minority of gifted, wilful people." Obstetric registrars are normally selected neither for their gifts nor for their wilfulness, and therefore stand condemned.

Though they might not quote his opinion verbatim, most people seem to agree with Orwell. Men slink furtively past their 30th birthday hoping it won't bite them: by combing their hair forward and playing more squash they convince themselves for a time that they can still pass for a mature twenty-nine. Ultimately, however, the realisation dawns that something has happened – the change from bright young thing to aging trendy has occurred. This metamorphosis is, like the menopause, recognisable only in retrospect, and hits the obstetric registrar hard. Like all junior hospital doctors, his career from nursery school to royal college has been based firmly on the principle of "jam tomorrow": hope of deferred pleasure has made him – on occasion – burn the midnight oil rather than the candle at both ends. He finds it hard to believe that his life is half over, with the jampot still unopened. Indeed, junior consultants whisper to him that there is no jam, only bread and dripping. This is why older obstetric registrars are a tight-lipped lot, given to wondering if a career in general practice would rejuvenate them.

Alchemists have so far failed to discover either the elixir of life or a way of increasing consultants' salaries. The obstetric registrar needs some other antidote to the poison of Orwellian gloom. One remedy would be a more positive attitude to the trauma of becoming thirty. After all, our other decades are regarded as significant milestones: the 11-plus, the 21st birthday, "life begins at 40," the male menopause, retirement and the end of one's allotted span. The fourth decade should also be entered with a bang rather than a whimper. A little propaganda would soon make thirty the only age to be: the gauche twenties, with all the embarrassment of high testosterone levels, would rightly be regarded as passé. Greetings-card manufacturers would be delighted to co-operate, and the doctors' mess would have another excuse for a party – with Beatles' records, of course.

1979

## *Is This a Record?*

When stars of the Top Twenty, rich beyond the dreams of avarice, buy a fifty-room mansion in Surrey or a croft in the Scottish Highlands, they usually announce plans for converting the basement (or the cowshed) into a recording studio. I could never understand this enthusiasm for bringing work home – after all, the successful Harley Street surgeon rarely converts his own attic into an operating suite – until I recently watched a record being made.

The days are long past when the performers all had to assemble at the same time and the same place to make music together. Nowadays each member of a group records his contribution independently, starting with the drummer and ending up, hours, days, or weeks later, with the singer, who interprets the lyrics while listening through headphones to the accompaniment. No longer does a duff note from the second trumpet bring the entire ensemble grinding to a halt: the massive tape is simply rewound, the trumpet track erased and perfection achieved the second time around. Thus playing becomes technically easier: the difficult trick is for musicians to achieve a zestful rendition or an atmosphere of romance despite standing in a little room full of electrical cables.

The responsibility for the final version of the whole piece rests with the producer, who sits at a huge console of switches from which he controls performers and machinery, like a cross between Andre Previn and Brian Trubshaw. His authority is absolute: where Toscanini had to subdue the occasional rogue bassoon by force of personality alone, the producer can crush insurrection completely by the twist of a knob. After the musicians have been paid off he re-runs their work, adding a crescendo here, subtracting a diminuendo there, until he is happy with the result. Notes of which he disapproves end up on the auditory equivalent of the cutting room floor. Although it is the artistes whose names are printed on the record label, they may in fact be little more than colours on the palette of this omnipotent creator. Small wonder, then, that they nurse aspirations to exercise editorial control, and crown their careers by constructing their own seats of power.

1977

## *North of the Border*

The Scottish border hills looked pleasant enough on an icy winter's day, when viewed through from the heated interior of a saloon car. In Edinburgh we had sleet and gales, while here in the country snow lay in corries, the Tweed was swelling in spate, and fields near the river were under water after spectacular floods that had brought down several bridges in the area. Dusk was approaching and lights appeared in farmhouses as the inhabitants retreated indoors from the freezing wind. Stopping for afternoon tea, we felt lucky to have found a hotel still open in what was clearly the nadir of the low season.

Two Englishmen in deerstalkers followed us in. They asked the clerk for accommodation and fishing permits but were directed elsewhere: the hotel, it seemed, was already packed with anglers. As we huddled by the fire other Englishmen in hairy hats strode in and out, all clad in identical woollies and weatherproofing, carrying rods and lines, and apparently having the time of their lives. Two men with Costwold burrs took off their insulated waistcoats and sat near us discussing the best method of putting down a horse. An ebullient Scotsman in green waders flapped over to them, took off his deerstalker, and beamed that he'd had to leave the river early because his companion had put a hook right through her finger. "I got it out with a pair of pliers," he twinkled, gesturing at the first interosseous space. "Damn sore, mind." After he left they discussed the best way of removing a barb – a procedure which, one gathered, needs two pairs of pliers and lots of whisky. Running a reflective tongue over my hard palate, I finished my buttered scone and we headed for the effete calm of our urban home.

1978

## *Under the Covers*

I saw blood dripping from an eye-socket. Nearby, a platinum blonde winked at me, her decolletage heavy with lust. I half-turned: a volcano vomited rock, incandescent lava ripping through the earth's crust.... The whole Dali-esque mirage had risen in front of me as I entered our local bookshop. Innocently seeking a new copy of Roget's Thesaurus,

I found myself grabbed, jostled, pummelled, bruised, buffetted, assaulted, battered, and given one in the eye by a bunch of hardbacks, as colourful a galaxy of advertising men's creations as I have seen outside a fairground. Two months ago, at Christmas time, shimmering book displays had been just another part of the tinsel season, but now, on a pale February afternoon in a university bookshop, they seemed needlessly lurid.

I remember when dust-jackets were matt brown affairs that merely protected books from dust, and I can even remember paperbacks in uniform green and white, with titles in demure black type. Nowadays books are becoming like long-playing records and after-shave lotion – products secondary to their packaging. For centuries books have struggled to live up to their publishers' glowing claims, and now the glossy '70s have made "puffing" one of the visual arts, thanks to laminated plastic and luminous ink.

When my eyes grew accustomed to the glare, I realised that many of the works fell within my own specialty. All of obstetrics and gynaecology was there: menarche, menstruation, sexual intercourse, vaginal discharge, cystitis, pregnancy, breast-feeding, child care, and the climacteric – each being championed, vilified, or put firmly in its place by a posse of forceful lady authors. It appears that women buy instruction manuals on physiological functions as enthusiastically as men buy road maps. And on the covers, photogenic females suckled, looked indignant, or sank into picturesque post-coital slumber. Several times I picked up a volume only to replace it again. Normally easily seduced by books, this time I felt overwhelmed. Like a voyeur in a nudist camp, I realised with growing irritation that it was all too much for me. I found my dowdy thesaurus, and crept, slunk, tottered and slipped away.

1979

## *To Market*

Looking back, it already seems unreal, though I still have the receipts to prove that it happened. I remember following my family as they dodged through a dim cavern full of cars and noise, up a wet concrete staircase, along a brick passageway and then – scuttling past a glimpse of daylight – into a bright colossal barn full of women and merchandise. My wife slid out a wire trolley the size of a haywain. With experienced glee my children swung aboard as outriggers, and the whole caravan headed for the groceries.

Food was stacked row on row, yard after yard. Meat came in polythene with little computerised figures. Toilet rolls beyond number were randomly piled in hoppers big as grain elevators. Somewhere there were loudspeakers, suave with cryptic messages, and on a dais a uniformed overseer sent her uniformed lieutenants on forays into the crowd. In this aseptic warehouse everything gleamed, including the floor – except where clothes were sold: here we walked on wide strips of carpet which were, I suppose, the result of a study of sales psychology. How the psychologist must have been fascinated by our primitive avian urge to fill the trolley's gaping mouth.

All the denizens of this Asimov fantasy were in a trance. They walked slowly forwards with their heads pointing to one side, frowning in concentration as they studied labels, yet magically avoiding collisions between their mammoth vehicles. Eye-to-eye contact was taboo, even when the preoccupied masses pressed towards the cash registers, which were operated by humanoids with lowered eyes intent on price tags and machine keys. Only when I paused at the separate kiosks selling liquor and cigarettes did I meet an unforced smile.

Burdened and bankrupt, I returned to the multistorey car park. My wife tells me that a supermarket is cheap, hygienic, and less tiring than a day's dealing with a series of old-fashioned shopkeepers. For me, back at work, even the antenatal clinic seems cosy by comparison.

1980

## *Public Launch*

A street explosion in a seaside town – surely not a bomb or a gun, and hardly loud enough for a gas-stove. Holidaymaking and uninterested, I wander into Boots, and it happens again: a sharp slap, like a packing-case falling on the road. Shoppers look round with frowns, amusement, or unconcem, and the pharmacist appears from his sanctum. He says, "*Two flares – the lifeboat*," gazes at the cloudless sky, and fades again behind his bottles.

The Friday crowds move fractionally faster as we loafers are drawn to the harbour. The tide is out and silent watchers throng the harbour wall as the little blue-and-white boat is towed on a trolley across the sand by a caterpillared tractor. It turns and pauses by the water's edge while half a dozen men in orange oilskins climb aboard by ladder. The tractor reverses far into the sea and with a jerk the boat is off, sitting low in the water and moving out quickly over a flat calm. The crowd of spectators sighs and starts to disperse. My son climbs down from my shoulders and I notice there was no rail at the edge of the quay. A man with dyed hair and binoculars says, "A light aircraft come down – didn't you see the Nimrod?"

The icecream man by the lifeboat station glows with reflected glory. "We got the message at ten to three. Ship in trouble seven miles out, so they needed the big boat. The inshore boat can hit the water in a minute flat." Inside the lifeboat shed are displays of dog-eared pictures – stolid former coxswains, wrecks, and a launching in earlier days with teams of men instead of a tractor. A bored man in gumboots is hosing things down, and a three-wheeled car with an RNLI sticker sits outside. Everyone is matter-of-fact, selfconsciously immune to the admiration of tourists: there must be many like me who, even on a sunny day, get a lump in the throat with memories of tragic headlines – of fishing hamlets decimated by this cool, unsalaried heroism. I notice that the collecting box is padded inside, so that my loose change doesn't even rattle.

1980

## *Beginners, Please*

Scene: an auditorium. The houselights are on and the stage is bare. Enter two DOCTORS and a SOLICITOR, each carrying big square spotlights and rolls of black insulated cable. They place these on the floor. Exeunt, panting. Enter a TECHNICAL DIRECTOR, carrying a huge toolkit in a blue metal holdall. He stands centre-stage, gazing upwards thoughtfully. Re-enter DOCTORS, sweating, with more lights and cables. They ask how much more stuff there is. They groan and exeunt.

Noises off. SOLICITOR drags an enormous stepladder onstage. He and TECHNICAL DIRECTOR set it upright, and by pulling ropes and levers extend it precariously to its full height of 15 feet. They look at each other. Re-enter FIRST DOCTOR. They send him up the ladder and pass him spotlights, which he hangs from bars in the roof.

Disturbance at the back of the hall. Enter several RUDE MECHANICALS carrying a piano. They place it in the rear stalls. SECOND DOCTOR re-enters and suggests it should go onstage. RUDE MECHANICALS register amazement, clutch their lumbar muscles, and refer to their job description. TECHNICAL DIRECTOR issues a brief command. Piano is moved and RUDE MECHANICALS exeunt muttering.

Enter DOCTORS' WIVES, carrying expensive parcels, followed by DOCTORS' CHILDREN, sucking lollipops. WIVES gasp and point. TECHNICAL DIRECTOR assures them ladder is safe and, anyway, metal bar to which FIRST DOCTOR is clinging is strong enough to bear his weight. CHILDREN shriek happily and head for best seats.

Enter STRANGERS dressed in sandals, cowboy hats, and wispy beards. They are carrying loudspeakers and microphone stands. Exeunt OMNES to help them. FIRST DOCTOR remains half-invisible in roof, making incoherent noises. Tableau. Re-enter OMNES, carrying more loudspeakers and cable. STRANGERS croak and grasp their throats.

FIRST DOCTOR, now flushed and dusty, descends ladder and exits. Pregnant pause. Re-enter FIRST DOCTOR with crate of ale. OMNES drink.

Suddenly all six loudspeakers blast out punk rock music at deafening volume. TECHNICAL DIRECTOR crawls beaming over tangle of cable and gives thumbs-up sign. STRANGERS beam back. DOCTORS turn pale.

Silence again. Somewhere in roof SOLICITOR'S disembodied voice is heard cursing. Spotlights go on and off apparently at random, while TECHNICAL DIRECTOR raps out instructions sounding like trigonometric formulae. STRANGERS apply lengths of insulating tape to anything that moves. Loudspeakers repeatedly count up to three. FIRST DOCTOR searches in vain for full can of ale. SECOND DOCTOR plays piano introspectively. Finally the ladder is taken down with a crash. The comedy can begin. 1980

*Autobiographical note:*
From 1982 to 1990 I was a Consultant/Senior Lecturer in Leicester.

# *Edinburgh Medicine*

## *The Drife Diaries –*
## *Part One*

Teviot Place is awash with rumours that an Edinburgh doctor is threatening to publish the diaries he kept during his undergraduate days in the "swinging sixties". His former fellow-students, now distinguished medical men, are said to have offered large sums as "hush money" to "Doctor X", and several Edinburgh publishing houses

*The author as a student in the 1960s*

have experienced burglaries, arson attacks, and telephone calls hinting at complications should the publisher ever need medical treatment. In a major journalistic coup, *Edinburgh Medicine* has secured exclusive rights to these manuscripts. After consulting our lawyers (who advise us that their authorship must remain secret) we present the first instalment from *"The Drife Diaries"*.

### *March 2nd*

Got up. Had breakfast. Corn Flakes supply getting low again. Must learn to cook something else (Sunday's luncheon-party fell a bit flat after second course.) Am worried about autobiography. Due to graduate next year and still hardly any sex and violence for Chapter One (high hopes re tomorrow night's party, though). Need more s & v if autobiog. is to be international blockbuster. Memo: must develop popular style. No use writing like medical textbook.

Today's Resolution: try out diff. styles to find the best one.

### *March 6th*

Got up. Had breakfast. Doing Gen. Medicine so plenty of time to read my Sherlock Holmes Omnibus. That reminds me: must practise a new style each day ...

I was roused from my slumber at a later than usual hour, and as I opened my eyes I beheld a look of the gravest anxiety on the handsome visage of my old friend and flatmate, Tony.

"Come!" he cried, laying down the ladle and tin basin he had been beating together over my recumbent head. "The game is afoot!"

"Dear heaven!" cried I in a fervour of dreadful anticipation. "Has this accursed thing happened again?"

My friend spoke not a word, yet even as I searched for the neck-hole of my kaftan I could not help but notice his tight-set lips and stern countenance. When he spoke, however, his voice was quiet and perfectly controlled.

"Nev has locked himself in the bog again." The words struck a chill into my very soul.

"With the water-pistol?" I stammered.

Tony nodded, grim-faced. "And my catapult." He did not miss the change in my expression.

"Yes, my friend," he sighed. "I thought it well hidden. Would that I had banished it from this flat altogether as you so earnestly beseeched me!"

* * *

Our little toilet overlooked the garden of Mrs Dalgleish, our worthy but officious next-door neighbour. She it was who, only the previous afternoon, had engaged our volatile flatmate in a discussion of the utmost animation over the question of the rota for scrubbing the common stair. And she it was who, in but a few minutes' time, would carry into the garden a basket of washing, bend over and – unless Tony and I could effect an urgent intervention – suffer unthinkable revenge at the hands of the temporarily deranged Neville.

Twice before he had lost control of himself in this fashion after being bested in debate by our sturdy neighbour, and she had promised that should a third attack be visited upon her, we would be prosecuted with the full vigour of the law. Who then would come forward to say that Neville's violent nature was but the dark reflection of a brilliant mind? Who then would care that he was destined to become one of Edinburgh's leading haematologists? Nought but disgrace beckoned, unless Tony and I could persuade him to abandon his vengeful purpose.

"Come out, Nev, I'm bursting!" I cried, as we beat with our fists upon the stout oak door.

"Naff off, guys," came the response from within. "This time she's going to get it right between the ischial tuberosities."

Tony and I could clearly see that it was useless to reason with him further while his mind remained inflamed with fury. Tony's classic profile darkened for a brief moment, and then became resolute once more. "Wait here," he snapped. "I'll wake The Hulk". In an instant he was gone, and there was no sound but a demonic chuckle from behind the closed door, and the twang of elastic as Neville essayed practice shots at Englebert, the Dalgleish tortoiseshell.

In a moment Tony had returned, and with him was the towering figure of our fourth flatmate, Douglas, known throughout Marchmont as The Hulk. In outdoor clothes he was an awesome sight, but now, clad in his night attire of rugby shorts and anorak (for his was the coldest bedroom) he seemed to fill the tiny lobby with knees and shoulders.

"Kill, Hulk!" snapped Tony, pointing at the toilet door. In an instant the lock was shattered and we three fell upon the astonished Neville as he crouched with catapult poised at the open window. I caught a glimpse of Mrs Dalgleish, inviolate and unaware of the titanic struggle being waged on her behalf, but at that moment The Hulk fell on top of me and I knew no more …

## *April 5th*

Got up. Had breakfast. I'll say one thing for Neurology at the Northern – plenty of opportunities for study. Superb hospital library with several Jeeves books …

* * *

With a discreet cough, the ward maid shimmied into Sister's office bearing a salver with a much-needed pick-me-up.

"Down the hatch!" I croaked, screwing up the pallid features and downing the steaming brew in a single gulp. For a moment nothing happened, and then all H was L L . I felt like a patient whose sigmoidoscopist has suddenly developed St Vitus' dance.

"I say!" I yipped, gazing around me with a wild surprise and preparing to head for the wide open spaces.

"Steady, lad," said Sister, laying a restraining hand on my knee. "I know hospital coffee takes a bit of getting used to."

She gazed at me over her half-glasses and under her bushy eyebrows, and slowly the internal maelstrom subsided. Dunking a thoughtful chocolate digestive, she continued, "I understand you're in a spot of trouble".

Under normal circs, of course, a gallant scion such as myself does not unburden himself to those of the distaff persuasion. Stiff upper l. and all that. But there was something about Sister – the row of medal ribbons, perhaps, or the flash of hunting Stewart when she crossed her legs – that invited confidence.

"Yes, actually," I stammered. "Well, sort of."

"The election, I believe?" she said, still skewering me with the steely gaze like Rob Roy interrogating a captured Redcoat.

It was pointless to resist.

"Mmm, ya," I replied, spraying crumbs of Rich Tea over her starched lap. "I think I've blown it."

"Fiddlesticks!" she snapped, in the voice that had caused sudden loss of tone in many a consultant sphincter. "Would William Wallace have said that? Or Robert the Bruce? Or John Reith?"

"Dash it," I riposted with spirit. "None of them tried to become Moderator Ludorum Laetitiarumque".

"Who dares wins," Sister murmured calmly. "Who else is in for it"?

"Andrew Burton," I hissed the name between clenched teeth. The ghastly Burton had been my arch-enemy ever since we shared a body in the Dissecting Room. When I tell you that this fiend in human form had nipped up there during a lecture, re-plumbed the coeliac trunk, and waited sniggering behind his *Scotsman* crossword while I traced the superior pancreatico-duodenal artery into the gall bladder, I think you will have a pretty clear idea of the kind of villain I was up against.

"Andew Burton?" said Sister, frowning. "I seem to remember the name."

"Extended," I prompted, "and very smooth."

"Ah yes," she nodded. "My nurses called him Andrex. Well now, we can't have a chap like that becoming Moderator Ludorum Laetitiarumque. You'll have to stop him, laddie!"

She prodded me in the solar plexus with a ball-point inscribed *A present frae Kyleakin.*

"But Sister," I gulped feebly. "He's like a cross between Terry Wogan and Al Capone. There's simply no stopping him."

"Snap out of it, laddie!" Her tone was chilled steel. "Where's your backbone? Are you a man or a mouse?" I opened my mouth to protest that this was no time for a Basic Sciences viva, but something in her eye stopped me. I stood up and brushed the crumbs from my cagoul. My jaw was firm. My eye almost certainly glinted. This woman's words had turned me from a jellyfish into a superbly engineered fighting machine."

"Golly, Sister," I rapped. "How can I ever thank you?"

She looked up at me and her bosom heaved under the navy-blue serge. "Kiss me, you fool," she breathed.

## *April 6th*

Got up. Had breakfast. Nev. has lent me his Damon Runyon book – says it was made into a successful musical, and I should try the style. (Nev reckons if my autobiog. is a blockbuster, he'll be famous. Little does he know I'll change all the names, sexes, towns of origin and perversions to protect my royalties.) Anyway, here goes …

This fine evening I am sitting with a group of prominent citizens on the steps of the Royal Infirmary, speaking of this and that and watching the broads with the bedpans going about their business, when all of a sudden I notice four guys approaching me on the sidewalk. They are four very well known characters up and down Lauriston Place, and one is a very tall and very obnoxious guy known to one and all as Andrex. Andrex is giving me a long cold stare which suggests strongly that he is sorer than a prolapsed haemorrhoid at me for running against him for the Moderatorship, and the three fellow-citizens with him are wearing expressions of such sorrowful reproachfulness that I begin to feel distinctly nervous. Andrex raises his voice above the sound of knuckle-cracking and tries the diplomatic approach.

"Listen, frog-face," he says, "ever since I was a tiny baby on my mummy's knee I cherish the ambition that some day I will be Moderator Ludorum Laetitiarumque, and I do not care for some greasy schmo to try to blow it away. Furthermore my companions here are so touched by my aspirations that they are investing a substantial number of potatoes on the outcome of the impending election."

I think it disrespectful to reply from a sitting position but it is no easy matter to rise when I have Andrex's pal Broncho standing on my left hand and Gertrude the Gorilla standing on my right hand.

"Believe me," says I, "I have no wish to make myself disagreeable to peaceloving citizens such as yourselves, but my white-haired mother's heart is set on seeing her flesh and blood installed as Moderator and being as I am an only child what else can I do?"

I can see that Gertrude the Gorilla is touched by my filial devotion for he blinks his one good eye and eases the pressure on my right mitt. The fourth member of the deputation, Slit-mouth Charlie, ceases swishing the air in a meaningful fashion with his rolled-up *Evening News* and turns to look at Andrex.

Andrex snaps his fingers and his henchmen back off. "In that case," says he, "I have a proposition. I suggest we and our advisers meet in equal numbers to discuss our differences. Shall we say Thirlestane and Spottiswoode at midnight?"

* * *

Well, midnight sees Nev, Tony and me dragging the unwilling Hulk towards the corner of Thirlestane and Spottiswoode. "I am missing my beddy-byes," wails The Hulk. "My hotty-botty will have cooled down by now." The Hulk is a guy of regular habits, who likes to hit the cocoa on the chime of ten. In the distance we can see strung out across Spottiswoode a line of shadows.

"Two bob says Hulk will put 'em all in A&E without us doing nothin' but wind him up," whispers Nev.

You see, we are putting it about that The Hulk has gone off on his elective to Borneo so we figure we have the advantage of surprise. I am therefore more than a little astonished that the shadows do not vanish as soon as The Hulk appears, and I begin to suspect that Andrex has invited many old cronies to join the congregation. Up ahead I hear his high-pitched laugh.

"You bums are surrounded!" he shrieks. "This evening my colleagues and I are spreading the word around the neighbourhood that the Marchmont Sharks are planning a surprise attack. The Warrender Jets are seriously displeased and offer to escort us safely home. Renounce your candidacy, Wimp, or my allies will turn you into oatmeal porridge."

Behind us we hear the creaking of the leather jackets of a dozen Jimmies. It dawns on me that The Hulk is very silent and when I look at him I see he is now asleep standing up. When this happens nothing west of Krakatoa wakens him. I come over somewhat thoughtful and watch my past life floating in front of me. All of a sudden I hear a doll's voice from a nearby doorway. "In here!" says the voice and figuring that an undignified retreat is preferable to three months in traction I pass swiftly through, slam the door and let the Jets bruise their toecaps kicking the other side ...

(The concluding instalment from the sensational Drife Diaries will appear in the next *Edinburgh Medicine*, writs permitting.)

*Edinburgh Medicine*, December 1987

## *The Drife Diaries – Part Two*

The story so far: In these sensational revelations of life as an Edinburgh undergraduate in the "Swinging Sixties", the anonymous diarist, mindful of future publication, tries varying literary styles. In Part 1 be began battling with Andrew Burton ("Andrex") for election as Moderator Ludorum Laetitiarumque of the Royal Medical Society. Outnumbered in a street-fight by Andrex, his cronies and the Warrender Jets, the author and his colleagues (Nev, Tony and The Hulk) took refuge up a close at the invitation of a mysterious young woman. They fell asleep. NOW READ ON ...

*April 7th*

Got up. Had breakfast brought down the stairs by the most beautiful girl I've ever seen. This must be love. I may have said that before [Editor's note: see Dec 5th, Jan 26th, Feb 4th and 19th, March 1st etc, etc] but this time it's for real. It's like something out of Mills and Boon, so that's the style I'll try today.

Her tiny, delicate hands trembled as she shyly held out the bacon butty, and for a moment, as I took it from her, our fingertips touched. In that instant a thrill like an electric charge ran through me, and I shivered involuntarily. Her cherry-red lips parted and her clear brow furrowed in a worried little frown. "Are you cold?" she whispered solicitously.

"It's nothing," I laughed, my twinkling blue eyes making fun of her concern.

"It's just that ... I mean, I couldn't help noticing that your friend has taken your clothes," she said, flushing prettily as she averted her gaze.

"Hulk likes to keep warm," I explained, rolling modestly over onto my flat, well-muscled tummy as I tried to unwrap my trousers from around his neck. He had put my Y-fronts over his head, and I desperately hoped that they were her favourite colour.

"Can I turn round now?" she whispered tremulously, her eyes screwed up tight and her heart beating wildly in her bosom.

"Just a minute," I answered, deftly flicking my tie into place. "There!"

She turned and gasped involuntarily as her eyes fell on my broad shoulders, slim hips and long athletic limbs. The little laughter lines crinkled around my piercing blue eyes as I grinned boyishly but tenderly down at her. Trembling, she lifted a hand to brush a speck of dust from my lapel. "You haven't told me your name," I breathed roguishly.

"It's Edwina," she replied, and as a shaft of sun from the fanlight caught her flame-red hair I thought for the thousandth time how beautiful she was.

"Mine's …"

"I know," she replied. "I've seen your picture on the election posters."

"Then …" I breathed, a wild hope rising in my bosom. "Does this mean … does this mean I can count on your vote?"

"Oh!" her voice suddenly broke into a wild sob. "O would that it did!" I stared at her, aghast and uncomprehending. "You see," she continued, "I am but a poor Psych and Soc student. Yes, and proud of it too!" Her little jaw lifted and her eyes flashed with spirit. "But a grand gentleman like you would never be seen with the likes of me. We are of two worlds which can never meet. To see each other again would only cause untold pain and suffering, so … farewell, my love!"

Choking back a sob, she turned and fled like a faerie spirit up the stairs. Ere I could follow, a door slammed above me, and a great weight pressed upon my heart. I knew I could never win her back unless some miracle happened. Wearily I turned back to my recumbent colleagues, squeezed their earlobes and rubbed their sternums. What had Edinburgh to offer me now? The crown of the Moderator Ludorum Laetitiarumque – even if I won it – seemed hollow, and as we stumbled out into the sunshine of Spottiswoode Road, I realised that without love, life's glittering prizes are but tinsel.

At the corner of the street, as I turned for one last glimpse of the happiness that had so nearly been mine, my heart leapt into my mouth. Smoke! Smoke was drifting in a thin stream from the doorway we had just left! My mind was in a whirl as we rushed breathlessly back along the street. Had the poor distraught darling allowed her own bacon butty to burst into flames under the grill? I knew she was a girl of too much spirit to resort to deliberate self-immolation, however deep her despair.

Heedless of our own safety we rushed into the smoke-filled close and up the stairs to a door with a dozen hand-written cards stuck to it. My heart went out to the lovely child forced to live in such squalor, probably with students of politics, philosophy or even, though I shuddered at the thought, Eng Lit. Clouds of smoke billowed under the door and through the letterbox, but in a trice The Hulk had put his shoulder to the door and charged into the flames. I tried to follow but I was beaten back by the flying bodies of semi-conscious philosophers as The Hulk unceremoniously emptied the flat of its occupants.

I waited in an agony of suspense for what seemed like hours and then my heart leapt in my bosom as I saw, dimly through the smoke, The Hulk with Edwina's limp form under his arm. He had somehow found a bucket and was dousing the burning walls. "Catch!" he yelled, and deftly threw the elfin child into my outstretched arms. She lay there motionless.

"Is she … is she …?" gasped Nev and Tony.

"Are you … are you …?" I choked, full of grimmest foreboding.

Edwina lay still and her eyelids fluttered open.. "Am I … am I …?" she breathed faintly, then her little body began to struggle. "Put me down," she cried. "I must go to him!"

She broke free, rushed back into the smouldering ruins and threw her arms around The Hulk's waist. His sooty anorak was torn, and she reached up shyly to touch the singed hair on his manly chest. "My hero!" she cried, and I could see from the way that she and The Hulk gazed into each other's eyes that there was no place for me now in her life. I turned away, my eyes moist with unshed tears.

"Don't take it hard, man," said Tony, who had experience in these matters. "She's got fat legs."

## *April 20th*

Got up. Had breakfast. The cornflakes last a lot longer now that The Hulk spends so much time in Spottiswoode Road. Also, we get to read his *Times* in the morning. Am now a big fan of Bernard Levin. People say they detect his influence in my final election pamphlet.

In the ordinary run of events, though I must confess that for me events seldom if ever run in an ordinary way, and indeed I suppose that when one looks closely at the events in any person's life is probably the exception rather than the rule, all of which has the salutary effect of making my opening phrase a contradiction in terms, I should be reluctant to return to a subject, however fascinating, outrageous, provocative, hilarious or, to use a much debased word in its original sense, important, that I had already discussed a few days ago. But the matter I wish to lay before you is so fundamental to the well-being of every man, woman and child, nay every dog, cat and monkey in the venerated if not venerable medical school of ours that I make no apology for again attempting to draw my readers' attention to it, for I am referring to an impending event which future generations may come to regard as the fulcrum on which our tired civilisation swung either downwards to everlasting perdition or, and I am not yet so cynical as to dismiss this second possibility without serious consideration, upwards out of the abyss over which our species is suspended.

Anyone who has not been entombed in a soundproof vault for the last three months will by now have realised that my subject is the Homeric battle being waged over the office of Moderator Ludorum Laetitiarumque, a struggle between good and evil; between right and wrong; between light and darkness; between truth and falsehood, between hope and desperation; between me and Andrew Burton.

But there is a small faction within this university which is dedicated to the overthrow of democracy, a grim, hard-faced faction to which the very words "ludorum" and "laetitiarum" mean

Unfortunately, the rules of the election give each candidate only 300 words for his final election address, but I reckon this should impress the plebs.

*May 15th*

Stayed in bed. Didn't feel like breakfast after last night's fiasco. Should have pandered to the masses like that clown Burton. Must practise a style more appropriate to the electorate. What about that very successful chap Hargreaves?

Mr Student was excited. He was so excited he almost missed the ward-round. That made Mr Paediatrican very angry.

Usually Mr Paediatrician was calm. Nothing upset Mr Paediatrician. Not even when his little patients made his shirt all wet. Not even when his little patients swung on his tie shouting, "Me Tarzan!" Mr Paediatrician loved his little patients. But he did not love Mr Student. Oh, no!

When Mr Student arrived halfway through the ward-round, Mr Paediatrician looked at him very hard. "How kind of you to turn up," he said. "I'm touched." But he did not look touched. Oh, no! Then Mr Paediatrician started asking Mr Student questions. Very difficult questions. Poor Mr Student! He did not know the answers! He did not know about dysgammaglobulinaemia! He did not know about the Waterhouse-Friedrichson syndrome! He did not know about the cerebral sclerosis of Pelizaeus-Merzbacher! In fact Mr Student did not know anything at all!

Mr Paediatrician grew angrier and angrier. "You are a great hairy moron!" he told Mr Student. "Write out one hundred times, I must know the difference between glossoptosis and glomerulosclerosis." And he made Mr Student stand in the corner all day.

By the evening Mr Student was not excited any more. He was sad. He was sadder than he had ever been in his life. Mr Student had missed his supper. He was hungry as well as sad. And tonight of all nights! Tonight was election night. Mr Student thought to himself, "Nobody will want to elect a sad person like me." And the more he thought this, the sadder he got. So Mr Student decided to try and cheer himself up. He went to Mr McEwan's. For a quick one. And another quick one. And another. And a magical thing happened. Mr Student slowly turned into Mr Happy!

Mr Happy smiled a great big smile. He decided to have a quick one too! And another! And then Mr Happy had a thought. "Time for the election!" he thought. And off he went.

The election was held in a room with a big chair. Mr President sat in the big chair. Mr President was very important. And he knew it. He banged the table with a bone. A leg bone.

Mr Happy thought of the man whose leg bone it was. Trying to walk around with no bone in his leg. And Mr Happy began to giggle. He giggled and giggled. He giggled and giggled and giggled. Mr President looked at Mr Happy. Mr Happy tried to stop giggling. He turned red. Then he turned purple. But he managed to stop giggling. Just.

Mr President asked Mr Secretary to read the minutes. They were very long minutes. Mr Happy began to fidget. He was feeling uncomfortable. More and more uncomfortable. Mr Happy crossed his legs. Mr Secretary kept on reading. Mr Andrex raised a point of order. "Oh God!" said Mr Happy.

He crossed his legs the other way. But it didn't help. Mr Happy was going to have to nip outside. He stood up. He fell over. He got up. He fell over again. His friends were amazed! More magic! Mr Happy had turned into Mr Topsy-Turvy!

His friends laughed! His friends whistled! His friends fell off their chairs and drummed their heels on the carpet. What a good time they were having!

Everyone agreed it was the best election they ever had. Everyone except Mr Topsy-Turvy. He didn't know anything about it. Mr Topsy-Turvy had done a Very Big Wee-Wee and then fallen fast asleep! By the time he woke up the magic had worn off, and he was Mr Student again. And everyone had gone home. Poor Mr Student!

## *September 17th*

Breakfast in bed! Great things, electives in Kirkcaldy. The natives here speak some strange language and read nothing but ethnic novels.

Sunset over the Lang Toun is aye bonnie, wi' the reek o' the lums gangin' slowly heavenwards frae the corbie-stane gables. But yestreen, on the hill abune the toun, wi' the distant piping o' the whaups and peewits and the laverocks pouring their wee bitty song o'er the ripening corn, 'twas a true Celtic twilight.

The silver firth gleamed in the blude-red sun like a fallen claymore on the green plaid o' the fields. As I hied me o'er the heather the memories o' the bygane year swirled around me like October mists. Och, but now I should be looking forward through the gloaming to the future.

Was it the second sight I had? Else how was it I kent – and firm as Aberdeen granite was my kenning – that Nev would one day return to his native hearth as a consultant? That braw Tony's destiny was a group practice on the South Coast o' England, and that the muckle Hulk would soon become a psychiatrist in Australia?

As for yon Andrex, aye, becoming Moderator Ludorum Laetitiarumque was but the first step in a brilliant medicopolitical career but might yet lead to his achieving the secretaryship of a BMA Division.

And what of his glaikit friends, Broncho, Gertrude the Gorilla and Slit-mouth Charlie? As I sat amid the bracken, gazing at the shadows deepening on the Lammermuirs and slipping my brawny arm round the yielding waist of Nurse O'Reilly, I thought, "Who cares?"

THE END

# *BMJ*

## *Birthday Bidding*

From the descending jumbo, Singapore's Chinatown had been a Legoland of skyscrapers, but close up on a warm Saturday night the streets seemed dilapidated. Signs were bilingual and exotic: "May Sin, Hairdresser," "Oriental Slasher Emporium" (prices, I hoped), and, on the back of a car, "Another Toyota from Borneo Motors."

Through the silence among the shuttered shops came an imperative monotone like a country auctioneer's; when I headed towards it I found a street party. A roof had been erected over the roadway with lights and electric fans hanging from the temporary rafters. A few hundred Chinese people sat in family groups at round tables, the men in open necked shirts, the little girls in party frocks. Food was being cooked at temporary barbecues on the pavements, and on a dais a perfectly bald auctioneer with a microphone and a team of assistants was working hard to sell ornaments and potted plants. A huge red shrine had been set up with rows of small brass bowls in front of tiers of painted figures, and six-foot ornamental candles stood unlit nearby.

I stared from a distance – a solitary European – as a ceremonial dragon worked by a dozen men with poles danced round the shrine, its jaw flapping and short brightly coloured antennae wobbling. When I asked a bystander if I could buy beer from a trestle table I was made to sit as a guest while one man found a glass, two more produced bottles of beer, and another brought a paper cup full of ice cubes. A young woman with a beautiful toddler explained that tomorrow was their god's birthday. The auction suddenly ended and people streamed slowly away, pausing to buy handfuls of incense sticks and place them in the brass bowls. "Come back tomorrow," I was told, "and see the procession."

At noon next day the parade set off: lorries – old Bedfords and new Mitsubishis – bright with banners and flags, deafening percussion bands with gongs and drums, baggy trousered boys waving more flags, men carrying long leafy boughs with lemonade bottles tied to one end, a self-conscious god walking along in frightening makeup and a green costume, and the sinuous dancing dragon. No women took part, and only a few spectators watched as the procession wound its halting way past dusty building sites before disappearing out of the sun's glare between the shining, silent skyscrapers.

1987

## *The Legend*

The yellow cab dropped me at a nondescript doorway. Inside, in the semidarkness, a young man in a tuxedo blocked my way: "Standing bar only, sir – fifteen dollars." I stretched my arm through the throng to buy a Budweiser, pushed further down the room, and explained to another bouncer that I was looking for some friends. A waitress found me the last unoccupied wooden chair, almost hidden in the crush of people and tables.

A moment later the club became even darker and spotlights picked out a trio on the little stage. Grand piano, string bass, and drums played mainly with the brushes. Even I, no jazz fanatic, could tell they were good, and when the announcement came I realised that they were the backing group to one of the genre's living legends.

After a couple of numbers the applause persisted and began to swell as a foot appeared on the tiny wooden staircase beside the stage. Dressed in flowing red, the legend herself slowly descended. Flashbulbs popped. She started a scat song which soon focused into the line, "Don't take no flashes!" The snapshotting continued. The legend stopped and with an electric mixture of threats and coquettishness persuaded her fans not to photograph her "because it hurts my eyes." Those eyes had seen it all. They could kill a clattering waitress at 30 paces.

The legend had first recorded "Misty" 30 years previously and she was a perfectionist. Tonight, it seemed, things were not quite right. She wanted more bass on the mike and more obedience from the audience. Even when she melted into infectious giggles we had the uneasy feeling that if we didn't love her enough she'd stalk off in a huff. She introduced the band whose names, in spite of their Dixie grins, sounded like a firm of British solicitors. Her Gershwin medley was punctuated with affectionate applause. Concentrating on producing beautiful sounds, she mopped her brow with a little hankie and occasionally scratched her cheek while singing. When she drew attention to a sensuous lyric (.... Taste me with your kisses ... Find the secret places ..") with a disgusted grimace, we fell around with laughter. She ended with Sondheim – an unexpected framework for her rococo blues, stood up from her stool, blew kisses, and processed towards the little staircase. Three hundred adoring New Yorkers shouted for more, but she didn't come back.

1987

## *Apres Nous...*

"Ferme en hiver," said the notice; but on a warm July evening there were cowbells in the Alpine pastures and the single track road climbed the mountainside among snowless firs. The Col du Coq begins near the monastery of Chartreuse, rises higher than Ben Nevis, and then twists down a cliff face on its way towards Grenoble. As we crawled upwards in second gear we wondered why the Parti Communiste Francais had recently painted neat white hammer and sickle emblems at intervals in the middle of the road. Then we saw the tiny gravelly laybys filled with darkened Renault vans and the cardboard arrow, sponsored by Peugeot, delineating what was presumably one of the more demanding stages of the world's greatest cycle race.

Next morning knots of people gathered at the hairpin bends. Two armed policemen closed the road to cars but allowed a trio of elderly cyclists to pedal doggedly upwards. We feared a Horatius-like confrontation with the descending horde but soon a police car swept downwards and a sergeant gesticulated, ".... personne... meme les bicyclistes...." His grey headed superior gazed, silent and Godfatherly, from the back seat.

After a pause two advertising lorries ("Coca-Cola, c'est ca!") rushed past, followed by a vintage fire engine with a Michelin man sitting on the ladder. Groups of cars with stickers in primary colours almost bumped one another as they hurtled around the bends. Half a dozen go karts careered along with giant bottles of lavatory cleaner attached to them. A car advertising fly killer was accompanied by another with a giant insect expiring supine on its roof. A motorcycle combination raced down the hill on two wheels with a massive beer bottle in the sidecar. From two cars in the shape of the train grande vitesse handfuls of paper hats were hurled at the spectators. Vans stopped briefly to sell souvenirs. Another Michelin man stood on the saddle of his motorbike to wave to the crowd. A bright yellow car zoomed along with an identical full size car upside down on its roof. Overhead a helicopter zigzagged towards us. On the road a long gap was followed by the international press, carloads of gendarmes, the headlights of police motor-cyclists, and then the television cars.

The competitors themselves appeared preoccupied, perhaps feeling that as mere cyclists they were rather an anti-climax.

1987

## *Learning the Hard Way*

"Very hot!" said an oriental voice sympathetically.

I nodded, sweating. The man, smartly dressed with a small attaché case, was walking beside me on the crowded Bangkok pavement. Obviously I was English, he remarked: in October he was coming to England to study. He mentioned a provincial university: "The best after Oxford and Cambridge, I think?" I politely agreed. He was a teacher but as today was a religious holiday he was going to his temple.

"You like to see? It's round the corner." Why not, I thought. "Too hot to walk," he said and hailed a tuk-tuk.

We roared down to the river and took a water taxi up a broad canal. With an unchanging grave expression he pointed out families bathing beside their wooden houses.

"No middle class in Bangkok – only rich and poor."

We alighted at a Buddhist temple, glittering red and gold, and walked reverently through its grounds. Hundreds of monks in saffron robes sat in the main building, some turning to watch us curiously. Over the loudspeakers an aged voice chanted a long prayer. Families ate lunch beside a wall containing cremated ashes and small memorials.

"They believe their relative's spirit will come and eat with them." My friend motioned me to wait and returned with a bowl of cut flowers. We removed our shoes and he placed his flowers among others in front of a shrine with a photograph of the temple's founder. "A great man," he said intensely.

Returning by water taxi, we stopped at a cafe. Over lunch, he talked of his village and told me what a privilege it was to practise his English with me. He ordered more beer than I wanted and refused to let me pay. We exchanged addresses. The colourful boat took us back across the river and stopped 20 yards from the quay.

"He needs money," said my friend, "and I do not have enough."

"How much?" said I, comprehending at last.

The boatman looked inscrutably at my friend, who looked at my wallet. The fare, it transpired, was nicely covered by all the money I had on me, leaving just enough for the tuk-tuk back to my hotel. My friend's address, I later discovered, was false. (Mine, fortunately, had been a post office box.) Next day, as a solitary sightseer, I was regularly approached by smartly dressed men. I stared blankly at them and pretended to be Scandinavian.

1988

## *Balcony Scene*

Naturally all the lectures were being given in English, even though we were onlv a few kilometres from Transylvania. British and Hungarian speakers were alternating at 10 minute intervals, and outside the tall windows the leafy campus was dappled with sunshine.

Hungary's warmth and colour had come as a surprise to us, brainwashed as we were by Le Carre novels into expecting Eastern Europe to be drab, wet, and humourless. The city of Debrecen was full of the unexpected: its church was a stronghold of Calvinism despite being less than 160 km from Russia and only 320 km from the birthplace of the present Pope, and its nightclub boasted stunning showgirls all the way from Havana.

Walking to our meeting in the medical school we had passed

animated groups of students and now we were finding it increasingly difficult to concentrate on the talk. Through our open first floor windows came the sound of musical instruments and voices, distant at first and then organised into a choir outside our building. The speaker goodnaturedly gave up the struggle and our host headed for the door with an apologetic smile. "It is graduation day and my students have come to say goodbye. The meeting is adjourned for three minutes."

We crowded on to the balconies. Beneath us were nearly 100 beaming students, dressed informally, some holding balloons and others flowers. They were singing accompanied by a brass section, percussion, and guitar. A Hungarian folk melody was followed by what seemed to be a specially written song, which drew laughter from the staff and uncomprehending smiles from the British. Then the crowd burst into *Gaudeamus Igitur.*

"Extraordinary how potent cheap music is," wrote Noel Coward in another balcony scene, and I learnt later that I was not the only visitor to feel a lump in the throat at the familiar tune with its optimistic lyric in the ancient academic lingua franca. We waved and applauded as the students loaded trombone, French horn, and tuba on to a hospital trolley and straggled away in the sunshine. Our meeting continued and I wondered why English had replaced Latin as the international language of medicine and science, if not of music. Later I asked one of our hosts why, living between Germany and Russia, he had bothered to learn English. "To tell the truth," he said, "I wanted to find out what the Beatles were saying."

1989

# *BMJ*
# *"Opinion"*
# *1988-1990*

## *Looking Carol in the Face*

Carol is a stocky woman, who usually wears a grubby windcheater. She has lank brown hair and wears no make up, and her husband is a labourer with fingernails that betray his interest in car mechanics. They are pleasant, unimaginative people who have enough determination to cope cheerfully with living in a poor suburb, but neither of them aspires to upward mobility. They seem enviably content on their cluttered council estate, and their only problem is Carol's blocked fallopian tubes.

Like other gynaecologists, I see a fair amount of infertility caused by tubal problems. After surgery has been tried unsuccessfully the next step is in vitro fertilisation (IVF), a procedure that patients usually want desperately even when its failure rate has been explained. What I say to them is: "Unfortunately IVF isn't available on the NHS, but I can refer you to one of the private clinics near here. The waiting lists aren't long. The cost varies, but it's of the order of £1000 for each course of treatment. You may need several courses before you get pregnant." In Carol's case the meaning of these words is: "Push off."

*The first time is the worst*

Turning patients away is a new experience for me. The most upsetting thing about it is how easy it is becoming. Something that was formerly unthinkable is now part of my repertoire. With any shameful action the first time is the worst, the second time is easier, and eventually it hardly bothers you. This is how Agatha Christie's villains used to describe their homicidal careers, and the same applies to lesser misdemeanours like mugging, embezzlement, or refusing treatment to people who can't afford it. For the common criminal this loss of innocence is a solitary process, but things are easier for the doctor who embarks on a career of withholding treatment from the poor. He has the sympathy of his peer group, the approval of society, and the encouragement of the government.

He can also expect resigned acceptance from the patients themselves. You see, Carol comes from Anglo-Saxon stock. Her people have lived in England's feudal society since before the Norman Conquest and have never expected the same treatment as their betters. The English peasantry still regard socialised medicine with popeyed amazement. When I give patients an immediate date for operation their jaws drop and they gasp that they expected to wait at least a year. If I tell a woman with, say, a premature menopause that her condition is untreatable she will become thoughtful and stammer: "Well, I'll just have to go private, then." The yeomen and yeowomen of England expect the NHS to offer a second rate service, and infertile patients don't even look surprised, much less angry, when I tell them that their dynasty must come to a halt because expensive fertility treatment is not for the likes of them.

*Disappointment compounded by debt*

According to the Voluntary Licensing Authority for Human In Vitro Fertilisation and Embryology, only one of Britain's 30 centres is funded wholly by the NHS and access to treatment "continues to be determined largely by a couple's financial resources, a matter of continuing concern to the Authority." This restriction has been received by the profession with a mixture of resignation and enthusiasm. Some specialists have moved wholly into the private sector, while academic units have adopted compromise solutions, which mean that patients pay for only part of their care. Couples slightly better off than Carol may indeed raise a bank loan or sell their house to pay for private treatment. More often than not IVF is unsuccessful, and the luckless couple face disappointment compounded by debt.

Why has the country accepted that IVF cannot be free to all? It is not just because the service is new and expensive – we can afford new linear accelerators for cancer treatment. It may be because nobody dies of infertility, but – at least at the time of going to press – NHS treatment still isn't restricted to lethal diseases. Perhaps we feel that people like Carol don't deserve free care because blocked tubes are often the result of gonococcal salpingitis. Nevertheless, the NHS doesn't refuse to treat the drunk who drives into a lamp post or the heavy smoker with lung cancer, so I doubt whether primitive morality is the real reason. Part of the problem may be our awareness that the last thing this planet needs is more babies – but we seem happy to treat women whose infertility is due to anovulation.

*Pity, not sympathy*

I think that there are two reasons why infertile couples do not excite public sympathy. The first is that unlike sick babies, crippled children, or pregnant women they don't look vulnerable. They look healthy, they keep busy, and usually they are reticent – even sullen – about their problem. The second, more powerful, reason is that each of us supports the NHS partly through fear that we may need it. Any day now we may develop a cancer, have an accident, or suffer a heart attack. We commiserate with such afflictions because we know we may be next. Those of us with children have lost the sympathy born of fear. Among the many emotions we feel in the puerperium is a trace of smugness. Though we may pity our infertile neighbours, once we have children we can never again fully sympathise with them.

*Not the right Victorian values*

The Victorians felt comfortable with pity and made charity a virtue, but, so far, Britain's return to Victorian values has not meant a rebirth of sentimentality. Our attitude to infertile peasants is one of yuppie indifference, and I doubt whether this will mature into compassion during Carol's reproductive lifetime. As Carol's consultation ends the tableau has its comic aspect. The patient waddles off philosophically; the doctor, red faced, drums his fingers and glares at the dictaphone; the student frowns with respectful incomprehension; and the nurse looks at her watch. The implications crowd in on me and I wonder which non-essential service will be next to move into the private sector. Conscious of the team's morale, however, I bite back sardonic comments and call for the next patient, hoping that it will be someone I won't be ashamed to look in the face.

## *Power Dressing for Men*

In these days of equal opportunity medical men are still disadvantaged by a lack of advice about fashion. Every week the colour supplements hand out suggestions to women on how to dress. In the quality papers the women's sections – thinly disguised by titles like "The Monday Page" – discuss technical details of how to stop conversation at a board meeting by turning up in the right outfit. The rising female doctor, having outgrown the stage of granny glasses and organic sweatshirts, merely needs to follow the published instructions in order to have a head start at any medical meeting.

The male, however, finds life more difficult. For one thing, his fashions alter so slowly that he may not notice the change. This was illustrated by a recent letter in *The Times* from a headmaster complaining that his pupils became convulsed when he wore a kipper tie. His plight underlines the rarely acknowledged fact that schoolboys are important arbiters of male style. They influence trends by pointing, whistling, and falling over clutching their sides. It is thanks to them that flared trousers have followed drainpipes and Oxford bags into the pages of comic costume history. So my first rule for power dressing is that supervision by a son or nephew is vital, just as a French maid used to be essential to the debutante.

*Pinstripe or chalkstripe?*

A second problem for the professional man is that his range is limited. His female counterpart may dominate that important meeting by wearing a suit of pure primary colour, but he knows instinctively that he cannot do this. He must agonise between the fairly dark grey and the very dark grey; between the pinstripe and the chalkstripe. It's comforting to remember that medicine is less restricting than the other professions. Barristers are limited to deciding which shade of black has the best chance of impressing the judge, and archbishops have to know only which purple goes best with their complexion. The doctor has slightly more scope for self expression, but in the hothouse environment of the committee room or postgraduate centre we all tend to look similar, and for scoring points nuances are crucial.

Published medicosartorial guidelines are almost non-existent. The glossies are no good for doctors, with their pictures of slim young men looking like characters from Thunderbirds and wearing greatcoats big enough for two. Those of us with Phil Silvers hairstyles and mid-trimester waistlines get no help from the newspapers, and, let's face it, our needs have been completely ignored by the medical press. Until now, that is. Here are some tips I've picked up over the years.

*Hard to impress colleagues*

First, the suit. Few medical men have time to change between emerging from the consulting room and attending a meeting, so the suit has to be chosen to impress both patients and colleagues. Patients are easy: anything expensive will do, provided that it is slightly old fashioned. Indeed, patients, brought up on television fiction and BUPA commercials, are so surprised to find intelligent human life in the medical profession that they hardly notice the clothes. Colleagues are a good deal harder to impress. The message you are trying to put over is that you are busier than they are. Certainly the suit should be expensive, but it should be a little rumpled. (Not too rumpled – we don't want to look like a scientist, do we?) It should look as if it was chosen with the help of a family tailor and a wife with impeccable taste, but it should have a slight air of suffering, as though too much has been asked of it. Nothing in excess, you understand – no frayed edges or missing buttons – but it should suggest that it belongs to a man who has more important things than clothes on his mind.

Naturally, the suit should be a two piece. The waistcoat has, alas, been rendered obsolete by central heating, as recent photographs of the Cabinet have underlined. (I mourn its passing, but nowadays black tie dinners are the only occasions when I wear a waistcoat – a strange satin garment that looks like a cross between a cummerbund and a brassiere and makes me feel like Bob Monkhouse.) The waistcoat's demise focuses attention on the shirt, particularly nowadays when at meetings from May to September it is conventional to remove your jacket. The shirt should be slightly too large – at the waist for obvious reasons but also at the neck as this implies slight muscle atrophy after ceasing to play rugby. Short sleeved shirts are permissible for paediatricians, but for other doctors sleeves are de rigueur. Cuff links are mandatory, but be careful – they reveal so much about your personality. If in doubt go for gold.

The tie is traditionally the only item that a man actually chooses as opposed to lifting automatically from his wardrobe. You will already know whether or not you are a bowtie wearer, as this is a matter more of lifestyle than of dress. (Bowtie wearers are never left alone with other men's wives.) Most doctors choose a conventional necktie with an affiliation: royal colleges are to be preferred to schools or regiments, which smack of nostalgia, but best of all is a club with an obscure purpose and no more than a dozen members.

*Ideal place for bloodstains*

Next, a word about bloodstains. It is all too easy to overdo these. The aim is to show that you still carry out practical procedures, but you don't want people to think that you are clumsy. Bloodstains should therefore not be seen on the body area, collar, or spectacles and should never be more than 2 mm in diameter. The cuff is the ideal place for most doctors, though for obstetricians the socks are a possible alternative.

Finally, those all-important accessories. These should be chosen to suit the occasion. For scientific conferences a pullover will ensure that you aren't browbeaten by the lab boys. At clinical meetings a vest will add weight to those trenchant opinions. A Telecom bleep impresses nobody except possibly the Women's Institute: even there, it should on no account go off. Your accessories, like the rest of your outfit, should make you feel comfortable and your colleagues uncomfortable: to that extent power dressing is the same for both sexes. A doctor, however, should aim to look slightly less than perfect. You don't want people saying that you're dressed to kill.

## *My Grandchild's Birth*

I hope that it will be the next century before I become a grandfather, but the millennium is only 12 years away. I wonder how my 10 year old and her classmates will have their babies? People used to think that space age parturition would entail futuristic technology ("Beam me out, Scotty"), but the chances are that my daughter will want to give birth just as previous generations did. My mother, in a pre-NHS nursing home, was attended by a Welsh midwife, who became my godmother. My wife was looked after in hospital by senior midwives and by the consultant, my boss. My sister had both her sons in her local general practitioner unit. In different settings they all received first rate care with one common factor: each was attended by an experienced midwife in direct contact with an experienced doctor. This luxury, I am afraid, is denied to the average British woman giving birth.

*Officers and NCOs*

The typical British labour ward does not have enough staff to allow each woman to have her own midwife. Student midwives, auxiliaries, or medical students help out, with qualified midwives moving between rooms as required. If a problem develops the midwives do not deal directly with consultant obstetricians. The hospital midwife – who may have many years of experience – calls a senior house officer, who has usually been in post for less than six months and is probably training to become a general practitioner. The senior house officer may then ask advice from the registrar, who is employed on a short term contract and is almost certainly worried about his or her career. The consultant is regarded by the team as a remote figure to be invoked only as a last resort.

I find it difficult to understand how a midwife copes with the ignominy of deferring to an inexperienced senior house officer whenever a complication occurs, but some midwives find the relationship rewarding. The best analogy is a military one: the senior house officer is a junior officer and the midwife a non-commissioned officer. The senior house officers are being trained to take responsibility and senior midwives become skilled in leading them to the correct decisions. The system, however, fails if the senior house officer will not heed good advice: midwives respect the medical hierarchy and bypass the juniors only in desperate circumstances. The relationship also becomes strained if the midwife herself is inexperienced, and hospital midwifery is unattractive to young women. According to the Royal College of Midwives, 17% of staff midwife posts are unfilled, which means several thousand vacancies throughout the country, mainly in the large hospitals in our cities.

*Collecting gongs*

Unattractive jobs may always be filled if the money is good enough, but the midwives' pay structure is based on negotiators' logic rather than common sense. When a woman gives up work as a staff nurse to become a student midwife her salary does not drop and when she then works as a qualified midwife her salary does not increase. Midwives, who greatly resent being called "nurses," have for years tolerated nurses' pay. The bizarre salary structure encourages "gong collecting," and midwifery training schools contain a high proportion of nurses who have no ambition to become midwives. "Midder" is one more diploma that will enable a nurse to apply for a sister's post in another specialty, just as obtaining the DRCOG helps the career of a general practitioner trainee who has no intention of delivering babies.

Training people in skills that they will never use is a disease endemic in the NHS, and its most florid manifestation is on the labour ward. Many more registrars are trained than are needed, but this problem is tackled in *Achieving a Balance*, with its long overdue proposal that the number of registrars should be related to the number of vacancies for consultants. Reducing the number of registrars, however, will tend to increase the number of senior house officers, which leads to still more stress for the midwives who help to train them. The last thing our labour wards need is more inexperienced senior house officers, but they do need more midwives. The logical solution is to replace many of the senior house officers with midwives. Few midwives will refuse the increased responsibility, and the main resistance to this change will come not from the labour wards but from general practice.

General practitioners will argue that their trainees need obstetric experience because providing antenatal care is part of general practice and because trainees should be eligible for the "obstetric list," which increases the income of the practice they eventually join. Nevertheless, in an era when errors of judgment in the labour ward cost £lm each it is doubtful whether the staffing structure of the maternity hospitals can continue to be determined mainly by the needs of general practice. As the exponential rise in litigation continues and as women resist high rates of caesarean section and high technology, the "defensive obstetrics" of the next century will entail the supervision of pregnancy and labour by fully qualified practitioners - midwives and consultants.

*Isolated midwives*

Midwives are jealous of their role as practitioners in their own right, but their independence has brought them problems. Too few to carry political weight, they are bracketed in pay negotiations with trade unions unsympathetic to the idea that they should be paid more than nurses. Fearful of domination by male specialists, midwives keep their distance from consultants at an official level: obstetricians and midwives do not sit on one another's appointment committees and liaison between their respective royal colleges is minimal. Instead midwives are becoming more and more identified with anti-hospital pressure groups and with general practitioners, who have neither the power nor the inclination to support the hospital midwife. (This trend, incidentally, isolates midwives from their patients, who continue to vote with their feet for delivery in consultant units.) The sooner midwives and obstetricians begin collaborating at an official level as they do at the bedside the sooner midwives will cease to have the image and the paypackets of nurses.

I hope my daughter reproduces and I hope that I live to see it. Unless she decides otherwise she will inevitably be looked after by a senior midwife liaising directly with a consultant – because the baby's grandfather is an obstetrician. Those of her classmates who deliver in the expanding private sector will receive similar care. If the NHS survives into the twenty first century I hope that it will provide the same standard for her less affluent contemporaries.

## *The One-Minute Doctor*

The new-look NHS will need a new breed of doctor. Bold. Decisive. An entrepreneur. With the kind of managerial skills you read about in airport paperbacks such as *The Effective Executive* or *The One Minute Manager*. Skills like these aren't taught in medical school. They're learnt in the tough competitive world of business. If doctors are going to manage their hospitals they need to learn these skills. Fast. This article won't make you a top medical executive overnight. But it may help.

*But I don't want to manage my hospital*

Of course you don't. You want to treat patients. That's what most doctors want. But let's just ask ourselves why. Is it because that's what you've always done? Or maybe because that's what you were taught to do at medical school? Or is it because it makes you feel good? These reasons don't really stand up to managerial scrutiny, do they? At first I resisted becoming a manager. Then I realised my reasons weren't good enough. They were excuses, not reasons. I was making excuses to avoid the biggest challenge that can face a doctor – the challenge of being a manager.

*Give me one good reason why I should manage*

I'll do better than that – I'll give you two. Here's number one. You can't treat patients if you've got nothing to treat them with. And if you don't compete for resources at a managerial level – boy, will your patients suffer. It's that simple. Now for reason number two. Management is its own reward. Right now you probably think management is a means to an end. Okay, that's fine for beginners. But when you really get into management you'll discover that it can be an end in itself. That's when you're really managing.

*This sounds good. Tell me more*

You're getting interested, aren't you? That's what management does for people. It provides a constant challenge. Admit it, doctoring doesn't do that for you any more, does it? Doctoring is a small scale activity. You see one patient at a time. They all have the same little aches and pains. The same fears. Most of their problems can't be cured. And if you cure a patient, so what? You get a good feeling. A little gratitude, maybe. But if you're a successful manager you get something a lot better. Hard cash. Cash to build a bigger hospital and generate gratitude by the bucketload. So even the idealist in you is happy.

*Have I got what it takes to be a good manager?*

Go to the station and take a train. Sit in the first class carriage for a change. Look around. Are you as good as these people? Of course you are. The only difference between them and you is you've paid for your ticket out of your own pocket. Maybe they are better groomed than you. Maybe they have got louder voices. But these are just the trappings of management. You'll achieve these too, given time. All it takes is to want them badly enough.

*But I'm a doctor*

So what? Everybody has a problem. Yours is your medical background. Don't be ashamed of it. Face it. Your medical training has given you attitudes which could stop you being an effective manager. So drop them. Once you've made that decision, it's easy. Maybe you're worried because you care about people. That's okay. Managers care about people too – they have to, to be good managers. Your real problem is that you care about people more than you care about management. You'd rather see a patient than attend a management meeting. Admit it. Your priorities are wrong. Once you get your priorities right, being a doctor is not a problem.

*What should my priorities be, then?*

Your priority is to be a successful manager. It's that simple. In any business the manager is responsible to the shareholders. In your case, that means the taxpayers. (For the time being.) Priority number one is to keep them happy. Which means saving their money. Priority number two is to keep the customers happy. In some businesses this is a big problem. If the product is cars, say, customers will shop around for quality. But you're lucky because your product is health care. Your customers – the patients – don't know about quality. What they know about is availability. So your priority in delivering health care is quantity, not quality.

*So how do I deliver health care in bulk?*

Congratulations. You've just asked a management style question. This shows you're already thinking in the right way. Now for the answer. Think throughput. If you're in a surgical specialty high throughput means lots of operations. Remember: nobody but you knows if the operations are necessary or not. But your number one priority is to the shareholders – so get operating. If you're not in a surgical specialty high throughput means lots of consultations. Remember: what you say to the patients doesn't matter. In fact, the less you say to them, the higher the throughput. Look again at the title of this article. The one minute consultation may be an impossible dream, but it's what you're aiming at.

*It sounds easy*

It is easy. All it takes is unlearning some outmoded attitudes. Listening to patients is out: operating on them is in. It's that simple. And never forget your customer has a choice. If he wants old fashioned health care there's always the private sector – your competition. But unlike other businesses the more customers you drive into the arms of the competition the happier the shareholders will be. Fewer customers mean shorter queues and bigger savings. The patients are happy. The doctors are happy. The taxpayers are happy. And who better to drive the customers into the private sector than you? In the public sector you're a manager: in the private sector you're a doctor. From every viewpoint it's the perfect combination. Happy managing.

## *A Calvinist on the Copacabana*

When you tell the ward sister you're off to a conference in Rio she raises her eyebrows. In Portuguese the word "Rio" means river but in English it means hedonism, and no amount of dignified reassurance will restore sister's eyebrows to normal. In vain you remark that the World Congress of Gynaecology and Obstetrics happens only once every three years, that you are an invited speaker, and that you have an economy class air ticket. Sister clearly feels that a congress in Rio for the consultant is the equivalent of a trip to Benidorm for the unemployed, and you have an uncomfortable feeling that she's right.

Nobody speaks highly of large medical congresses. They are an inefficient way of exchanging scientific knowledge and they have little effect on clinical practice. This at least was the consensus among the dozens of British doctors at Rio, and no doubt similar cynicism was rife among delegates from the eighty-four other countries represented there. What then attracted several thousand of us to such an apparently futile exercise? Social contacts are said to be more important than the formal business at these meetings, but I saw little mingling between national groups, apart from individuals renewing acquaintanceships. Was it merely herd instinct that made us head for a prearranged waterhole every three years?

### *Rationalising the herd instinct*

If so, the instinct was rationalised in various ways. For the office bearers of the international federation the congress was their raison d'etre and their main fundraising event. For the local organisers this huge gathering enhanced the status of their country within the specialty and of the specialty within their country. For visiting gynaecological dignitaries the trip was a flag waving exercise, and for the generous multinational companies it was a marketing opportunity. Speakers were motivated by a mixture of duty and vanity and listeners by the tax advantages of combining learning with tourism. Accompanying journalists seemed driven by a desire to write bland articles praising the city, the organisers, and the pharmaceutical products.

For a presbyterian Scot, however, an international jamboree in a developing country brings a sense of unease. My colleagues and I represented conspicuous consumption in the midst of equally conspicuous poverty. A round of drinks at one of our posh hotels cost a week's minimum wage for a Brazilian labourer. By night tourists emerging from a musical spectacular were met by child beggars. By day the congress's trade stands promoted expensive technology in a country on the brink of bankruptcy. Surrounded by a population with a maternal mortality rate 10 times that of Europe we found it hard to enthuse about subjects like hot flushes or acne.

*Beyond the armed guards*

The congress organisers took pains to insulate us from Rio's problems. They supplied special transport, ringed the lecture theatres with military police, and advised us to avoid walking, taking public buses, or wearing jewellery. I quickly found out why. On my first walk, in dirty plimsolls and without a wristwatch, I was soon propositioned by a lady of the night. "No comprende," I said unconvincingly as she extolled her coital expertise in basic and all too comprehensible English. Trotting beside me she smiled seductively and, in the middle of a Copacabana pavement, her right hand lunged at my flies. A few moments later, pleased at escaping with my virtue, I realised that her left hand had emptied my pockets.

After that I hid my banknotes in an unaccustomed place and held on to them whenever I took a stroll. At the end of the fashionable Ipanema beach is a cliff road with no pavement, and to avoid the traffic I walked like a schoolboy along a low wall overlooking the sea. Beneath my feet, invisible from the passing taxis, were corrugated iron shanty homes with blue jeans drying in the sun. A brown skinned woman in a wet bikini walked up from the sea and smiled, showing gaps in her teeth. A few yards away, behind the high fence, steel gates, and armed guards of the Sheraton Hotel, were well oiled sunbathers with perfect dentition. Rich and poor live cheek by jowl, ignoring each other except for stereotyped interactions: toff gives to beggar; bargain hunter haggles with hawker; businessman appraises prostitute; victim is held up by mugger. In Britain muggers used to be called footpads, and in Rio the social order resembles that of nineteenth century England. Beneath its tropical beauty the city is like the London of Charles Dickens.

The congress itself was a success. The scientific committee's brilliantly appropriate programme soft pedalled high tech medicine but avoided patronising the Third World. We were gently but persistently reminded that throughout the world hundreds of thousands of women still die avoidably each year as a result of pregnancy. We also witnessed a star performance. In a perceptive lecture entitled "The seven deadly sins of the health services," Dr Fathalla of Egypt showed how health care everywhere is afflicted by the same sins, such as doctors' pride, lawyers' greed, and politicians' sloth. Dr Fathalla delivered his insights with such grace and compassion that at the end his audience of jaded foreigners rose spontaneously with a standing ovation – the first and probably the last that I shall join at a medical lecture on a Thursday morning.

*A hint of our future*

My only quibble was with his last slide, which asked for *"the energy to change what can be changed, the patience to accept what cannot be changed, and the wisdom to know the difference."* This prayer, I decided, is merely an elegantly phrased excuse for inertia. The second of its requests has been granted in bountiful abundance to most of us, including doctors. Britain emerged from Dickensian squalor because a few idealists challenged "the wisdom to know the difference." Thanks to them our poor became affluent, with beneficial effects on maternal mortality if not on Benidorm. Rio, however, still has the rich man in his villa (or hotel) and the poor man at his gate. In pre NHS Britain, doctors earned their living from the rich and dispensed charity to the poor – a system of medical care that still operates in many countries and indeed is being reintroduced into ours. What worried me, as a Calvinist on the Copacabana, was that Rio may be not only a reminder of British society a hundred years ago but also a hint of our future.

## *How to do it: Telephone a Hospital*

Mr Punch's advice to those about to marry was: "Don't" and the same should be said to anyone thinking of telephoning a hospital. Ask yourself, is your call really necessary? If it is a matter of life or death you can dial 999 and ask the police to go round. If you want to cheer up a patient or make advances to a member of staff call Interflora. If you want to discuss a medical problem leave a message at the consultant's private rooms. In all other circumstances send a letter.

If you don't want to take this advice, however, you should proceed as follows. Firstly, empty your bladder. Next, get yourself a packet of sandwiches, a flask of coffee, and a crossword puzzle, and sit in a firm but comfortable chair. You may be tempted to allow hope to triumph over experience by omitting these simple preparations, but don't – you know you will regret it.

Now find out the hospital's telephone number. This is not as easy as it seems. The telephone directory will be of little help. St Winifred's Hospital in the village of Loose Chippings will not be listed under "Saint" or "Winifred" or "Hospital" or "Loose" or "Chippings." In the Loamshire telephone directory it will be listed under "Loamshire" because it is administered by the Loamshire Health Authority. When you have found the number there is little purpose in dialling it because it will have been changed. Hospitals now seem to change their numbers every two years or so, presumably to reduce pressure on their switchboards.

You will have to phone directory inquiries. Try to sound confident that the hospital does indeed exist: the operator will not realise that she has to look under "Loamshire." It will also help if you have some knowledge of the layout of the building you are calling because you may be asked whether you want the Mafeking Street annexe, the central supplies department, or the Queen Mary Wing. Don't ask for all of them: directory inquiries have instructions to give out only two numbers at a time, so you will have to guess.

When you ring a hospital there will be no reply. With old fashioned switchboards this was because the porter who doubled as the telephonist was carrying urgent specimens to the laboratory. With the new electronic switchboards the endless ringing brings a novel element of uncertainty. Have you dialled the right number? Is your call in a queue? Is the switchboard dealing with a major emergency? Has the computerised apparatus routed your call straight to an empty office in the administration block?

*Using up nervous energy*

It is at this point that you risk becoming irritated as you think of the things that you could be doing with the time you are wasting on the end of the telephone. The way to deal with this problem is to have someone make the call for you. Secretaries remain normotensive because they know that simply getting through on the telephone is an achievement in itself, whereas bosses (such as you) tend to use up nervous energy thinking of what they would like to say when somebody answers.

If you have no secretary now is the time to start on your crossword puzzle. **DO NOT DRINK ALL YOUR COFFEE YET**. Eventually the ringing tone will be replaced by a high pitched whine. Dial again. Repeat the process as necessary. To your surprise, one of these calls will be answered on the first ring. This is a moment of critical importance. Engrossed in your crossword you will have forgotten what you are telephoning about. (It helps to make a note of the reason for your call in the margin close to the crossword before starting on the first clue.)

The switchboard will give you between three and five seconds to state your business. Do not waste time inquiring about the major emergency. If there is one the switchboard may start to tell you all about it, and if there isn't they will assume you are being sarcastic and cut you off. What you should do is to ask politely for the person you want. Speak clearly. The switchboard, sounding mystified, will ask you to repeat the name. They will then say, "This is Loamshire General Hospital. You want Loamshire Royal Infirmary." Keep calm and don't forget to ask for the Royal Infirmary's telephone number. Then go back to the start of this article and ask yourself again if your call is really necessary. Beware of the false logic that says "I have wasted all this time so I'm not going to give up now." Give up and write a letter.

If you are determined to continue, go through the procedure again with the new number. When the hospital answers don't expect to speak to the consultant you are trying to contact. The only calls that are put through direct to consultants are from patients with vague psychosomatic disorders. Do not expect the switchboard to know the ward on which the consultant works or the name of his registrar. Bear in mind that in any hospital with three or more consultants two of them are bound to have the same surname.

Your best bet is to ask for the secretaries of the specialty in which your consultant practises. That way you have at least a fighting chance of speaking to someone who has heard of him. The person who takes the call will be the secretary to one of the other consultants. She will say, "I'm sorry, I don't know where Dr So-and-So is and his secretary is out at lunch. Can I take a message?" This is where you have to find some consolation in defeat. Give your name and say, "I have to contact Dr So-and-So very urgently about a prescription he wrote. Please ask him to ring me. I shan't be at home tonight but I'm easily available on the telephone at my hospital."

## *Doctors, Lawyers and Experts*

Barristers' offices are not designed for medical conferences. They are pleasant, book lined rooms with old fashioned furniture, but they are not quite big enough. When a group of doctors arrives a polite youth in a suit is sent out to comb adjacent chambers for more chairs. The conference proceeds at an unhurried pace, and tea is taken. Some of the doctors are there because they are being sued and others are expert advisers, and the only way to tell who is who is that the doctors being sued turn up in good time for the meeting.

Each doctor is questioned by counsel, the host. As an expert one can relax and compare counsel's history taking technique with ours. The main difference is that counsel has time. He does not arrive late after walking past a queue of resentful litigants with their bawling offspring only to find that the case notes have been lost by the records department. Instead, each of the pages is neatly numbered, from one to several hundred, ready for analysis.

*Feigned ignorance*

Counsel seems unfailingly polite and delightfully ignorant about medicine. As a rule, the more nonsense a doctor talks, the more polite counsel becomes. The doctor may be halfway home in the train before realising that he has been exposed as a blusterer – or he may never know. Counsel's feigned ignorance traps us into revealing ourselves: under his innocent gaze we puff ourselves up and waffle. Counsel listens respectfully and eventually concludes that, although he sees exactly what we mean, he fears that a senile and prejudiced judge may find for the other side. Only occasionally does his mask slip – a chance remark disclosing that he is word perfect on hundreds of pages of evidence or that he has heard the technique of hysterectomy explained umpteen times before.

I like counsel. He has self confidence and common sense, and he thinks logically. His job is simply to predict how the judge will react – a task made easier by the fact that he and the judge come from the same sector of society. He has confidence because he belongs to the profession that makes the rules. The career structure is such that if he reaches the top he will enter the House of Lords – a distinction automatic for lawyers and bishops but far from automatic for ours, the lowliest of the three professions. Leading doctors may receive knighthoods if they don't annoy the government, but doctors enter the Upper House only at the whim of the Prime Minister.

Counsel's ability to think logically is both enviable and frustrating. I envy the way he makes medical problems seem simple and I envy his down to earth style: despite his pukka accent he speaks for the man on the Clapham omnibus. It is frustrating, however, to realise when talking to lawyers that our professions have so little in common intellectually. Lawyers are trained to progress logically from one argument to the next and much depends on how the arguments are presented. Doctors are trained in the scientific method, which prefers experiment to deductive reasoning and minimises the cult of personality.

At the interface between law and medicine stands the medical expert. Expert witnesses are no more expert in medical matters than any of their specialist colleagues. Indeed, because experts are commonly retired doctors or senior figures concerned mainly with administration their skill in practical procedures may be less than that of their registrars. What they are expert at is dealing with lawyers. Lawyers prefer experts whom they can understand, who seem authoritative and who are unlikely to change their minds. The last quality is the most important. Cases that reach court entail a divergence of medical opinion, and the last thing counsel wants is an expert who might admit under pressure that the other side might be right.

*Trial by flattery*

Experts are therefore chosen for, shall we say, the robustness of their opinions. They are then subjected to trial by flattery. Lawyers listen to the expert with deference because of his medical knowledge. Back in hospital, doctors listen to him with respect because of his legal experience. In these heady circumstances no expert can remain humble for long. Slowly at first, he begins to believe that he really is an expert, and he becomes increasingly sure of his infallibility as the years progress without his being contradicted (except in court, which is part of the game).

Our medicolegal system has two fundamental flaws. One is that British justice is adversarial. Two lawyers present opposing arguments and one or other wins. This system has the advantage of administrative convenience, but from any other point of view it is primitive. To have to decide that a doctor is either negligent or competent is ridiculous; the truth usually lies somewhere between. To persuade two medical experts to give opposite points of view is an affront to medicine. In private these two doctors will agree on most aspects of the case, but in public the system forces them to come to diametrically opposed conclusions. Without meaning to, the lawyers are making fools of us. I believe that medicolegal cases in Britain, as in parts of Europe, should be decided by an inquisitorial system rather than by confrontation. Impartial experts should give advice to the judge without being coached by the contestants.

The second flaw is that medical experts are chosen by lawyers, not by doctors. Thus a judge may accept an idiosyncratic or out of date opinion from an impressive looking doctor who has no reputation outside lawyers' offices. Yet that one doctor's opinion, by influencing the judge's decision, can have a more profound effect on practice than the recommendations of a royal college with its democratically elected council and its specialist committees. Doctors, as good citizens, have great respect for the law, but we tend to forget that court decisions are based on medical advice. The advice given by expert witnesses depends on their age, on where they practise (or practised), and sometimes on personal prejudice. It ought to be susceptible to peer review. We cannot demand the right to referee judges' decisions, but we ought to monitor the "expert" advice given to the courts and subject it to debate within our own profession.

## *Lunar House*

Lunar House is an office block beside a dual carriageway in Croydon, a few minutes' walk from the station. Your registrar or senior house officer may know it, for it is the place where the Home Office inspects the papers of aliens. My Egyptian registrar has to go there regularly and accepts the 240 mile round trip with smiling fatalism. The same could not be said about his Australian predecessor, whose pithy comments about Croydon in general and the Home Office in particular made me curious to see the place.

The trick is to be near the head of the queue at 8 30 am. Delightful staff at the door give you a numbered ticket and direct you to the first floor, which is a mixture of post office and airport. Rows of yellow benches face a long wall of glass partitions. Fluttering signs like flight indicators show what number is being called and a loudspeaker tells you which desk to go to. Of the 34 desks, only seven had clients while I waited. Five were out of use and at another five the clerk had disappeared leaving a jacket or cardigan over the chairback. At the remaining 17 the clerks were chatting to one another.

It would have taken two hours for me to be called. I interrupted a clerk, who was discussing holiday rotas with a colleague, to ask how many doctors he saw. "I can't give you that information," he replied. Eventually he guessed at five doctors each day. "Postgraduates studying here," he added.

My registrar need not attend in person. He could post his passport and wait for eight to 12 weeks (at least) for it to be returned. That would not appeal to me. I feel uneasy abroad when my passport is taken away for a few hours. For the pessimist there is no guarantee that his passport will ever come back: the Home Office once dealt with the problem of its postal workload by not opening its mailbags. For cautious doctors from Penzance to Wick there is no alternative to an excursion to Croydon.

The numbers are substantial. Approximately 4000 doctors have limited registration with the General Medical Council. Not all of these are aliens, but some with full registration are. After the Preliminary Language Assessment Board examination the Home Office allows four years for postgraduate training, and during this time the doctor must make regular pilgrimages to Croydon and wait for hours to assure a clerk that he intends leaving Britain when his training is over.

*People approach as supplicants*

Normally when a clerk keeps someone waiting unnecessarily the client ought to make a scene. In Lunar House this does not happen. People approach the desks as supplicants, hoping no irregularity will be found in their papers. As a native with a passport good for a decade, I could have complained but I didn't feel angry enough. After all, I could get up and leave. The aliens, however, had to sit and watch the clerks socialising while they calculated how long it would take to be seen and get back to Victoria, then Euston, then Crewe or wherever.

The clerks are neither malicious nor stupid. They have two problems. Firstly, they are ill informed. The doctors they keep waiting are more than "postgraduates studying here." Many are part of the backbone of the NHS. For example, almost 60% of the obstetric registrars in England are overseas graduates. If alien doctors were not allowed to work here casualty departments and labour wards up and down the country would be in trouble and might have to close. These registrars and senior house officers are classed as postgraduate students by the Home Office but if one of our relatives has a car crash or needs a caesarean section these doctors suddenly become qualified to treat her.

The clerks' second problem is that they are acting as we want them to act. All nations like to keep foreigners waiting. We have all queued at airports to have our passports needlessly stamped: I suppose travellers who give their occupation as "international terrorist" are turned away but I have never seen this happen. Making people wait is a way of establishing superiority. Inferiors "wait upon" their betters, which is why punctuality is the politeness of kings. During his state visit Mr Gorbachev's car swept into Windsor Castle on the stroke of noon because anything else would have been an insult. We doctors keep our patients waiting ostensibly because we are so busy, but it is interesting to work out how far up the social scale our patient has to be for her time to be more valuable than ours.

*Synonym for unhelpfulness*

This is the unconscious reason why we tolerate the arrogance of the Home Office towards our colleagues. Consciously, however, nobody wants to inconvenience overseas doctors working in the NHS. But what alternatives are there, short of abolishing all immigration controls for all medical graduates? One possible alternative would be courtesy and efficiency. These would be radical innovations for the Home Office, whose name has become a synonym for unhelpfulness. Accustomed to dealing with people who have no votes and who speak with funny accents, its staff would no doubt be genuinely puzzled by the idea that their clientele deserves prompt service.

Nevertheless, the idea is worth pursuing. The next time our registrar asks for a day or two off to go to Croydon we can write to the Home Secretary asking why his staff need more than three months to open an envelope and stamp a doctor's passport. We might even suggest that the three main institutions dealing with overseas doctors could communicate with one another – something that does not happen at present. Health authorities, the Home Office, and the General Medical Council are each connected to British Telecom's well advertised facilities, and in this computer age it should not require personal visits for the Home Office to be told which aliens are being employed to prop up the NHS. The Home Office may argue that it does not have the resources to work out ways of making life easier for overworked obstetric registrars, but its civil servants would surely be more usefully employed helping doctors than discussing holiday rotas.

## *Body Language for Beginners*

When television cameras first appeared in the House of Commons many MPs were coached on how to present themselves to the nation. One of the main lessons was that the impression speakers give depends to only a small extent on the words they choose. More important is their tone of voice and more important still is their body language. The impact of fine words about, say, blood, toil, tears, and sweat is negated if the speakers are energetically scratching themselves through their trouser pockets or if the people behind them are searching for a dropped contact lens.

This lesson is also important for doctors but unfortunately it is not taught to us as students. For decades medical schools have been ruled by those who believe that the highest quality to which a doctor can aspire is invisibility. We are taught that the practitioner should sit in the shadows of his consulting room uttering a series of encouraging grunts while the patient tells his story. Students come to believe that taking a good history is the acme of the art of medicine and that healing the sick is the prerogative of the pharmacist.

After graduation, however, it dawns on us that we have to talk to patients as well as listen – indeed, that what we say is more important than what we write on the prescription form. We learn by trial and error to make ourselves understood and our main error is that we rely on words. Thanks to the Commons I now know that I should use my body, too, and I hasten to pass on what I have learnt so far about the messages it can convey.

### *Beginning and ending the interview*

Firstly, the arms. Consultations are started with the right arm, which should be extended towards the patient. This manoeuvre has to be carried out with precision or it may be misunderstood. The palm must face towards the doctor's left. If it faces downwards the patient may try to kiss your hand, and if it faces upwards he may reach for his wallet. Do not flex the fingers too much or the patient will expect good news. Do not extend the arm too rapidly or swing it from side to side; the patient may counter with an uppercut.

The left arm is used to end the interview. This is done by abducting the arm at the shoulder, flexing the elbow and pronating forearm, while at the same time turning your head to the left. Whether or not you are wearing a watch, this gesture is universally understood. If the patient keeps talking you may have to reinforce the hint by closing the case notes, audibly if necessary. If this does not work you should stand up, again flexing the left elbow and extending the right arm as described above. If the patient still does not move hand him his coat or, if appropriate, zip up his bomber jacket.

Some patients, by contrast, are oversensitive to the doctor looking at his or her watch. They will clam up if your glance strays near your left wrist, even if you try to disguise the action by stretching up to a high shelf or brushing dust vigorously from your sleeve. In these circumstances look at the patient's watch or, if this is out of sight, the nurse's, which is usually pinned close to her name badge. In these days of concern about sexual harassment, however, take care when peering at the nurse's breast, especially if you are shortsighted.

Now for the rest of the body. On ward rounds the consultant's body can speak volumes. Common mistakes are to remain in a standing position (intimidating the patient), to hide behind the case notes (ignoring the patient), or to form a huddle with the houseman and registrar (excluding the patient). If you sit on the bed you will establish better eye contact, but if you lie on it you will be suspended from duty. Casually straightening the patient's newspaper shows that you cannot cope with upside down reading. Never lean on anything in the ward: nowadays everything either moves or folds up.

In the consulting room your body may give away tell tale signs of inattention. These include tapping your feet, opening your desk drawers, or balancing on two legs of your chair. Saying "Yes, yes, please go on" as you pick yourself up from the floor is unconvincing because it contradicts what your body is telling the patient. Here is some more of the body's vocabulary. Leaning forward signifies earnestness or deafness. Stroking your beard indicates thoughtfulness but stroking your moustache indicates vanity. Putting away your pen shows that you have made up your mind and some straight talking is to follow. Taking off your glasses means that you are speaking from the heart, but the effect is lost unless you memorise beforehand exactly where the patient is.

*Immobility is the key*

Practise expressing attentiveness through your body. You do this by keeping still, as demonstrated every night on television. On the screen fidgeting implies distraction, so stars from Michael Aspel to Clint Eastwood have built successful careers on immobility. Lack of body movement focuses attention on the eyes, and the doctor's eyes should express concern. Not for us the twinkle of a Bonnie Langford or a Russ Abbott. Behind the doctor's calm gaze should lie pain – not merely the distress of overwork but sadness at the tragedy of life. It helps if you have a hidden sorrow, which is why, years ago, the Lancet included haemorrhoids in a list of prerequisites for the successful practitioner.

Now to the difficult matter of body contact between doctor and patient. During a formal examination contact is ritualised to protect both parties, but at other times touch can form a bond between them. Nowadays most doctors use the laying on of hands for diagnostic purposes only, leaving therapeutic touching to osteopaths and physiotherapists. Nevertheless, some patients become visibly brighter after being examined, and it occurs to me that the healing powers of the rubber glove and tendon hammer are perhaps underrated these days.

Finally, your body can talk to your colleagues. Again, remember the importance of immobility: on the lecture platform it shows poise; in the committee room it shows stubbornness; and on social occasions it encourages others to buy the drinks. Cultivate a slight stoop, which gives you a concerned air in conversation and distinguishes you from sales representatives. A limp is permissible in the skiing season. You should avoid coughs and tics but it is best not to look too robust. Colleagues rarely trust a really healthy looking doctor.

## *Rogue Mail*

For many of us the first task of the day is to sift the real letters from the junk mail. This can be difficult. No longer are all circulars posted in Hampshire: now they may be marked "Private and confidential" or addressed in feminine handwriting. Nevertheless, the busy doctor usually works out which letters to drop unread into the waste bin. In case you wondered what you were missing by doing so here is a selection from my postbag.

*The Consultant Obstetrician,*
*Leicester Royal Infirmary*
*Date as postmark*

Dear Doctor,

Episiotomy is a common procedure, but little research has been done on it. Surprisingly, there are no data on whether right sided episiotomies are better than left sided ones. To answer this vital question, I am sending the enclosed questionnaire to 500 random obstetricians. It is ENTIRELY CONFIDENTIAL (the reference number is to check on non-responders).

Please remember to fill in your date and place of graduation, and to estimate as closely as you can the number of episiotomies you repaired at each stage of your training. Pages 37-45 need be completed only by left handed doctors. Question 73(d) contains an error: it should read "How many one legged patients have you delivered since obtaining the MRCOG?" The questionnaire should take only two hours to complete. Your cooperation is crucial if my study is to stand anv chance of publication.

Yours faithfully,

J O DRIFE FRCSED,
University of Leicester

It gives me genuine personal pleasure to inform you, Dr FRCSED, that you have been elected by our Board of Advisers for inclusion in the exclusive Directory of Doctors of Achievement of the Twentieth Century. I enclose our questionnaire. Please TYPE the details of your education and military service in the boxes as indicated. Due to pressure of space we cannot include details of your academic publications (if any) but these may be summarised in no more than FIVE words. This prestigious reference work is scheduled for publication within a few months and you, Dr FRCSED, can order it at the special prepublication price of £155.75. If you know of anyone else who should be included please send them the enclosed spare questionnaire. Once again, Dr FRCSED, my congratulations on the honour of your inclusion in this exclusive directory, which comes in a variety of luxury bindings to enhance your home.

Yours very sincerely,

*Sehr geehrter Kollege!*

*DAS HANDBUCH VON EPISIOTOMIE*
*Herausgeber:*
*Prof Dr Med Otto Klistiermenger, MD.*

Eine NEUE sehr wichtige Publikation! 25 Bander!
Inhalt:
Bander 1-8: Pathologische Anatomie der Pelvischemuskulatur
Bander 9-16: Klassifizierung von Fleischwunden im Niederkunft
Bander 17-25: Chirurgischtechnicken fur Episiotomireparatur.

"Ein musst fur alle gynakologischen Buchstander!"
Arch Episiot.

*From: The Chief Medical Officer*
*To: All Doctors in the United Kingdom*

Dear Doctor,

IMPORTANT NOTICE

Hairline cracks have been reported in the heels of some surgical boots manufactured by Fratri Lacrimacristi of Italy. The fault in the suppliers' quality control department has now been rectified. The boots bear the trademark "PIED ANGELICA" on the instep. They may be liable to give way under pressure as, for example, in jumping off a bus or Morris dancing. Only LEFT boots are affected. As none of the affected batch has yet been released for sale this notice is for information only, though the withdrawal and replacement of stocks may cause some inconvenience. I am closely monitoring the situation.

Yours faithfully,

*Dr J Drife (or executor),*
*Leicester*

Dear Dr Drife,

Only last week a doctor friend of mine, an obstetrician like yourself, left home for work as usual. He got into his fully serviced car, put on his seatbelt, and drove carefully to work. He parked considerately and walked safely across the car park to the hospital. Having completed a conscientious ward round he hurried to the outpatient clinic still wearing his stethoscope round his neck. Unfortunately, due to NHS cutbacks, the revolving door of the clinic was malfunctioning and when a gust of wind caught his stethoscope a terrible accident occurred. FORTUNATELY, HE WAS FULLY INSURED, so his dependants can look forward to a financially secure future. He had realised the importance of dealing with people who understand the special problems of doctors. Do not leave your family's future at risk for a moment longer: send the enclosed reply paid card NOW!

Yours sincerely,

*To: Fellows and Members, RCGP and RCOG,*
*and to members, Royal College of Midwives and Chartered Society of Physiotherapists*

Dear Colleague,
British Episiotomy Society

We feel the time is right for the foundation of a new society to enhance dialogue between GPs, obstetricians, midwives, etc. At present there is no national forum for discussing the physical, psychological, and sociological aspects of perineal incision. Our aim is to create an interactive group of committed practitioners who can advance the understanding of episiotomy, increase public awareness, and lobby parliament. We have been fortunate in obtaining initial support from Megadrug Pharmaceuticals, makers of "Cloud 9," a local anaesthetic spray which does not damage the ozone layer. Our first meeting will be held in Jersey, well known to viewers of *Bergerac*, and the speaker will be writer and broadcaster Lucy de Loom, author of the best seller *Fourchette ou Couteau?* I enclose a banker's order for the modest annual subscription and look forward to meeting you in Jersey.

Yours faithfully,

Reading all my mail was a harrowing experience. So many unrepeatable offers, so little disposable income. I'm afraid the worthy causes remain unsupported and the pharmaceutical innovations unprescribed, and all I have is a sense of guilt about those pulped trees and that expressionless postman. There are eight doctors in our street and we all avoid his eye. What did he do, we wonder, to deserve his punishment posting?

# *"Soundings"* *1991-2006*

*During this time I was Professor of Obstetrics and Gynaecology in Leeds.*

## *Operation Notes*

Operating today. ?Time to write article between cases. ?Why surgeons always write notes in telegraphese with no auxiliary verbs. Save time, perhaps. ?Why hospital notes always put question mark at beginning of sentence, not end. Complete mystery. Perhaps all hospitals originally staffed by Spaniards.

Surgeons and playwrights only people who work in pyjamas. But playwrights' pyjamas fit, I bet. Surgeons' not fit. Hospital laundry think surgical teams either Harlem Globetrotters or Seven Dwarfs. ?Why some surgical pyjamas have flies. Unnecessary – surgeons oliguric while operating. ?Deliberate insult by sewing room – flies only 1 cm diameter.

Furthermore, flies permanently open. Doctor's dilemma: ?ignore flies – risk upsetting student nurses (worse, amusing them); ?seal with sticking plaster – but pink too conspicuous, draw glances. Mind you, nurses use sticking plaster on theatre dresses – otherwise spectacular decolletage, surgeons distracted, patient at risk.

Watch out, thief about in changing room. Pyjama pocket not big enough bleep, watch, pen, chequebook, credit cards, filofax. Find locker with key. Key disappear hole in pocket damn blast, tie round neck on gauze bandage.

Where in blazes boots with name on? Forced wear clogs marked "student." Athlete's foot for sure. Clomp around taking surreptitious look everyone's heels. If catch student with consultant boots, have guts garters.

Surgical hats all disposable nowadays. High quality paper. "Made in Texas," says box, "assembled in Mexico." Mind boggles. Paper hat traffic across Rio Grande, then transatlantic shipment – rum, molasses, paper hats. ?Why NHS choose Mexican hats. ?DoH worldwide hatfinding tour: find perfect hat – meet British Standard, not disintegrate midway through operation.

Flight of fancy. Hat trials in England and Mexico. Final test – hot lights, really incompetent surgeon, bathed in sweat throughout operation. Wonder why hats necessary anyway: most surgeons balding – in distinguished sort of way.

Scrub up now. Nailbrushes individually wrapped. Impossible open plastic packaging. Not allowed use teeth. Brushes made in Europe: multilingual instructions all over box. Now know how say "'fingernails" eight languages. English, French, German, Spanish, er, Italian.... No, Italian, Spanish. ?Which one Norwegian.

Never managed get hang elbow taps. ?Left cold, right hot. ?Inwards off, outwards on. ?Other way round. Every hospital different. Sometimes think plumber visit weekly, change round. Three minutes later temperature just right, then houseman finish at other end, turn off her taps with flourish, surgeon utter silent scream.

Teach student scrubbing. Drop towel, Mr Smith. No, just drop it. Yes, on floor. ?Where else. Give me strength God. Thought sterile technique primordial instinct – like fear, rage. Forgot has to be learned.

Hate disposable gowns. Even higher quality paper. Cannot believe cheaper than laundry. Rio Grande long way off, heaven's sake. ?Why so cheap: ?nearer rainforest, ?cheap labour. Pity Mexican peasant – assemble hats all day, wife in cardboard city, dozen bambinos. And probably illiterate, poor thing.

## *Three Nations*

Like other expatriate Scottish doctors, I am sometimes guilty of sentimentalising the land of my graduation. I look back fondly through heather tinted spectacles at a medically self sufficient country with adequate numbers of doctors, where private medicine – though not unknown – seemed an unnecessary self indulgence for snobbish patients. Then I tell myself this is mere tartan nostalgia: Scots are, after all, less healthy than the English and the NHS has similar problems north and south of the border.

Picture my surprise, then, when I found hard evidence for my patriotic prejudice. Recently the Royal College of Obstetricians and Gynaecologists conducted a census of doctors in maternity units, relating staff levels to the number of deliveries. In Scotland there is one consultant obstetrician to 416 births, around London the ratio is one to 697 and in Yorkshire (where I now work) there is one consultant to 1005 births. Of course, there is a similar discrepancy in the numbers of medical schools – one for every million people in Scotland and London, and one for every three million in the English provinces.

Scotland has exported doctors ever since the eighteenth century, when her universities embraced clinical medicine. Oxford and Cambridge, by contrast, did not found clinical schools until 1939 and 1975 respectively, and for centuries English students gravitated to the capital for clinical teaching. Thus today Britain has three medical nations – Scotland, England, and London. Scotland and London are still purveyors of consultants to the rest of the country: the RCOG survey showed that in obstetrics the ratio of senior registrars to deliveries is 1:2078 in Scotland, 1:3024 in London, and 1:5082 in England.

In the past it would have been unreasonable to distinguish between London and the rest of England, but nowadays the concept of capital cities is becoming dated. In the era of the fax machine it is no longer necessary for a nation's talent to be concentrated in one town. Medicine's London centred attitude can irritate – for example, when London hospitals mount nationwide appeals for money. Londoners do not reciprocate with donations to, say, Oldham or Leeds, which respectively pioneered in vitro fertilisation and renal dialysis.

Much more annoying, however, is the upheaval in the provinces from a health service reorganisation aimed primarily at London. The concept of hospitals competing with one another may make sense within the boundary of the M25 but is meaningless in most of England. But politicians and civil servants live in the home counties, see only London medicine, and indeed expect doctors to travel to meet them in Westminster or in Southwark. The only times that senior politicians enter provincial hospitals are after plane crashes.

Forty million people live in the English provinces. Their needs should be considered first, not last, in reforms of the health service. In spite of lip service paid to reallocating resources we are far from seeing NHS money being distributed fairly among Britain's three medical nations. In the next NHS reform – not, I guess, so far away – the planners should for once start with the regions, aiming at creating sixteen equal nations instead of three unequal ones.

## *Coats of Many Colours*

My fourteenth graduation ceremonial, counting my own and other people's. Haven't missed one since becoming a consultant. The one annual chance for a professor to dress up in technicolor plumage and flaunt status. No opportunity for academic showmanship in NHS clinics – no framed diplomas on walls, like consulting rooms in cartoons. Pity. Might be fun to have the clerk not only change names on the board but take down and put up framed degrees – all Latin, sealing wax, and Iacobus Owen Drifus. Give queue something to think about, what?

Each year resolve to arrive at graduation suave, cool, plenty of time, but medical faculty usually ends up dashing in, seconds to spare. Shouldn't squeeze in quick hysterectomy before the organ recital, but ceremonial seems like skiving, somehow. Frantic rush from operating theatre to great hall, then horrors, realise that gown hirers in different building. Accost nearest graduand – where did you get that gown? Graduand blinks, parents stare aghast – has university changed its mind after all? Eventually find Aladdin's cave of academic dress. Hand over ticket: man leafs laboriously through downmarket black gowns, ignoring hand signals that mine is red one at the end.

Edinburgh MD gown designed for draughty Scottish lecture hall in winter, not quartermile sprint in July. Arrive glowing at hall, put on hat over perspiring forehead. Hat unbelievably silly, worse every year. Try different angles: look like either Statue of Liberty or Bart Simpson. Why no one tell me this before I apply for university? UCCA should organise show with catwalk, or at least send candidates illustrations of robes. Emeritus professor appears in elegant gown with sumptuous colours; under envious questioning admits it was run up to his own specifications by friendly tailor. Prettiest hat is Leeds PhD – broad brim, floppy top, like Queen Mum at Garter ceremony.

Line up in twos, introduce ourselves, worry whether gowns clash. Start walking out of step, sign of academic integrity. Hood, attached by loop to shirt button, threatens to pull shirt up, strangle wearer. Parents turn heads slightly as we process down centre aisle. Column splits: up on to platform, turn and face congregation. Gosh, say parents, Bart Simpson asphyxiating. Sit down, adjust shirt, remove hat at last thank goodness.

Always enjoy ceremony, though know chancellor's speech by heart now. Watch graduands' faces: by turns blasé, embarrassed, amused, then anticipation and, at moment of truth, pure pleasure. Parents proud but more circumspect. Everyone self conscious – even chancellor on best behaviour, knows one hiccup would destroy magic. My delight tempered by realisation that I now identify with grey haired parents, not tanned graduands.

Afterwards sherry, strawberries, cameras. Congratulate pretty graduate. Pretty graduate reminds me we last met in pass-fail viva. Now my turn to be lost for snappy answer, but it doesn't matter. All smiles today: shared happiness of great life event. Birth of new doctors after long gestation. Or rather, christening: stress of labour gone but not forgotten. Only at this ceremony men too wear silly hats.

## *One in Three*

It shocked me when I worked out that one third of British women will have a therapeutic abortion. I checked my figures. Our abortion rate is 15/1000 women aged 15-44. During 30 years, that adds up to 450/1000 – nearly one in two. But some women have more than one termination. In 1989, of the 170,463 English and Welsh women undergoing abortion, 36,821 had already had at least one. That means four fifths had not, so the rate of first time abortions is 12/1000. During 30 years, that's 360/1000 – one in three. I tried another way. In 1989 there were 690,961 births in England and Wales. The average family has two children, so about 346,000 were first births. With 133,642 first abortions, that's one first abortion to three first births.

On reflection, what's shocking is that this figure took so much working out. The statistics are public and have changed little in seventeen years. They now stand as a national monument to the inadequacy of sex education and contraceptive provision in Britain. *One in three* should be carved on Mrs Bottomley's desk and painted on the teacups at the Department of Health. At present the department's idea of promoting women's health begins and ends with screening: its image of Today's Woman is a pair of breasts attached to a cervix. The government's response to the continuing epidemic of unwanted pregnancy has been to encourage the closure of family planning clinics.

Britain's abortion rate is lower than those in, say, Russia or Japan, where most women experience abortion, some many times. In Holland, by contrast, the rate is 5/1000 – one third of ours – though abortion is readily available. I assumed this was due to easy access to contraception, but a Dutch colleague told me there is more to it than that. In Holland, he said, families discuss the subject openly. That gave me pause: I talk a lot about family planning but not at our own dinner table.

So will one in three remain unchanged – a side effect of the British tradition that sex is for seaside postcards and Sunday papers but not for rational discussion? I hope not. We have altered other national indicators of ill health. Sixty years ago the maternal death rate seemed immutable, but it fell dramatically once the problem was tackled by health workers and government together. The current abortion rate ought to generate a similar response. Instead it provokes mere debate, posturings from pressure groups, and a vague British wish that sex had never been invented.

Who will take the initiative? The Department of Health did nothing about advertising contraception until the advent of AIDS. Politicians believe – erroneously – that the only votes in abortion come from trying to ban it, so they do nothing and 40,000 teenage girls go through hell every year as a result. We all thought that abortions happen to a little group of recidivists. We should remember *one in three* next time we go to the theatre or to a dinner party. Or – especially – when we wait outside the school to take our daughters home.

## *Have Slides, Will Travel*

Unfamiliar envelope: invitation to lecture abroad. Pleasure tinged with disbelief – really necessary fly me all that way for just 45 minutes plus questions? And shouldn't they be asking someone older? Accept with alacrity before they change minds. If Hon Sec's head on platter afterwards, his problem not mine.

Months pass, then last minute dash to medical photography. Cynical cartoons on wall, including picture of hysterical photographers saying "You want it WHEN?" Receptionist tries to keep straight face at yet another supplicant with impossible deadline.

Slides completed, minutes to spare. Photographer much better than desktop slidemaker: computer doesn't frown and click tongue to discourage lecturer from producing overcomplicated slides.

Essential that slides are simple, even if they make lecturer look simple too. Slidemaking twentieth century skill: fun to imagine great minds of history distilling wisdom into two by twos. If projectors around in first century AD, might have had St Paul's slides to the Corinthians:

**3 CHARITY**

- **suffereth long**
- **is kind**
- **envieth not**
- **vaunteth not itself**
- **is not puffed up**

Stop daydreaming, return to slide cabinet for old faithfuls. Usually end up including something old, something new, something borrowed.... Prefer to take too many, make final selection just before lecture. Feel insecure travelling with slides – can't trust them to suitcase. No use if sent Schipol, Anchorage, Luton, returned three weeks later. Keep on person, ideally – should have slide belt like money belt, coat with lots of pockets like tout, or bandoliers (slidoliers?) like Mexican bandit.

Trouble is, slides very heavy en masse. Stagger through green channel with knees giving way. Sure to be body searched. "Excuse me, sir. About these pictures. You say they are for a conference of gynaecologists?"

Medical audiences all supposed to understand English. Not so projectionists. Like golf caddies they can humble the most experienced pro. In projection room they read tabloids during question time, create memorable experiences when lights go down. For example, Arabic speaking projectionist carefully took slides from holder row by row reading from right to left, not left to right. Worse things happen in China, probably.

Big congress: load slides myself, watch carousel sealed, taken away. Night of separation anxiety. When correct picture appears on screen next day, relax – but too soon. Slides all different thicknesses, so each comes up slightly blurred. Lecture develops into series of epic struggles. First: lecturer versus projectionist ("I said focus, please"). Native speaker disappears into projection room to translate lecturer's pleas.

Round two: projectionist versus projector. Audience agog as image expands, contracts, moves in and out of focus, while red dot of laser pointer bounces randomly around screen, walls, ceiling. Actual words of lecture now peripheral to gripping visual spectacle.

Still, at least audience stay awake.

## *Medicine as Circus*

If three men in jeans turned up at my clinic and asked if they could watch I should refuse. Consultations are private, I'd tell them: the community health council would take a dim view of my allowing strangers in. The men might argue that sick people are fascinating and that it is in doctors' interests to let the public see how a hospital works. I would reply that patients don't like voyeurs, and have them thrown out.

If, however, the three men turned up with arc lights, a furry microphone, and a television camera my reaction would be different. Provided they had permission from the hospital manager, I would probably help. I might ask patients to do us a favour by appearing. Why, I wonder, would I allow millions of strangers to watch me at work while I would kick out three?

The answer, of course, is vanity. Fame is the spur that drives us on to television, though we try to disguise it. We say we are helping health education, enhancing public relations, raising money, or applying political pressure. Enlarging one's private practice has – at least in the past – been an unacceptable reason for appearing on television, but encouraging referrals to one's hospital is OK. Indeed, some NHS trusts employ public relations staff to assist the process.

The media like hospitals because they are packed with human interest stories. Children battling bravely against cancer are best – consent to publicity being given by the anguished parents. Sick adults can be almost as heart tugging. At least twice in recent months television has shown dying patients – with permission from the recently bereaved relatives. Our profession generally enjoyed the resulting programmes because the doctors came over well.

When publicity favours us we think it must be good. We rarely ask whether appearing on television is best for our patients. All professions confuse their clients' interests with their own. Parliament agonised about being televised because of fear that MPs might appear uncouth, and British courtrooms do not admit cameras because it would mean that the lawyers were no longer in absolute control. But both parliament and the courts have public galleries and, of course, should be televised. Medicine is confidential and should not, however much it inflates our egos and our professional image.

Media people accuse me of paternalism. Patients, they say, can decide for themselves whether to appear and doctors have no right to interfere. I accept this, and when patients ask my help with publicity I do not refuse. However, I don't like initiating the process. I'm not a recruiting sergeant for television companies or NHS publicists. I do not believe that patients should arrive in hospital to find a camera crew already installed. You'll notice that ill people on television are usually NHS patients: among the things private patients pay for is the right to be treated with dignity. There seems to be no machinery to stop hospitals turning themselves into circuses. Another job for the ethical committee?

## *The Seven Bleeps*

As junior hospital doctors mature, their white coats become crisper, their frowns become more authoritative, and even their bleeps metamorphose. The milestones of bleep development are reminiscent of Shakespeare's seven ages.

The houseman's bleep, like a toddler, vocalises constantly, keeping its wearer in touch with the trivia of hospital life – a new rash, a tissued drip, or unprescribed sleeping tablets. The recent graduate tolerates this like a proud parent, indulging the bleep's whims. He learns bleep play, paging himself as it hides in the laundry basket.

Next, the bleep develops new reflexes, somehow connected with the doctor's nervous system. For example, the recto-bleep reflex ensures that whenever the houseman sits on a toilet his bleep goes off. If this primitive reflex persists it may result in diverticular disease in the doctor and non-accidental injury to the bleep.

When the bleep starts to talk it speaks in a harsh, atmospheric tone like a railway announcer. It listens to the doctor's consultations, and when he is about to break really bad news or receive an intimate confidence, it suddenly bursts out, asking him to ring the casualty department. After suffering months of such abuse, the hospital doctor becomes emotionally withdrawn and indeed may remain incapable of empathising with patients ever again.

The crash bleep is the apotheosis of its power. As soon as it sounds, the wearer leaps up, suffers coronary spasm, and rushes out of the room. The bleep pauses dramatically, and then says, "Testing, testing." In some hospitals the crash bleep's distinctive note is a series of fast tones: in others, slow tones. Moving from one hospital to another is a stimulating experience.

The registrar stage is like adolescence, as the wearer begins to show signs of disobedience. These first appear when doctor and bleep are attending a lecture. The bleep goes off in (of course) a quiet part of the meeting. The speaker, despite being used to such interruptions, loses his thread. The registrar stares fixedly ahead – as if being bleeped, like passing wind, was something that could be blamed on his neighbour. The whole audience tenses for the second bleep. When it comes, the registrar frowns to indicate that this puzzling phenomenon has never happened before, gathers his white coat around him and heads for the door, closing it with elaborate precautions against causing any disturbance.

The most remarkable stage is the senior registrar's bleep, which works by telepathy, for it contains no batteries. This is how the senior registrar filters out the unimportant messages – which is 95% of them. For the remaining 5%, thought transference or an astute switchboard operator ensure that the senior registrar appears just when needed, or calls in after the problem has been safely dealt with.

The consultant needs a bleep with more gadgets than other people's bleeps. Ideally it should be thin as a credit card, with a memory, a liquid crystal display, and a 200 mile radius, and should give advice to the senior house officer without bothering the consultant at all.

## *Rags to Riches*

In his monologue on menstruation, the comedian Ben Elton asks his audience what it would be like if men had periods. He imagines W G Grace speaking at a cricketing dinner. "There I was," he roars, "halfway to the wicket and what d'you think – MY PERIOD STARTED!" His point is that if menses were masculine they would not be taboo.

After twenty years of talking to women about their periods, I should hate to menstruate. The human ovarian cycle is one of Nature's more heartless practical jokes. Sheep come into season once a year; rabbits are induced ovulators, but only women (and a few monkeys) have to cope with monthly incontinence of blood. I would resent carrying a handbag, queuing for inadequate toilets, and smiling through my uterine contractions.

Because I'm male I don't menstruate, and the same applies to most MPs and civil servants. This is why the government thinks it is reasonable to tax the menstrual flow. As if 37 years of monthly bleeds were not misery enough, HM Customs and Excise charge value added tax (VAT) on sanitary protection.

How much profit does the state make from menstruation? A packet of 40 sanitary towels costs £3 to £5 depending on the brand. A woman who uses a whole packet each month will spend £40 to £65 a year. With over 13 million menstruating women in Britain, the market could be worth £500 million a year, but the manufacturers of tampons give a more conservative estimate of £179 million – VAT on this figure amounts to over £30 million a year.

On current prices the average woman will pay about £100 tax on her periods during her life. A woman who consults you with genuine menorrhagia, however, will pay considerably more. A packet of twenty regular tampons costs about £1.74 but a packet of forty super absorbent tampons costs £3.49. If you take a detailed history of menorrhagia you will find that some women pad themselves up with a tampon and more than one towel in order to go to work. Even if your patient ends up with a hysterectomy the state will still have made a profit from her disorder.

Services that are exempt from VAT include those of doctors, dentists, and opticians, and – perhaps less predictably – betting and gaming and the provision of credit. Zero rated items include the dispensing of prescriptions, aids for handicapped people, food, books, newspapers, houseboats, and children's clothes. The list gives an endearing insight into what the well educated British male considers important. Condoms, needless to say, are taxed at the full rate. AIDS, which has made condoms respectable, might change this, but can anything stop civil servants sniggering about sanitary towels?

Women don't complain because it isn't done to make a fuss about your periods. Women who reach positions of influence don't want to lose face by talking about menstruation, and in any case such women are usually comfortably off and postmenopausal. The sums are trivial – £30 million doesn't buy much nowadays – but the principle isn't. It is disgraceful to tax menorrhagia.

## *A Doctor Writhes*

Do you have any rules about entry?" I bellowed. This was the first time I had been to a nightclub in Yorkshire. The man behind the half door leaned forward, grinned, and yelled, "Gotta be smartly dressed."

We agreed that in my black pinstripe suit, waistcoat, watch chain, and college tie, I was well on the safe side of the "no jeans" regulations. I paid £2.50 and entered. The music pounded even more loudly, lights flashed, and a mass of bodies seethed on the dance floor. Behind a railing on a mezzanine were more swaying people. There was a bar but hardly anyone stood beside it. Stroboscopes came on for a few seconds and went off. Multiple spotlights changed colour. It was like one of those 2 am television shows from Preston or Coventry, except that no one came up to me and started pulling faces.

When my students had invited me to join their celebrations I had envisaged discos I remembered from the sixties – people grouped by gender for most of the evening, shouted conversations, and intermittent dancing to records that jumped if you stamped your foot. The nineties version was a revelation: if you wanted to dance, you danced, and the club had a system of stimuli that plugged directly into your hypothalamus. Conversation was impossible. People joined the throng in groups, jumped around, and went away again. This was tribal, as far from the valse veleta as you could imagine, and in its way more sophisticated.

I could recognise nobody and began to think that my students, flushed with their exam success, had gone home. Then I saw them in the middle of the floor, where the music was loud enough to feel. The beat thudded down from the roof and throbbed up through the floor.

"Great sound system," yelled one, "pain threshold but no distortion." My body responded with Jacksonian movements – Hughlings Jackson, unfortunately, not Michael. One toe began to twitch, then a leg, then the other limbs joined in.

This was a purely physical experience – like swimming, except that one was immersed in sound rather than water. The enveloping rhythms made the ambience even more intrauterine, and like foetuses our movements were only partially coordinated. I began to enjoy myself and writhed with growing gusto, though I drew the line at jumping up and down on the spot. Bald head nodding, paunch wobbling, I gyrated around my tiny personal space. The students pretended not to notice.

The onset of chest pain reminded me it was time to make an excuse and leave. In this freestyle place, however, no excuses were necessary and indeed it was difficult to catch the eye of one's pogosticking host. I drove sweatily home with my ears ringing. The first time I had experienced tinnitus was in 1965 after a Rolling Stones concert in a Cardiff cinema, where the deafening noise had come mainly from the screaming audience. I decided I could afford to sacrifice a few ear cells every quarter century.

## *Are Breasts Redundant Organs?*

Sometimes when I'm lecturing I point out how easy it would be to abolish breast cancer. My suggestion tends to outrage the men in the audience and I have to reassure them that my proposition is philosophical, not practical. Women listeners, however, usually react more thoughtfully.

Breast cancer becomes more common with age and will eventually affect at least one in seventeen women in Britain. Screening may improve survival rates but does not aim at abolishing the disease altogether. The way to eradicate breast cancer is to remove the breasts before the cancer develops. The age at which she has the operation may be left to the woman. With the insertion of implants it could be carried out at any age, but the sensible option would be prophylactic mastectomy either at the completion of her family or at the menopause.

My suggestion is so shocking that I am beginning to lose my nerve as I type this. Why? The reason lies in the emotional importance not of the milk glands but of the fat that surrounds them. It is this fat that swells at puberty and makes a girl realise she is a woman. The fat has nothing to do with lactation but is a sexual signal, like the chimpanzee's swollen perineum. Men respond because they are programmed to do so, not because of cultural influences.

We hate to think that we are affected by instinct. Like hypnotists' victims we rationalise our reactions, but our feelings about breasts are far from logical. Women blame men for bad attitudes but the breast is much more important psychologically to women than to men. For a woman it is the main symbol of her femininity, and this is why she wants to retain it long after she has attracted a mate.

Even when a breast turns malignant a woman often wants to keep it. This is hardly rational. Many women in Britain undergo hysterectomy and few of them feel they are losing their femininity, but both sexes see mastectomy as unacceptably mutilating. Rationally, prophylactic mastectomy involves nothing more than excising a redundant gland and a pad of fat. Society should not deny this option to women, particularly those with a family history of breast cancer.

You can see, can't you, why my lecture upsets people. Men ask how I would like to be castrated, and look as if they mean this as a practical, not a philosophical, proposition. The analogy is inaccurate because, unlike the testis, the breast at 50 has no function apart from its psychological one. I refer questioners to my own secondary sexual characteristics and point out that if my beard had a 6% chance of turning malignant I would shave it off.

The audience eyes me warily, no doubt feeling there is something weird about a man who talks about removing normal breasts. They may be right. Perhaps all this is a distorted grief reaction to the deaths, over the years, of relatives, friends, and colleagues, killed painfully by glands they didn't need.

## Breasts and the media

The first hint of trouble came on Maundy Thursday. A reporter phoned, sounding excited.

"Has anyone else rung?" she said.

"No."

"They will," she replied.

The BMJ had appeared with my "philosophical proposition" that prophylactic mastectomy could prevent cancer.

Good Friday's front page had accurate but highly selective quotes, and added that a London colleague thought my article "offensive." (The reporter had sent him a copy by fax.) Now the first papers had a controversy, other reporters followed. Most sounded shocked. Few had read the BMJ. A grilling on local radio was followed by a roasting on national television.

On Saturday a tabloid carried my sinister picture – lip curled, eyes shifty – lifted from the Nine o'Clock News. Now I know why politicians appear with fixed smiles. BskyB phoned to say a crew was on its way from Lincolnshire. The two young men – shell shocked after attempting to turn Skegness into interesting television – set up lights, read my article, and shot a sympathetic interview for Europe's hotel rooms.

A tough lady columnist phoned my wife, who disappointed her by supporting me. That evening, on a family outing to the theatre, my children pointed out news hoardings: YORKS DOC SPARKS CANCER STORM. At The Rivals I half expected Mrs Malaprop to lean over the footlights and ask me about mastoidectomy.

On Easter Sunday my father phoned, sounding as if he had had a hard time at church. Next morning I was beamed by satellite to Australia. The formula was becoming familiar – amiable technicians, terse producer .... and lastly the presenter, charming until the microphones went live, then affecting outrage.

On Tuesday during a phone-in on local radio, an irate man said, "I just hope my sister isn't listening to this." It seemed to me he was speaking for everyone. Then, from a tiny studio, I was put through to Radio Oxford. After snatches of music on my headphones, I heard the interviewer speaking to an oncologist. For the first time in six days I heard a supportive voice on the air. I was close to tears.

Next day the handwritten envelopes started arriving, at first mainly from readers of a tabloid which had made me "Wally of the Week." Half the letters were abusive and hinted at castration: I replied with a fact sheet comparing testicular and breast cancer. The others were from women asking for mastectomy. The most upsetting was from a dying woman who wished I had written 10 years ago.

My own patients were unfazed. One grinned that before her hysterectomy she would write HANDS OFF on her chest. Another, worried about her family history, requested mastectomy after delivery.

A few weeks on, I can again start the day without a knot in my stomach. It was a surprise to find how paranoid one becomes under pressure. It was disappointing to find that the world's journalists still regard the breasts as sex objects. And it was interesting to hear how many women and doctors agree with me but won't say so for fear of the media.

## *I-spy Hospital Architecture*

Visiting hospitals can be tedious. Whether you're an SHO seeking the personnel department or a professor searching for the postgraduate centre, you end up in a cul de sac by the boilerhouse or at an empty desk marked "Enquiries," wishing you were elsewhere. Next time, brighten your visit by spotting how a hospital's architecture reveals its history.

In a Victorian hospital, I-spy portakabins. Old buildings with sturdy joists and lots of space between wards are ideal for perching plasterboard sheds on roofs and flower beds. If you can't see them, follow signs marked "Academic Department of ..."

The 1930s were the golden age of hospital carpentry, with solid parquet floors, and I-spy doors with handles that actually work. These are quite unlike contemporary handles, which last about four weeks before falling off in a shower of small screws and powdered plywood.

The 1940s' contribution to hospital architecture was the Nissen hut – or, as it was later called, the doctors' residence. These buildings, originally dubbed "temporary" to fool the enemy, are marvellously durable. I-spy wallpaper, a tribute to the taste of wartime interior decorators who chose pattems of such timeless beauty that nobody can bear to replace them.

The fashion in the 1960s was to construct hospitals out of materials that had fallen off the backs of lorries. I-spy the bottom half of a lift, stuck between floors with muffled sounds of engineers working above. Sixties' plumbing is easily recognised by its characteristic sounds: when someone somewhere empties a bath, every sink in the building gurgles. I-spy the doctor standing in front of such a sink. The basin behind him gloops and glugs, the patient stares wide eyed at his waistcoat, and the doctor gravely remarks, "No more curried eggs for me."

The 1970s saw the introduction of standardisation. Every British hospital was issued with an extremely large chimney. You rarely see smoke issuing from it: its purpose is to allow the hospital to be identified from the other side of town, so that visitors can navigate through the 1970s one way system. I-spy also standard signposts. NHS policy is to fill each post with as many signs as possible, in identical lettering and with randomised arrows, but always to omit the personnel department and the postgraduate centre.

In the 1980s architects decided to hide all hospital stairs. This was to symbolise a complete break from the previous century, when hospitals consisted mainly of staircases – the internal ones magnificent, the external ones functional. In a modem hospital, I-spy (eventually) the concealed staircase – cramped, unmarked, and reached through a door with no handles.

Progress in the 'nineties means shopping malls. The foyer of a British hospital now resembles a high street, with banks, newsagents, bookshops, and I-spy the twee hairdresser, "Doctor McCurls." As patients move from hospital to community, shops are moving in the opposite direction. Soon all patients will be outside, the ground floor will be devoted to retailing, and the doctors will be undisturbed, up the hidden stairs.

## *New Logos for All*

One of the reformed health service's growth industries is the designing of letterheads. Referrals from GPs now arrive under pen and ink drawings of idyllic rural surgeries, the aim being to rub salt in the wounds of hospital consultants in their windowless basements. New NHS trusts have notepaper with at the top a morale-boosting designer motif and at the bottom a punchy slogan reassuring readers with 20/20 vision that the trust cares for patients and is still part of the NHS.

Universities are starting to join in. After centuries of monochrome gothic shields they are bursting into colour with stylised versions of their coats of arms. So far, they have drawn back from putting messages at the bottom of the page saying that they still teach students and are part of Britain's higher education system. Perhaps they feel it would be unwise to go public with such unfashionable sentiments.

Slogans on notepaper are nothing new but they used to be written in Latin and incorporated into the logo itself. For years I was baffled by Oxford University's book with its mysterious motto DOMIMINA NUSTIO ILLUMEA, until I worked out that I should read down the left hand page and then the right. Of course. DOMINUS ILLUMINA TIO MEA. "Master, light my uncle."

Generally, consultants still prefer traditional letterheads, with their names in capitals in the centre, the hospital address at one side, and the consulting rooms at the other. The only concession to the '90s has been the creeping introduction of the portable phone number. Fax numbers remain few, however, owing either to our unease with the written word or to disbelief that our handwriting can be digitalised.

Nevertheless, other people are personalising their stationery with little punning pictures based on their names, or cartoons depicting their trade. Their considerable humorous potential is sadly denied to doctors, but perhaps we can twinkle at the world without losing our gravitas. A paediatrician could have his name in Adrian Mole writing, for example, and per-haps e-ven have a speshul spel chek on his word pro-cess-or. A cytopathologist could have an artistic cluster of dyskaryotic cells, and a social medicine specialist could have a bicycle.

The trendy cholecystectomist would want a keyhole, but such stark symbols might look too masonic and we may do better to borrow images from the world of art. An ear, nose, and throat surgeon could have a van Gogh self portrait or maybe a head from Picasso's Guernica. For discretion's sake those who practise below the navel might resort to the subtlety of Highway Code symbols: "One way street" would suit a proctologist and "No U turns" a psychosexual expert.

Always reliable, if old fashioned, is a monogram – the literary equivalent of the personalised number plate. For me, though, an ornate JOD risks my being mistaken for the Almighty. Perhaps the safest course for an academic is to remember the collective noun for professors ("an absence") and leave the top of the paper blank.

## *Towering Inferno*

The hospital fire alarm is a litmus test. When it sounds, staff divide into two groups – those who quit the building and those who stay. The quitters are people for whom an emergency evacuation is welcome excitement to punctuate their day. The stayers think themselves so important that they must remain at their posts until flames lick their stethoscopes. Which group is right?

In twenty-one years of hospital life I have found a perfect negative correlation between fire alarms and fires. I've survived two hospital fires. In the first I was having tea in sister's office at night when we heard feet scurrying in the ward above. We finished our tea and went to investigate. I met a fireman dashing upstairs unrolling a hose. After thoroughly dousing the male surgical patients' sitting room he left.

A year later, I was in the same office when the same scurrying began. Now an experienced registrar, I explained to the nurses that the noise meant the hospital was on fire. This fire crew was even more impressive: an officer dashed upstairs to the sitting room, emerged with a smouldering television in his arms and ran outside, where three fire tenders turned their hoses on it. It sat, black and wet, in the car park for the rest of the week.

In those days the fire alarms didn't work. Since then the nation's hospitals have been equipped with sophisticated devices that burst into ear splitting life every time a man with a drill puts up a shelf somewhere in the building. Doors close automatically, men with bunches of keys and portable telephones march around and tell you to stop working, enormous numbers of staff whom no one has ever seen before congregate on the pavement, and fire engines waa-waa their way to the wrong entrance.

Heroes in yellow helmets comb the hospital, find the man with the drill, and tell him to stop. An older officer with a white helmet searches the building again slowly, just to make sure it isn't on fire, before allowing the men with the keys to turn off the alarms and let people back inside.

This performance is repeated irregularly throughout the year and rehearsals are held every week. Testing occurs in the middle of a weekday morning, and is timed to coincide with the most short tempered consultant's outpatient clinic. During that morning, each sensor in the hospital is individually tested by someone who walks around setting off the entire system of bells and hooters at unpredictable intervals.

In contrast to the false alarms, testing is associated with a towering inferno. Smoke issues from the consultant's ears as he tries to empathise amid the decibels. The patient, to whom everything in hospital is strange, seems not to notice the nearby klaxon, but becomes a little agitated as her doctor spontaneously combusts while phoning the general manager. There should be a notice: "If the alarm sounds, throw a bucket of water over the nearest consultant."

## *Bonjour, Chin, and Goodbye*

The crickets on the Cote d'Azur send messages to potential mates by rubbing their legs together. They make quite a din on the corniches. The human inhabitants find less energetic ways of sending sexual signals. Young females go topless on the beach and strut in tight dresses on the promenade. Older males dye their hair and flaunt their wealth in casinos.

The Monegasque ambience of tanned bodies and Rolls-Royces makes even blasé yacht owners behave foolishly and had a potent effect on a British holidaymaker who last saw the sea on a trip to Scarborough. I stared in the mirror at my battered trainers and khaki shorts. This image would not do. What if I chanced upon paparazzi from Paris Match? How could I be mistaken for a friend of Eddie Barclay? My gaze focused on my beard.

The idea at first was designer stubble. In the garden, among the hibiscus, I chomped away with scissors and hand mirror. In the bathroom I blinked at the result. I looked like a clinical photograph of alopecia areata. I reached for the razor. As a student I had had a goatee beard which I thought made me look like a distinguished psychiatrist. Could this be recreated? Evidently not, according to my teenage children, roused from their sunbathing, aghast but fascinated. "I dare you, Dad," said my daughter. "Shave it off."

A demon gripped my Gillette. Four wide eyes peeped round the bathroom door. They had never in their lives seen my chin and I had not seen it for 25 years. Would my children like me, I wondered. Would I like myself? We emerged tentatively, my chin and I, and went in search of my wife, who had never seen it before either. Calmly she told the moustached stranger that he looked like my father. My daughter muttered something about Basil Fawlty and my son reassured me that Hitler had had blue eyes.

Next day we all agreed about the moustache and out came the razor again. With a few deft strokes I became the reincarnation of my grandfather, a Congregational minister in a small Scottish town. My wife beamed at her third husband in as many days. She had not expected such a promiscuous holiday. My daughter said I looked like a potato. I smiled an inoffensive little smile and the unanimous view was that I looked lovable.

I began to panic. The word "lovable" is applied to professors only within a year of retirement. A quarter of a century under cover had left my chin serene and unpugnacious. How would I cope back at work? I saw myself being ignored by relaxed hospital managers and patronised at smiling committee meetings. I could imagine my cheek being pinched affectionately by the dean as he took the advice of more Churchillian colleagues.

I disposed of my disposable razor and set off for a stroll along the prom, hoping to summon up enough testosterone to restore the status quo.

## *Doctor in the Library*

Now that medicine is a scientific discipline, you might expect medical libraries to be thronged with doctors keeping up to date. Usually, however, they contain only juniors, retired doctors, a few middle aged regulars, and an occasional eccentric sitting on the floor.

Medical libraries do not cater for the person who ought to use them most – the mature, busy doctor. If they did, they would keep public house hours and stay open all day on Sundays and holidays. Even then, however, few working doctors would use them. This is curious because medical practice brings many questions, most of which can be answered in the library. Sadly, doctors are not trained to search the literature, and must rely on editorials written by reviewers.

Reviewers, like their readers, are hard pressed clinicians. Fully stretched by day, they time their nocturnal raids on the library to fit in with family duties. After work they rush home, bolt dinner, and dandle offspring on their knee. The bedtime story is read with one eye on the clock, and when the last teddy is tucked in they dash to the car and roar back to the library.

Their ambition is to prowl the stacks, identifying papers telepathically in a mystic communion between intellect and shelf. They rarely reach this astral plane, and normally have to sit at a computer scrolling its ROM, or leaf through Index Medicus, relying on a sixth sense to weed out rat work and papers in Serbo-Croat, while scribbling references on the back of an envelope.

The journals that reviewers want are the recent ones. These are helpfully marked on the shelves by notices saying "At the Binder." The Binder, the reviewer imagines, is an aged craftsman somewhere in the Hebrides, meticulously gumming each page into place and leaving the glue to dry for several weeks before finally returning the volume by bicycle via Stomoway.

With an armful of Binder's cast offs the reviewer heads for the photocopier, to find it occupied by a schizoid undergraduate who proof reads each sheet of his essay before copying the next page. When the reviewer's turn comes it is almost closing time. A porter pointedly straightens chairs and rattles keys. Unabashed, the reviewer settles into a practised rhythm, starting at the end of each article, pressing hard on the journal's spine and wreaking dreadful revenge on the Binder.

At the closing bell a warm quire is ready for midnight reading. Some libraries torture reviewers by making them request formal permission for each photocopy. It takes longer to fill the forms than to make the copies. In vain reviewers protest that they are not going to sell the copies and that they are the authors of at least one of the papers – and were paid nothing for it. The library assistant, flushed with embarrassment, whispers resolutely that the law is the law. The Copyright Licensing Agency takes a more humane view: forms aren't necessary, provided the library has a licence. I can give you the reference if you like.

## *Usurers' Apprentices*

The annual reception for new medical students was a learning experience, at least for me. I discovered I'm a year older than I was in 1991 and have even less in common with these cheerful youngsters. Searching for shared experience, I talked about money. The students told me about their finances and I replied that on my first day at medical school I had received a cheque for £79, which had been enough to live on for the term. Their eyes glazed in boredom – 1964 was before they were born.

Mine, however, sparkled with reminiscence and arithmetic. To keep pace with the retail price index my £79 would now be £763. In 1992 this will just cover rent, gas, and food. It is possible for a provincial student to receive a maximum grant of £753 a term, but only if the parents' residual income is under £13 630 a year. None of the students I spoke to received anything like the full grant. A teacher's daughter told me she receives £300, but a doctor's daughter gets nothing.

Another fresher said that her father, a trade union official, will have to pay £500 a term for her upkeep. As the parent of a medical student he will be much worse off than if she had taken a three year course in politics. My own course in the 1960s included an intercalated BSc year which, looking back, I see transformed my life. If asked, my parents would have supported me during that extra year, but with the altruism of a 20 year old I might well have decided to refuse my place.

The government has frozen maintenance grants for the past three years. Students can make up the shortfall with official loans. They can now borrow up to £715 per year, which means that a medical student at the end of the course could be £3500 in debt. Banks already offer undergraduates free overdrafts of £400 and medical students can negotiate larger bank loans. Most of our senior students this year will be about £2000 in debt as they approach graduation, and the government's policy will encourage this figure to increase.

Debt is popular with the government, the banks, and indeed the electorate, who follow the nuances of usury every night on the television news. As a student I was appalled by debt, and even after graduating I was uneasy with the truth universally acknowledged by young men in red braces, that to progress in life you should take on as big a burden of debt as you possibly can. The current economic climate seems to be proving me right.

It cost the state about £2500 to support me during my student years. In an unwritten contract, I and my colleagues have repaid our debt in kind – first by being exploited as juniors, and now by overworking as consultants. Times change. Junior doctors' hours will decrease and – who knows? – some day consultants may charge by the hour for serving on local and national committees. Then, perhaps, the sight of young doctors starting their careers deep in debt may seem less sickening.

## *Oh Yes We Did!*

We had no hospital pantomime last year. Or if we did, nobody told me. Christmas Eve found me as usual at my word processor with a mug of cocoa and a death threat from some distant editor. My desk lamp was switched off to save electricity. My hands, in their fingerless mittens, typed by the glow of the Christmas tree lights in the hall. Suddenly my study door opened. I turned and stared in horror at a shadowy figure who stood there, beckoning. "Who are you?" I gasped.

"I am the Ghost of Pantomimes Past," it said. "Come!"

In my cardigan and slippers, I followed the apparition through endless foggy streets to a door I dimly recognised. "St Elsewhere's!" I cried. "The Sports and Social Club!"

People were dressed in flares and kipper ties. "Your 1974 pantomime," announced the phantom, "Snow White and the Group Practice."

The show was just starting. At the back of the hall the hospital electrician switched on a row of huge floodlights borrowed from the hospital car park. On stage two men blinked through horn rimmed glasses and grinned wanly. One said that in a packed programme tonight an obstetric registrar would sing "The Lost Chord," a chiropodist would sing "Underneath the Arches," and a choir of speech therapists would sing "Doo Wah Diddy Diddy Dum Diddy Doo." The other announced a newsflash: the East German pole vaulting champion had just become the West German pole vaulting champion. My eyes misted in nostalgia.

The reflected glare of the floodlights caught the Ghost of Pantomimes Past clapping her hands delightedly. She was wearing a leotard under a white coat with L plates and carrying a bleep. She looked ravishing, as doctors in leotards so often do, particularly when they are on call.

On stage, three Blue Peter presenters demonstrated how to carry out a hysterectomy with a toilet roll and double sided sticky tape. The audience, a complete cross-section of the hospital staff, laughed comfortably, waiting for the high spots to come – the barbed references to consultant foibles, the performers who had resorted to Dutch courage, the precarious costumes, and, above all, the in-jokes. "Just walk this way," murmured a porter with an earring, to deafening applause.

The overworked and underappreciated pianist played "Supercala-frajalisticexpialidocious" as a winsome Mary Poppins sang solemnly about neonatal necrotising enterocolitis. In the next sketch Dr Clark Kent turned into Superdoc to survive a weekend on call, and in the grand finale an avuncular consultant was pulled from the audience to become the chuckling victim of This Is Your Life, greeting a gleeful succession of illegitimate offspring and deformed ex-patients.

When the applause faded the ghost and I were back in my study. As she began to disappear I begged one last favour. Relenting, she slipped her arm from her sleeve. "Doctor," she said, "will I be able to play the trombone when my wrist sets?"

"Of course," I smiled.

"Marvellous," she replied, fading away, "I've always wanted to play the trombone."

## *No Lunch Please, We're Doctors*

From time to time people offer to take me out to lunch. This always perplexes me. Do they think I'm undernourished? Don't they understand I have work to do? Years ago I accepted one of these invitations. My morning clinic overran: I arrived late at the restaurant, bolted an omelette and Perrier, and hurried back to the hospital, hoping my absence hadn't been noticed. I decided then that I am not a lunch person.

Many colleagues feel the same. Lunch is something we vaguely associate with continuing medical education. A buffet is provided as an attractant to a midday lecture or, during an all day meeting, as a half time interval instead of a sponge down and a slice of lemon. As we pursue the coleslaw round the plate we assure one another that in our normal working day we settle for coffee and a KitKat.

I like to think, however, that deep down we are still three course trencherpersons keen on roly-poly or spotted dick in the afternoon. We won't admit it partly through fear of obesity and partly because of the lunch-is-for-wimps philosophy currently gripping the NHS. A manic drive for increased productivity has been added to the intrinsic pressure doctors have always suffered – a work ethic that makes the adjective "busy" a compliment rather than a commiseration.

For hospital doctors another problem is Britain's nine to five day. It is metabolically impossible to work after a good lunch without a siesta but by the time cerebral blood flow resumes in the late afternoon the appointment clerks have gone home, the clinic nurses are picking up their handbags, and the theatre staff are putting chairs on the table.

We used to have that fine British compromise, a lunch hour. It had more than nutritive value. When I was a houseman the doctors' mess provided peer support in the middle of a day of barely tolerable stress. During the egalitarian 1970s, however, doctors' dining facilities were attacked as elitist anachronisms. The separate room was replaced by a screened off table in the cafeteria. Soon the screens went and the doctors joined everyone else in the self service queue.

Nevertheless we still had a big dining table where housemen and consultants could sit together and talk. Consultants in those days seemed terribly urbane and amusing, putting our day to day problems into perspective with their eye popping anecdotes from the postwar era. For their part they could pick up clues about what was worrying the juniors, though this knowledge rarely if ever resulted in action.

Now the big table, too, has disappeared – transported, perhaps, to the hideaway where the managers dine. Doctors no longer synchronise lunches. Our hospital, miraculously, still has a consultants' dining room but it is not well patronised. Most of us are too busy with lunchtime meetings – grinding through agendas for setting up working parties to formulate mechanisms for examining problems that we used to sort out over lunch.

## *Suffering Stereotypes*

Eighty seven per cent of consultant obstetricians in Britain are male. We are appointed in our middle 30s and our average age at retirement is 59. Like most people in this country nowadays, we would call ourselves middle class. As far as our ethnic origins are concerned we are a mixed bunch (with an overrepresentation of Scots) but from the general public's point of view we are readily stereotyped as MAMOs (Middle Aged Male Obstetricians).

I could point out that I'm actually a Middle Aged Celtic Male

Obstetrician (MACMO) but this has little effect on my image. MAMOs and MACMOs are lumped together and viewed unflatteringly by the media, patients, and fellow professionals. Midwives, for example, are plied with disinformation about our attitudes. I have a collection of offensive cartoons from journals in the midwifery library: one portrays the obstetric establishment as a mad bull; another has the MAMO saying, "I recognise the stitches – who's the patient?" Medical journals don't carry rude drawings of midwives, but for women to snipe at MAMOs is right-on and legal.

Perhaps this merely reflects general attitudes to middle aged men. A dad in a television commercial is usually a fool, falling off his surfboard, failing to repair his car, or with a wife who snips the head off his chrysanthemum in a symbolic gesture that would cause outrage if the sexes were reversed. Sexist orthodoxy even affects the BMJ, which excises "he," "him," and "his" from my articles whenever possible in spite of my being not overtly neuter.

Most patients ignore such stereotyping, but I regularly see intelligent women who believe what they read. They attend classes which demonise MAMOs and they arrive in the antenatal clinic prepared for a debate. My cheery "Good morning" is met with a hostile stare and my heart sinks as I realise we have an awkward consultation ahead of us. Recently I spent 20 minutes with a healthy woman before she allowed herself to smile, and over an hour before all her questions were answered. The rest of the clinic degenerated towards chaos and was rescued only by our summoning extra juniors. Afterwards she wrote to me, remarking that I was less unpleasant than she had expected but complaining that the clinic had not run to time. Normally, I'm told, she is delightful company, but like her peers she has been conditioned to be aggressive to MAMOs.

It is rewarding to win the trust of such patients and convince them that stereotyping is unfair and inaccurate. I suspect, however, that over the years this pleasure will pall. In the operating theatre it is challenging to encounter adhesions and bleeding diatheses on occasion, but debilitating to face them on every list. Similarly in the clinic, a man could get tired of meeting week after week women who, never having seen him before, arrive assuming he is a chauvinist pig. I expect the average retirement age of MAMOs, already low, will continue to fall, and it will be the sensitive ones who go first.

## *Hospital Foyer, Evening*

Inside the entrance hall is a small cluster of visitors, and outside is an ambulance from an exotic extracontractual location. In the smoke lock between inner and outer front doors a patient in nightdress and Roland Rat slippers confers with a friend amid a sea of cigarette butts.

So far, so normal, but tonight something is wrong. The visitors look animated. A short man with a purple face and a smart coat hurries outside; another in a shabby suit disappears into the toilet, and a tall one crouches by the phone. The receptionist glares from behind her glass partition. I ask her if anything's the matter. She says she has called Security to halt a recital of Scots songs by these three gentlemen.

I return to the front door. The short man is swaying slightly, his open coat revealing in an inside pocket a bottle of noxious looking yellow fluid. His friend emerges from the toilet, unshaven and tousle headed. I weigh in with low level aggression. "Can I help you?" I say menacingly.

"We're visitors," replies the purple faced man.

Tricky. People who hang around hospitals always claim to be visiting. Young men in trainers, challenged in locker rooms, say they are looking for their sick grandmother in coronary care. You can usually tell vagabonds from visitors, however; rogues look confident and relatives look lost.

"Who are you visiting?" I ask pointedly if ungrammatically.

"My wife's in maternity," he protests.

If he had chosen any other ward I might have backed off, but his claim doesn't tally with his age and complexion, not to mention the yellow liquid. "Pull the other one," I reply.

The three men close round me. I pray they don't exhale simultaneously. The unshaven one thrusts his face into mine.

"You're frae Scotland!" he cries with sentimental delight. "Where abouts, pal?" he asks. The conversation has taken a dangerous turn. Filled with irrational fear that we'll discover a mutual acquaintance, I try to be firm.

"You've got to leave."

"We've called a taxi. We'll wait inside."

I express reservations. Their faces harden and they discuss nutting me. In these circumstances one either moves quickly or stands completely still. I choose immobility and advise against violence.

"Who are you, anyway?" they ask.

"I'm the professor," I reply, playing on the Caledonian respect for academia. The effect is gratifying. They stagger back wide eyed. They bow unsteadily and tug their forelocks.

"Good for you, son!" they beam, lining up to shake my hand.

Now we're bonded they can't tear themselves away. The unshaven one grasps my hand and holds it to his cheek, tearfully seeking reassurance that I'm not angry. The purple-faced man nudges me and whispers, "But I keep myself clean, eh?"

A taxi arrives. The driver takes one look and drives away, perhaps thinking this is a scene from *Rab C Nesbitt* or *Beadle's About*. I finally extricate myself. Eyes lowered, the receptionist keeps a straight face, at least until I get into the lift.

## *Visiting Time*

When I lived in Leicester, the saddest sight in town was opposite the hospital. Across the road from the gynaecology ward was the prison and at visiting time a queue of relatives would form at the gate. They were young women mostly, with children waiting to see their fathers. Those poor toddlers. Their lives were already in tatters only a year or two after they had slithered on to a delivery bed, naked and full of potential. As an obstetrician I took it personally.

In Leeds there is a decent distance between our hospital and the prison – a black, Victorian self parody on a hilltop across the valley. Tonight as I write this, it contains 332 men under the age of 25. Our medical school, a model of seventies architecture, has a similar number of male students about the same age. The two buildings could hardly be more different, and the same goes for their clientele. For the students, life is just beginning. The prisoners feel that life is over, and on average two of them commit suicide every year.

Visiting time in hospital means a jammed car park and warning buzzers from overloaded lifts. It is not only relatives who visit us. At Christmas there are carol singers and the Lord Mayor, and at Harvest Festival, people bring flowers and fruit. From time to time a celebrity, a television crew, or a newspaper reporter drop by. Regulars in local pubs raise money for us. To be honest, our patients don't need all this attention. It's sometimes difficult at Christmas to find someone to keep in and make a fuss over. The people who really need visiting are across the valley.

Prisoners, however, frighten us. Their image is of cynical, manipulative, even violent men – quite unlike hospital patients, who are vulnerable and grateful. Two thousand years ago St Matthew, describing the last judgment, could mention visiting those "sick or in prison" in the same verse. Nowadays prison visiting is left to a tiny group of volunteers. The only people who sing carols in gaols are the Salvation Army.

Our local prison is launching an initiative to integrate itself into the community. Not an easy task. It wants to be more open but at the same time to discourage evangelists and voyeurs. Unlike hospitals, which often use patients to gain publicity, it must protect the privacy of its residents. Nevertheless our prison, like others, has a scheme in which visitors chat to lonely inmates, weekly or fortnightly. The chaplains run it and take care that volunteers don't get too involved with prisoners. Of necessity there are constraints but I'm told they could do with more visitors: at present their team numbers 24. This in a city of 700 000 people.

Forty per cent of Britain's prison population is aged under 25, and many of these young men are already fathers. The cycle of deprivation is frighteningly short. The prison chaplains have invited me to pay a visit but I've made some excuse. I'm much too busy producing toddlers for the queue.

## *Staff President*

I had spoken at the medical students' annual dinner twice before, so I had lost the element of surprise. Student gatherings are intimations of mortality, making you wonder what happened to your physique, your youthful enthusiasm, and your sense of hilarity. Dimly you can recall the times when everything in medicine, particularly consultants, seemed funny. You suspect that viewed from a distance they still are, but once inside the consultant laager you cannot share the joke.

To feel confident with a student audience you need to know what image they have of you, and then play up to it. I am at a difficult age, metamorphosing from Friendly Young Consultant to Irascible Old Professor But All Right Really Once You Get To Know Him. Even in maturity there are surprises: recently I was intrigued to hear that a wrinkly colleague is a sex symbol. Having missed my parody in last year's revue, I was left guessing but it was flattering to be the staff president at the dinner.

During the reception the elegant revellers already looked uninhibited. The student president had an air of world weariness beyond his years, like those battle hardened young army officers in television interviews. I soon found out why. One of his committee drew me aside to explain that the kissogram was on a tight schedule and the speakers' timings might have to be altered. No problem, I told her suavely. It would have been uncool to admit I had never seen a kissogram before.

Two minutes into my speech, half the audience were listening and the others seemed quite happy making their table napkins into funny head-dresses. Then a note was passed to me: JIM PLEASE SING THE ANATOMY SONG. I glanced at my wife, who knows my musical repertoire and calls me Jim to my face, but she looked blank, wondering why I had faltered. I realised that another Jim was standing behind me, grinning at the audience in an unfocused way. I yielded graciously. An a cappella trio materialised, rendered some well crafted but unexpurgated lyrics about the dissecting room, and trooped off. Shaken, I continued. A few minutes later the kissogram arrived.

She was not tall but she was big and she carried a large microphone.

With a comfortable chuckle she took control. In frilly leotard decked with chains, she fastened onto the student president, metaphorically and literally. He quickly realised he would suffer more loss of face by resisting than by submitting.

"Good boy," she grinned. "Walkies!"

"Woof woof," he sighed, to riotous applause.

"What I need now," said the kissogram, "is . . ."

"Liposuction," cried a student.

"I'd lose my job, darling." She threatened him with her cat-o'-nine-tails. People stood on chairs, agog. The only time I had seen students so jaw droppingly attentive was during pass/fail vivas. Perhaps some thought the same about me. I had seen the evening as a rehearsal for a BMA dinner at which I'm speaking next month. Time will tell.

## *No More Heroes*

Our hospital is rediscovering art, with regular exhibitions of paintings and tapestries, and notices offering rewards for information leading to the recovery of last month's display. No sculpture so far, but some time I expect we shall have non-representational objects labelled "Healing" or "Gallstone III". What I'd like to see, however, are statues of some of the staff.

There are several of these in the old part of the hospital. Doctors in knee breeches gaze down on the entrance hall. Under a spotlight on the main staircase stands a bust of Leeds's most celebrated surgeon, Lord Moynihan. In the boardroom hangs a large oil painting of Lord Moynihan in academic robes. In the library is another sculpture of Lord Moynihan's head and in a glass case, God help us, a cast of Lord Moynihan's hands. Goodness knows what's in the gentlemen's toilet.

Moynihan died in 1936 and the fashion for immortalising hospital staff seems to have ended with him. This may change now that we are a trust. Perhaps the gardens of our next Phase One will have an equestrian statue of the chief executive. But not of a doctor. It's not that doctors have ceased to achieve great things. You don't have to be great to be sculpted: the most recent statue to appear in London was of Bomber Harris, and opposite our hospital an insignificant mayor looms in frock coat and traffic cone. What you need is to live in an age when people want heroes.

Institutionalised hero worship used to be the norm in medicine. As Lord Lister grew old, the BMJ noted his birthdays in increasingly fulsome terms and in 1912 his six page obituary (the first page edged in black) included an adoring poem, "The Chief." His Lancet obituary ran to eight pages and an editorial began: "Full of years and honours, the greatest Englishman of the nineteenth century has gone to his rest." There's a hint of jingoism there, in the heyday of the Empire, as well as a need for the emergent science of medicine to have a champion to compete with the armed forces' Wellington and Nelson.

Now that medicine is quietly self confident, great doctors get brief obituaries. Ian Donald, for example, or Patrick Steptoe, both of whose work revolutionised not only their own specialty but others too, received a few paragraphs and still no statues as far as I know. Besides, current fashion is very much against the idea of magnifying a man's virtues and glossing over his faults. Quite the reverse.

Individual doctors, however, love to look back fondly at their old chiefs and will describe with admiration even the most unpleasant eccentricities. The private need for heroes is constant in spite of changes in the public mood. In 1936 a Lancet eulogy of Moynihan, an egotist's egotist, pointed out that "his effect [on British surgery] was above all a psychological one." In today's hospitals the people who want to assert themselves are the managers. Was I really joking about that equestrian statue?

## *Not for Debate*

I have the impression that debates are becoming more common at medical meetings but perhaps I'm over sensitive. My specialty has more than its share of contentious issues – homebirth versus hospital . . . "pro choice" versus "pro life" . . . pro hormone replacement versus pro Germaine Greer. Such public polarisations create a culture of conflict within obstetrics and gynaecology which encourages junior doctors to see issues in terms of black and white. This worries me.

As a schoolboy I enjoyed the debating society but as an adult I prefer round table discussion. Unfortunately, debate is institutionalised in British life. Parliament, with its histrionics and predictable votes, is a bit of a sham, tacky at close quarters. Last year at our trust's first annual general meeting the board faced the public, which, apart from eccentrics and employees, consisted of party activists. One MP stood up and with windy rhetoric called on the chief executive to resign. An opposing MP gave us a ringing vote of confidence. Both then hurried smugly away to make the same noises elsewhere about another subject. I felt cheap because by being there I had endorsed the charade.

Our legal system is based on confrontation. During years of medicolegal work I have often heard counsel say: "I'm not telling you how to write your report, doctor, but could you leave out the sentence beginning....." The secret of debate lies in selection: you omit facts that weaken your case. This is no way to administer justice. Recently the Court of Appeal criticised police for suppressing evidence inconvenient to the prosecution in criminal cases. Massaging the data, however, is fundamental to civil proceedings. Outside the court opposing teams huddle together,whispering in case the other side finds something out. Surely courts are for exposing truth, not concealing it.

Debate, however, is more dramatic than discussion. The media know this. When a television researcher phones you up about a topical subject she gently presses you to be outspoken and then none too subtly asks if you know of a doctor with violently opposing views. By playing this game we risk producing an entertaining ding-dong which downgrades the image of medicine. Respect for politicians and lawyers has never been lower because an increasingly sophisticated public wants something more wholesome than mere posturing. On television a select committee looks and sounds more intelligent than the bluster of the House of Commons. In the law, Europe's inquisitorial system will sooner or later supplant Britain's anachronistic contests between barristers.

So next time a meetings organiser asks me to speak in a debate I should stifle my standard answer ("Sure: tell me later which side I'm on") and say, "Why not try a consensus statement? That would teach your audience what a tough world we really live in." One of the reasons why achieving consensus is such hard work is that we don't train ourselves to do it. Neither do we motivate our trainees to try: we give platforms to colourful characters rather than to the grey workers who actually move medicine forward.

## *Bow? Wow!*

I am often asked how to tie a bow tie. Well, not often, actually. Let me start again. People often look as if they want to ask how to tie a bow tie. They are nervous, however, about accosting me as bow tie wearers are widely (but erroneously) perceived as excessively friendly. Ballgoers ask during the second Buck's Fizz but never listen to the answer. People believe bow tie wearing is a congenital anomaly, like knowing how to spell. Perhaps it is: soon some researcher may isolate the gene and provoke debate about the ethics of prenatal screening for neckwear preference.

A bow tie excites onlookers because it is a symbol of masculinity – an exclusively male garment. (The only women wearers, Playboy bunnies, are now extinct.) Like the female suspender's, the bow tie's symbolic importance transcends its function, but its usefulness should not be underestimated. Unless he is an Iranian diplomat a man has to wear something under his collar, and for the gynaecologist a bow tie is ideal as it does not touch the patient when he stoops. (Touching the patient with your tie counts as sexual harassment in certain parts of London.)

There are pitfalls for bow tie wearers, of course. We are sometimes mistaken for waiters or, in tougher streets, doormen. This is why bow ties are so spotty and why those of us with savoir faire and myopic friends wear large, crumpled, or violently coloured ties, preferably with large, crumpled, or pale coloured jackets. The other pitfall for the tiro is tying the thing.

Which brings me to the purpose of this article – to give useful instruction and reduce the pre-dinner tension that sours so many medical marriages. Ideally I should stand behind you at the mirror and teach you as if performing that sketch about the Green Eye of the Little Yellow God. Failing that, cut out this page and keep it in the pocket of your second best dinner jacket.

Avoid the pre-knotted tie: it looks too perfect and cannot be loosened with a raffish flick during the rumba, and when pulled by a passing coquette it gives an embarrassing twang and bruises your thyroid. Your tie must be pliable and adjustable for length. When you put it round your neck the tips should just touch your xiphistemum.

Here are the secrets of the tying. First, ignore all diagrams. Second, get both ends the same length and tie it like a shoelace, tucking the first throw firmly against the collar. Third, don't despair when at first it looks like St Andrew's cross. Keep calm. Give a few delicate tugs here and there. It's straightening up, isn't it? Your image in the mirror is looking at you with respect, almost admiration.

The ultimate challenge is the bow tie of the Royal College of Obstetricians and Gynaecologists, with insignia that must finish the right way up. It tells the world you are respectable, independent minded, dextrous, and cool under pressure. What more could one aspire to?

## *I love it when you talk commas*

Like yin and yang there are two complementary kinds of people, the literate and the numerate. The literate think themselves superior but in general the numerate are richer. I'm told that, of the two qualities, numeracy is the more closely related to IQ, but what else do you expect if you measure intelligence by numbers? The "intelligence quotient" presumably involves long division, which immediately puts us wordies at a disadvantage.

I am not numerate. When I check my bank statement my tongue protrudes from the corner of my mouth. Fortunately, I can survive in the academic world thanks to a pocket calculator and the department of statistics. I treat both with a mixture of awe and off handedness – amazed at their cleverness when I think about it, but not thinking about it very often.

The verbal equivalent of the medical statistician is the medical editor. I don't mean grandees like ED, BMJ, who I imagine spends most of his time in full evening dress being chauffeured from embassy cocktail party to college power dinner. I mean subs like me who edit smaller, specialist journals and have to sharpen their own pencils. Our problem is that our scientist authors are numerati who treat the editorial process as we literati treat our calculators. They expect a machine to do it all for them. It's no use returning their papers and asking them to correct the grammar. The poor things thought it was perfect already.

We editors, unhappy to trust our proof readers with technical terms, sit late at our desks changing foetus to fetus and adnexae to adnexa and wondering whether anyone educated outside Scotland will notice or care. We curse our obsessiveness, reminding ourselves that Shakespeare didn't bother about spelling, but we can't stop. Part valet, part surgeon, we feel driven to send our authors out into the world's libraries tickety-boo with their infinitives unsplit and their colons excised. Nobody will know the part we played – certainly not the authors, who never notice that their proofs look different from their original manuscripts.

After years under the green eye-shade we can glance at a page and know there is a mistake on it somewhere, just as an auditor can smell something fishy on a balance sheet. Once in a while we receive a paper that is right in almost every particular (but never flawless – we can always find something to correct). When we discover one of these paragons the author shoots up in our estimation. Everyone has their criteria for judging other people – beauty, wealth, or ethical standards, for example. Editors judge their fellow humans by their punctuation.

Our biggest thrill is finding a kindred spirit. Sometimes we have to phone a last minute correction to the publisher. An efficient female voice answers.

"Page seven," we say, "Para three, line two. The apostrophe...."

She catches her breath. "My God! It's in the wrong place." We feel a wave of fellow feeling wafting down the line. We are not alone.

## *Managing Change*

Comedians mocked the news that it took 247 steps to change a light bulb in an NHS hospital, but I felt cheered. In these difficult times, the fact that somewhere in the NHS a light bulb has been successfully replaced is surely a cause for celebration. Doctors involved in management, however, were gobsmacked that this change was achieved in only 247 steps. We need to know more about this thrusting, no-nonsense hospital. Is it management led or clinician led? The two systems are quite different.

In a management led hospital, when a light bulb fails nothing happens. This is because light bulbs, unlike managers, work at night. When management is notified it assesses the problem by commissioning a study, either from independent consultants or by asking the nurses to grade lighting levels on a scale of one to 10 at two hour intervals. The nurses grumble that filling in forms about lighting detracts from their real work (filling in forms about nursing) but nevertheless they cooperate.

The study shows that the mean lighting level (MLL) over a 24 hour period is below EC guidelines. Meetings are held to agree a target MLL achievable within current financial constraints and to arrange an option appraisal, bearing in mind that the NHS Management Executive requires an annual 2% reduction in light bulbs across the board. A project manager is appointed. She suggests changing all the rooms so that the one which fails to meet its target MLL becomes a storeroom. She is promoted. Her plan is deferred till the next financial year.

In a clinician led hospital, light bulb failure is put on the agenda for the next consultants' meeting. The junior doctors' representative makes an impassioned plea for a new bulb, graphically describing how juniors are clerking patients by the light of a torch held between their teeth. If something isn't done, he says, he will write to Private Eye.

Dr A recalls that as a houseman during the war he had had to use candles in a similar way. The wax dropped on to the patients, but they never complained. Drs B and C reminisce about gas mantles in the old hospital. Dr D says that in his clinical opinion this light bulb has failed because the so called NHS reforms are pushing everyone and everything beyond the limits of human endurance or electrical resistance.

Professor E remarks that on a recent trip to America he saw an entire hospital lit by a single bulb and a fibreoptic system. Dr F asks about the wattage of the new light bulb, saying that in his experience patients prefer soft lights. Dr G disagrees, saying that good light is needed for safe practice. A lively discussion ensues. The committee cannot decide between 100 W and 60 W for the replacement. The senior registrar is asked to undertake a literature search and, if that provides no scientific basis for choosing either bulb, to organise a randomised controlled trial. This should mean that funds for the proposed bulb will come from the research budget. The meeting adjoums at sunset.

## *Caesarean Section under Water*

Like many ideas which change people's lives, the concept of underwater caesarean section (UCS) came to me by accident. Most obstetricians have had occasional requests for this procedure but I had unthinkingly dismissed them as the unrealistic aspirations of small scuba divers. I remained sceptical even when confronted with the convincing results of the Netherlands "spring tide" study, and with embarrassment I now recall making critical remarks about the Dutch decision to build a maternity hospital on a new polder.

Let me say at this point that I cannot claim all the credit for introducing UCS into Leeds. Future historians may remember not my name but that of H Cassidy, the plumber responsible for the fateful soldering of the water main above our caesarean section theatre. I was merely the obstetrician who happened to be operating that night, all our junior staff having been laid low by Beijing flu. Luck decreed that the rubber seals on the theatre doors had recently been replaced and that there was a spare anaesthetic machine to provide oxygen for the surgeon. The name of the unfortunate medical student who assisted me will, I hope, long be remembered.

Nevertheless, fortune favours the prepared mind. I was immediately struck by the fact that the patient signed herself out of hospital three hours after delivery, and I calculated that if this were to happen after the 70,000 caesarean sections performed every year in Britain, nearly half a million bed days could be saved.

The breakthrough came with the enthusiastic report of the government's expert group, which included economists, consumers, and hydrologists under a charismatic chairman. Having heard evidence from, among others, the Amphibious Midwives' Alliance and the Association for the Improvement of Marine Services, the group concluded that there is no scientific basis for claims that UCS is unsafe, as there have as yet been no large British trials. The Cousteau report, as it is now known, places responsibility squarely on NHS managers to provide UCS to women who request it.

Medical opinion has been slow to accept UCS. Doctors are worried that the surgeon's view might be obscured by blood, bubbles, or turbulence. These problems can indeed occur in theatres inadequately adapted for UCS and this is why hospitals are being urged to install purpose built UCS theatres (such as that available from Jimsplosh Ltd, Leeds) which incorporate facilities to clear away contaminated water and allow the accurate weighing of swabs under water. Trade unions, worried that UCS discriminates against non-swimmers, have been reassured by proposed changes to employment legislation, special training, and the provision of lead-filled theatre boots.

After the initial problems were sorted out, the reactions of women and their partners to UCS have been uniformly positive, and the public image of interventionist obstetrics has been improved by a number of beautifully photographed BBC2 documentaries. There are still conservative obstetricians who say UCS is just plain daft but to them I say this: UCS is no sillier than normal delivery under water.

## *Sound on Sex?*

After the Christmas parties, the gynae clinic. The 1994 diary is cracked open for the first urgent cases of the new year. My weekly operating list is on a Monday and the bank holidays have wrought their usual havoc with the theatre schedules. Still, the post-festive terminations have to be fitted in somehow.

Year after year, this traditional scene doesn't change. Despite papers in the BMJ showing how other countries reduce their rates of unwanted pregnancy, despite well intentioned targets in The Health of the Nation and despite fact filled reports from royal colleges, the teenage girls keep shuffling in. This year they're wearing Doc Martens but otherwise nothing has changed.

Last year our regional health authority commissioned a report on the sexual health of young people. Sympathetic, perceptive, and imaginative, our report analysed the problems and suggested solutions. The authority launched it with a flourish at a conference attended by teachers, media persons, and a government minister. I had been looking forward to the day but afterwards I suffered post-meeting depression.

The conference confirmed what our working party already knew – the key to preventing unwanted pregnancy lies with teachers, not doctors. Parents want schools to provide sex education and some schools are doing so, but it became clear that most teachers aren't going to help. How can they? During their own training they received no instruction in human sexuality, and now they're demoralised by the Department of Education's endless gimmicky initiatives.

To my knowledge, teachers have been demoralised by the government for at least 35 years. Government and teachers communicate by megaphone and the last thing they want to talk about is sex. Although it's easy to criticise ministers and civil servants for this, a gynaecologist's job is not to blame but to understand people's sexual problems. Our leaders have serious hang ups. The cabinet may be sound on economics but it is not sound on sex.

This may be because its members are mainly men educated at single sex schools, or because Cambridge University teaches its students little or nothing about normal heterosexual behaviour. More likely it's because as high achievers ministers have – or had – strong libidos, which they now try to conceal from the public, from the press, and probably from one another. Henry Kissinger may admit that power is an aphrodisiac but in Whitehall and Westminster you have to pretend to be an asexual hearty.

Sex makes British politicians take up ridiculous positions on the high moral ground. Unhappily for my clinic they're now insisting that teachers strike similar poses. Young people treat such insincerity with contempt. Other countries have shown that if you don't patronise the young you can alter their behaviour, but no such initiative is happening here. Not because politicians don't care but because they're terrified of the tabloids (whose journalists, by all accounts, are themselves far from monastic). More insidious than AIDS, the sexual disease of chronic hypocrisy is endemic among media and ministers, and my young patients are suffering the consequences.

## *Poet's Corner*

When I heard that the Virago Book of Birth Poetry had been published I dropped what I was doing and simply flew to the bookshop, fearful that all its copies might already have been snapped up by fellow aesthetes. I found the last one on the shelf and embraced it triumphantly, oblivious of the pointed way Waterstone's staff were staring at my rubber apron. But as I turned the book's brave, bloody, gutsy, inspirational pages, a sense of disappointment welled up inside me. Where were the obstetric contributions?

Today's typical obstetrician may not be a bright eyed consumptive wasting in a garret, but beneath his or her suavely tailored exterior throbs the heart of a poet. Here are just two examples of the kind of empathic verse missed by Virago's anthologist – one from a junior and one from a senior colleague.

NIGHT FEED

Another contraction starts
in the darkness
from the fundus spreading
through silent syncytial cells
squeezing wetly, acid squishing
till the one within cries out
Hey! I'm hungry!
says mister stomach
clogs on lino
endless corridor empty but for
me, weekend-weary, Sunday-sick
no pizza for the wicked
at 2am
then cold shock numbs my brain

I have no coins!
the food dispenser mocks me
chrome-bright, unnatural
its windows unblinking
its bending paper plates
sinuously seductive
but unattainable
alluringly lit behind glass
like Amsterdam tarts
only these are
Leeds butties

## OBSTETRIC EXTRACTION

I observe with clinical detachment
the droplets of sweat,
pallor, the bounding pulse
a most difficult case
perhaps beyond saving?
silence falls in the little room
deathly
broken by her shallow breathing
we crane attentively
is she trying to speak?
no
my colleague glances at me
and shakes his head sadly
but I must not give up
only I can save her now
coolly
I reach out my hand for the forceps
which clink as I assemble them
gleaming, dangerous saviours
tell me, I murmur,
whose instrument is this?
the candidate

raises a tear-stained face
a spark of recognition flares
Kielland's she stammers
yes we smile, relaxing.

## *The Printing on the Wall*

Graffitology (the study of graffiti) is now an established subdiscipline of the social sciences, but little attention has been paid to its medical equivalent. Hospital staff, too well behaved to write on walls but nonetheless keen on self expression, decorate their working environment with posters and newspaper cuttings. Their efforts are the subject of the emerging science of bluetackology.

Only selected walls are used. Operating theatres are free of plaques saying YOU DON'T HAVE TO BE MAD TO WORK HERE - BUT IT HELPS!!! and consulting rooms are usually bare in hospital, though not in the community. In a health centre I used to visit I found a notice above the couch: WORKING HERE IS LIKE WETTING YOUR PANTS IN A DARK SUIT – IT GIVES YOU A WARM FEELING BUT NOBODY NOTICES. I thought it patronising and removed it but the room's owner objected, arguing that it bonded deprived patients to their GP.

This plausible rationale seems naive to bluetackologists, who know there are three reasons for such wall decoration. One is to claim territory. Hospital staff, working in a building they don't own, personalise their space – the "teenager's bedroom" phenomenon. Postcards and DESIDERATA enhance secretaries' offices, but posters in waiting areas convey the message that the room belongs to the staff, not the patients.

The second reason is to reinforce hierarchy. Bluetackologists call this the "police station" phenomenon. Your local nick is festooned with posters which assume that you are stupid, never locking your front door and always consuming several lagers before driving. Similarly hospitals exhort their customers to get off their butts and stop eating junk food. Our antenatal clinic has a picture of a bruised toddler over the slogan FIFTEEN PINTS AND SIX WHISKIES A DAY AREN'T

DOING HER ANY GOOD. Our clients meekly accept our assumption that they are alcoholic child abusers.

The "police station" phenomenon is confined to the NHS. It's a long time since I was inside a private hospital but its decor, as I recall, treated its clientele as intelligent adults, not wayward children. I wonder whether postnatal wards in private maternity hospitals are designed to make mothers feel guilty about smoking or bottle feeding. I doubt it.

The third reason, which applies particularly to press cuttings, is the "silent scream" phenomenon. Pictures from the local rag may commemorate some happy event but national newspaper cuttings give a voice to staff who feel that nobody is listening. Such displays, thinly disguised as education, proliferate in schools of nursing and midwifery and in hospital coffee rooms. Sensational headlines (HUGE PAY RISE FOR NHS BOSSES; DOCTORS SUED IN OP BLUNDER) provide a comforting backdrop for disgruntled juniors and disenfranchised nurses. If managers ever visited these rooms they could learn something about morale even without having to go so far as actually talk to the staff.

One paradox still unexplained by bluetackology is that although everyone in a hospital feels the urge to put printing on the wall, nobody, alas, feels empowered to take it down.

## *Obituary*

It seems that the BMJ doesn't receive many "self written" obituaries. I'm disappointed but not surprised. Even for the non-superstitious among us, writing your own obituary feels spooky. Like marking your own exam paper, it's no substitute for an independent opinion on whether your efforts merited beta plus or alpha minus.

Still, the BMJ has a proud history of challenging the conventions of the genre. For example, Richard Gordon claimed that he learned to write fiction while working on BMJ obituaries. I applaud this creative attitude and I also question the custom of embargoing publication while the subject is still alive. Free of these petty restrictions the column could blossom, as follows.

James Owen Drife, a former BMJ contributor, died recently at the age of 87 as a result of an error while attempting to jump over nine paramedic ambulances on his Harley-Davidson. The accident led to the immediate disbanding of his stunt riding team, Hell's Gynaecologists.

For the first two decades, Drife's career was that of a conventional medical academic. At 48, however, he published the first of his racy Euronovels under his anagrammatic pseudonym, Jason de Merwife. His style, aimed unashamedly at the translators, was described by one critic as "like a dubbed film without the pictures." With plots drawn from his experience on the editorial board of the European Journal of Obstetrics and Gynecology, Drife pioneered the "shopping and refereeing" style of fiction now familiar on bahnhof bucherstanden throughout the continent.

In 1997 came his resignation from the NHS over consultant multiskilling. Drife had trained in an era when senior medical staff stayed within specialty boundaries. In the 1990s, however, purchasers became increasingly capricious in deciding year by year which services they wanted to buy, and trusts responded by rotating consultants through different specialties. A natural gynaecologist, Drife felt deeply unhappy in ear, nose, and throat surgery ("All those wee orifices!") and walked out in protest.

Suspicions later arose that his resignation had not been as spontaneous as it had seemed. During the preceding year he had been secretly learning the electric guitar. With characteristic vision, he had been one of the first doctors to realise that the growing numbers of wrinklies in the twenty first century would be willing to pay to be entertained. His roadshow combining sixties singsongs with a lecture on hormone replacement therapy became a prototype for many others.

The scandal that made his name a household word at this time is now thought to have been an ingenious publicity stunt. The medical secretary who announced that she had found Lord Lucan after spilling Tipp-Ex over part of Drife's picture later changed her name and moved to Marbella. His roadshow benefited from the furore, but as competition from imitators became more intense it was forced to become ever more spectacular. Most of the people who formed the pillion pyramid on his last fateful ride were former members of the RCOG council. All except Drife survived. It was how he would have wanted to go.

## *Five Star Consultants*

Theoretically, all consultants are created equal and remain so throughout their careers. This may produce a level playing field for private practice but it works to the disadvantage of the NHS. In no other walk of life is someone appointed to a secure job for 30 years with no hope of advancement and no need to keep up to date.

At present a consultant's only chance of promotion is to become a clinical director, but many clinicians regard a move into management as a retrograde step. What is needed is a career structure which formalises the natural progression that already occurs in consultants' lives.

In any new system everyone will have to be called consultant, so how can grades be differentiated? Names like subconsultant, superconsultant, or consultantissimo will be unacceptable to the profession. We ought to follow the example of the United States army, which ranks its generals from "one star" to "five star."

The one star consultant will have all necessary skills and be fully accredited under European legislation. Such doctors already exist and carry out consultant duties in the absence of their seniors: they are currently called by the quaint title "senior registrar."

Two stars will be equivalent to today's newly appointed consultants. These are the ones without middle grade junior support, who operate on Friday afternoons and are on call during bank holidays. Their letters are typed by the most junior secretary in the typing pool and their house officer shares duties in another specialty.

The three star consultant is firmly established and attends increasingly frequent meetings of hospital managers in various official capacities. There is a long waiting list for his or her NHS clinics, which become grossly overloaded, as do the associated operating lists. He or she feels responsible for everything from senior house officers' interviews to patients' complaints. Many consultants are content to remain at the three star level and their dedication is sometimes recognised by a distinction award, a myocardial infarction, or both.

Some, however, become four star consultants — those with national or international responsibilities. They run the nation's and the world's medical quangos, all of which regard themselves as indispensible to civilisation as we know it, and some of which are.

There are very few five star consultants. These are senior doctors who have put behind them the three or four star life and are again devoting themselves to medicine. They have sensible sized clinics and take an interest in their junior staff. If they have a fault it is that they talk a little too much about the old days, but nobody minds that.

Under this system hospitals will know what they are getting and will avoid having all consultants at the same level. Consultants could move, if they wish, between hospitals as they advance from grade to grade. Initial confusion that the stars represent a kind of Michelin guide to consultants will fade as people get used to what is clearly a much more sensible system than the present one.

## *Italian for Beginners*

My parents had a picture of Mount Vesuvius above the piano as a memento of their first meeting but they took a dim view of Neapolitans, who, they said, would pinch the wheels off your jeep if you stopped at traffic lights. I used to point out that in 1944 even the most law abiding Italian had had an excuse for behaving badly, but they never went back.

Fifty years on, I'm overcompensating. I grab any chance of an Italian trip, the most memorable so far being to a family planning congress at the Vatican. My wheels have remained unpinched. So when, at a recent conference near Italy's tendo achilles, the desk clerk advised us to stay in the hotel for safety, I scoffed. I persuaded some delegates to join me in a honking, traffic bound taxi ride to the mediaeval port and an ominously uncrowded ristorante.

Relaxed and talkative, we wandered back through deserted side streets at midnight. A leather jacketed native sidled close but he was, I noted, a bantamweight. I didn't see the motorcyclist until the native had grabbed my companion's shoulder bag and leapt towards the pillion. People say such things happen in a flash but this seemed like slow motion: I gawped; he stumbled; someone screamed; he scrambled aboard. Yelling abuse, I began to run but the motorcycle wobbled off, gathering speed.

The moment blew a hole in various facades. Our confident chatter was silenced by this flash of violence. Our sexual equality disappeared as we men bristled: we had failed as protectors and we wanted to hit somebody. Our sophistication crumbled as we realised we had broken all elementary rules of tourist survival.

At the hotel we glared at the clerk. With big sympathetic eyes he explained the Italian for bagsnatching (scippo) and for police station. At the questura centrale the policeman at the typewriter spoke no English but offered French. "Pres de la gare," I said, "Un voleur a pris le sac a main de cette femme avec son passeport et toutes ses cartes de credit."

"Prego," he said, "parlez Francais."

Eventually he issued a form which would allow her to leave the country at dawn as she had planned.

Next morning I walked back to the questura, darting suspicious looks at the sunlit crowds. The typewriter was manned by a different non-English speaker. Opposite him were rows of large pigeonholes, all empty save one which contained the wounded bag, minus cash but replete with passport and credit cards. My veneer of Britishness disintegrated. I erupted with a stream of delighted Euro-exclamations. The man beamed at me.

A lady clerk appeared. Eez theese your bag? No. Your wife's? Er, no. She raised her eyebrows and conferred at length with the typewriter man. He trusted me, she announced. Would I trust him? But of course. He typed for a long time. I signed the incomprehensible statement and he added an elaborate stamp. Clutching the bag under my jacket I made a lightly perfumed exit.

## *Professor Drife is on Holiday*

A deadline is a deadline, as the Prof said before he left for the airport, but I don't see why he should ask me to write his column for him. I think that's the registrar's job. It's a mean trick making the SHO do it. Still, maybe it was meant kindly. He said it counts as a publication. Perhaps he recognised my facility with language from my stylish discharge letters.

Not that he actually threatened me. None of that "remember who writes your reference" stuff, though I'm sure some consultants would have taken that line. Did you see that excellent television series Cardiac Arrest earlier this year? Nothing but bitchy nurses, arrogant consultants, and heroic SHOs – wasn't it true to life? Especially that bit where the consultant told the junior she wouldn't get a reference unless he had his wicked way with her. I expect that's why so few women get to be consultants.

Anyway, I don't need your reference thank you very much I would have told him. Aren't I a GP trainee and almost finished my six months? A certified expert in answering my pager, being nice to midwives, and clerking day cases, and fully up to date on the plot of Home and Away. Skills which will be highly prized in a rural dispensing practice in Much-Purchasing-in-the-Marsh.

If I ruled the world, GP trainees would be treated quite differently from SHOs who intend to specialise. What will happen to us when they become "Calman trainees"? (What a mouthful – they should be called "Calbabies.") At present all SHOs are apprenticed to the registrar. That's not much use when we're around for only six months. GP trainees should be attached directly to consultants.

Mind you, if we were really being trained for general practice we would drop most labour ward and operating theatre sessions and go out instead with the community midwives, as well as attending the consultant's private rooms.

Of course, that will never happen. The obstetric SHO job is designed to do two things to us. Firstly, to scare the pants off us by showing us all possible complications. Secondly, to give us so much night work that we never want to see another labouring woman as long as we live. The obstetric SHO job doesn't attract GPs to do obstetrics, it drives them away.

Most of the other hospital jobs on my rotation were no better. Six months' specialising in the left leg, six months on the right ear, and all for the greater glory of general practice. The more important a specialty thinks it is, the longer and more irrelevant the training. (Look at the pre-clinical medical course.) It's not so long since people went straight into general practice and learned on the job. May be those days will return now that nobody's applying for these rotations.

How many words is that? The Prof said that with this column you have to watch your length or the editor will cut you off without a

## *Tyndallising the Pill*

William Tyndale, the first person to translate the Bible into English, was strangled and burnt in 1536. He had become unpopular with an establishment which wished to keep knowledge away from the common people. In 1994 Tyndale would no doubt be a computer buff using the internet. I wonder if he would turn his attention to drug advertising.

American magazines like the New Yorker sometimes carry ads for prescription only medicines: the drug's benefits are described, and the reader is advised to ask a physician about it. I doubt if this is popular with American doctors but the US Food and Drug Administration (FDA) cannot stop it because the First Amendment protects freedom of speech. Nevertheless, the FDA has a voluntary code of practice and vets virtually all advertisements.

In Europe, with our long tradition of secrecy among the ruling and professional classes, freedom of speech is less of a problem. In Britain advertising prescription only medicines to the public is illegal and indeed is now banned by a European regulation. The common people therefore have only three ways to find out about drugs – through doctors, the media, or gossip. The one exception to this ban relates to vaccines, which are given to healthy people to prevent disease and can therefore be promoted by advertising.

The same logic, surely, applies to contraception. The Medicines Control Agency and its European counterparts may not have given much thought to family planning. One gets the impression that they imagine women approaching their doctors in trembling ignorance, baffled by the mystery of excessive fertility: the woman is then amazed by the news that a pill is available to prevent pregnancy, and the wise doctor explains all about it in simple language she can understand.

In reality, of course, a woman usually decides before seeing the doctor that she wants to start taking the pill. She has to be fairly strong to make this decision because her three sources of information all convey negative vibes about the pill. We doctors may feel that we give unbiased advice but our emphasis is on disease and side effects. The media are always looking for trouble and have no vested interest in telling women that the pill is actually good for their health.

If drug firms could advertise the pill (or other contraceptive methods, for that matter) direct to women, two results would follow. Firstly, women would be better informed about the pill's benefits because of the skills of the advertising copywriters. Secondly, the traditional hostility of journalists and editors towards the pill would be softened. Editorial copy is subtly influenced by what the advertisers are paying for.

Exempting contraceptives from the ban on direct advertising could improve women's health and save lives. In the complacent nineties this is hardly a reason to change the regulations – especially when the people affected are young women, a group easily ignored by bureaucrats. Older women, however, are more articulate and persistent. Changes may occur when the same arguments are applied to hormone replacement therapy.

## *The 1995 Name Awards*

Choosing the right name for an organisation is fundamental to its success. Virgin Atlantic or Body Shop would not have done so well if they had been called Branson Airways or Roddick's Cosmetics. A good name combines literal accuracy with a subliminal message. Here are my 1995 Name Awards, with three booby prizes and three winners.

*Third booby*: Department of Health. The word "department" has undertones of faceless eastern European bureaucracy and large impersonal shops. It does not have the cachet of the earlier "ministry," which speaks of religion and healing. We used to joke about "the men from the ministry" but we tugged our forelocks none the less. (Incidentally, have you noticed that the word "health," in a political context, now means "disease"?)

*Second booby*: House of Commons. Talking of forelock tugging, how can Britain become a classless society when its legislators are divided into lords and commoners? Their American equivalents, senators and representatives, have perfect names. By calling our politicians "common" we simply encourage their yob culture.

*Booby prize*: Privy Council. With supreme linguistic cackhandedness this name combines an unhappy literal meaning with an unfortunate subliminal message. In an era when much lip service is being paid to open government, this powerful institution (which, among other things, appoints lay members of the General Medical Council) not only is private but flaunts its secrecy in its title. Moreover, its name gives the impression that it meets in a shed at the bottom of the Buckingham Palace garden.

Now for the happier prizes.

*Third prize:* National Childbirth Trust (NCT). Many organisations have realised that there is no copyright on the word "national." Mary Whitehouse, for example, upgraded "Housewives' Clean Up TV Campaign" to "National Viewers' and Listeners' Association." The NCT, however, also incorporates the warm, primaeval word "childbirth." "Trust" is another magic word: although it is becoming overused, we should acknowledge the part it played in the recent NHS reforms. The public grudgingly accepted the new structure only because hospitals became trusts rather than, say, corporations.

*Second prize*: Royal Colleges. These continue to proliferate in various increasingly obscure medical specialties. Many are under 50 years old but nevertheless their names suggest gothic buildings with top-hatted choristers by the side of the Cam. The adjective "royal" is probably still an asset. The noun "college" is accurate in the sense of "closed shop" (as in "College of Cardinals") and conveys the positive if not totally accurate impression that their main purpose is education.

*Star prize:* King's Fund. Nobody outside London knows anything about this unelected organisation except that it keeps making pronouncements about how the NHS should be run. Its authority is never questioned because of its inspired name. In nine letters and an apostrophe it calls to the depths of the British character. "King's" invokes a long dead royal father figure and "fund" indicates largesse. Its real name, "King Edward's Hospital Fund for London," would only antagonise people but its short title, appealing so concisely to snobbery and Mammon, is a worthy winner.

## *Dear Wellwisher*

One of the success stories of the reformed NHS is the complaints procedure. In 1994 hospitals processed more complaints than ever before. Each complaint received an individual reply, but most could be dealt with by one of these standard letters.

*Dear Madam,*

I have investigated your complaint and I find that much of what you say is true. I apologise. May I point out, however, that nothing you said was news to me. We are way past the stage of identifying our problems and are now trying to solve them. We are already applying ourselves to most of the points in the first eight pages of your letter. I note you have also written to Esther Rantzen, Roger Cook, and Lynne Faulds Wood. If they think they could run this place any better they are welcome to try. They would have to do it on less money than they make at present.

Yours etc

*Dear Sir,*

Thank you for your letter. I too would like to improve our facilities for visitors, but I do not agree that this could be achieved by sacking all the managers and building car parks instead. You refer to the Channel Tunnel: my understanding is that the money for this was raised by the private sector and would not have come to the NHS. Even if, as you suggest, we did create a huge cavern under the centre of Leeds I am advised by the trust's geological consultants that it could cause the town hall to collapse.

I agree our lifts are sometimes crowded at visiting time but I deny that the trust has ever employed extra staff to dispose of the bodies of asphyxiated visitors. The board discussed your suggestion of external glass lifts like you saw in Singapore but we believe these would fall foul of the city planning department.

I am sorry you don't like our nurses' uniforms. The medical director informs me that there is no scientific basis for your view that starched aprons and frilly caps speed the recovery of male patients, or female ones either.

Yours etc

*Dear Madam,*

We have thoroughly investigated your complaint and found that it is entirely without foundation. Several managers were involved and a consultant was forced to cancel an operating list to attend our inquiry. Your farrago of trumped up accusations has consumed scarce NHS resources which the taxpayer intended for the care of sick people. I therefore enclose an invoice for the hours we have all wasted. As you see, even in the NHS our time does not come cheap.

Payment is required within seven days. If it is not received your name will be added to the managers' circulation list. This means that all communications—including those about holiday leave, withdrawal of out of date circulars, and arrangements for prescribing on bank holidays—will be sent to you and your children and your children's children for ever. Think about it. Payment may be made by instalments. There is no appeal mechanism.

Yours etc

## *The Chain Letter*

The bundle of papers from the manager was marked READ AND RETURN. Breaking my normal habit, I read. The circulars were quickly initialled. The glossy newsletter with its uplifting messages was wearily skimmed. Next, a letter from the general manager of St Elsewhere's, consisting of one sentence: "I can't believe I'm doing this." Attached to it was a wad of photocopies of similar memos, and a chain letter.

It had originated in Holland and promised good luck within four days if the recipient passed it on. Should the chain be broken, it warned, bad luck would follow. It was typed in capitals and the English was crude. The first British recipient had been a very high ranking soldier whose name was familiar even to an academic gynaecologist. He had extended the chain to brass hats at the Ministry of Defence.

They had passed it to the upper strata of the Metropolitan Police and then it had gone to NHS mandarins. Their covering notes said that they weren't sure they believed in it but they needed a bit of luck. One of them added, "There is some evidence that these letters work." Always a sceptic when medical people start quoting evidence, I noticed that several members of the chain had managed a famous London teaching hospital which was subsequently doomed by the Tomlinson report.

I must have been about nine years old when I last saw a chain letter. That had been handwritten, but the NHS letters in this chain were beautifully typed. I could tell they were from important people because their offhand prose showed they had been dictated languidly and their impeccable spelling meant that the secretaries were on high salaries. At each stage the letter had been sent to five people whose addresses were meticulously punctuated. Having just corrected my own clinic letters, I felt a twinge of envy.

Nevertheless, it was comforting to learn that the upper echelons of NHS management can find ways of keeping their expensive secretaries occupied. More important, it was instructive to discover what sort of letter stimulates them into action. Next time I want something done by a senior manager I shall imitate the style of that anonymous Netherlander:

DEAR FRIEND: ALTHOUGH WE NEVER MET I HOPE YOU WILL RESPOND. I HAVE A RABBIT'S FOOT AND IT HAS A STATISTICAL SIGNIFICANT SUCCESS RATE. IF I STICK A PIN IN IT YOUR GONADS WILL DROP OFF. BELIEVE ME I AM SERIOUS. I HAVE ALREADY WROTE MANY NHS MANAGERS AND ONE WHO DID NOT WRITE BACK IS DEAD. HE FELL INTO RIVER THAMES AND HIS BODY WAS FOUND IN BELLY OF SHARK WITH TOOTH MARKS ALL UP HIS LEG. NOW HEAR THIS. UNLESS I GET ANOTHER REGISTRAR I PUT INTO ACTION MY RABBIT'S FOOT. DO NOT GIVE ME RUBBISH ABOUT MANPOWER APPROVAL. PLEASE WRITE IN FOUR DAYS. IF YOU DO YOU WILL HAVE LOTS OF LUCK.

Then I shall simply sit back and wait for the reply: "I can't believe I'm agreeing to your request."

Speaking of disbelief, perhaps I should add that the only part of this article I made up was the paragraph in capitals.

## *The Eurospeaker*

As it becomes commonplace to go by train for lunch in Paris, postgraduate education will broaden its horizons. Soon you will be nipping over to European meetings to gather points for CME (Continental Medical Education). You may even be invited to speak. Having experienced PGME sans frontieres at various international gatherings, I offer some hints on how to adapt your lecturing style.

You are probably used to a static audience of people sitting down. This is not the European way. At a Euromeeting most of the audience files in and out during your talk. One by one, people open the door (admitting a babel from the lobby), look around expressionlessly, shuffle to a seat, listen for two or three minutes, and then shuffle out.

The organisers will have hired a photographer to impress everyone with the importance of the meeting. He waits until you are about to make a really important point and then flashes from the front row, putting you off completely. As you get into your stride again, he climbs on to the platform for a profile shot. Chewing meditatively, he then moves up the aisle making each row of listeners stiffen in turn. Like all photographers he believes that if he is not smiling he is invisible.

When you arrive you will find you have been allowed only half the time you were promised in the draft programme. You cope with this by using dual projection, which allows you to show all your slides anyway. Its other advantage is that it holds the audience's attention while they wait for the slides to become desynchronised. As dual projection has made your lecture incomprehensible, they have no way of knowing when this happens except by watching your face intently. For them the highlight of the talk will be when you try to tell the projectionist to hold the left hand side and go back two slides on the right hand screen.

It is important to project detailed graphs and to talk as quickly as possible, so everyone feels that the maximum amount of information has been squeezed into the time available. Include plenty of colloquial expressions, as this helps to educate the audience in contemporary English usage.

Refer frequently to London teaching hospitals by their abbreviated names and make lots of impromptu jokes about the Tomlinson report.

This flatters the listeners by making them feel that they belong to the British medical system.

They will respond by leaving the room and filing back with simultaneous translation headphones. They will spend most of the rest of your lecture trying to turn them on. Once they succeed, the translations will form a memorably polyglot accompaniment. This also gives the audience good value: as well as two slides (one for each eye) they get two lectures (one for each ear).

Finally, before and after your talk make sure you stick with the rest of the British contingent. Chatting to foreigners can be hard work and you need to save your energy for communicating.

## *The View from Ulm Minster*

We had not specially planned to be in Germany on VE day. Nor had we expected to climb Ulm cathedral spire, the tallest in the world. By the time I passed the bells I was sure I was going to die. At the top I peered down through my sweat at the town's reconstructed buildings. Eighty per cent of Ulm's houses had been destroyed by wartime bombing but its minster had been spared. I was surprised that in 1944 it had been possible to incinerate civilians with such finesse.

Our group of doctors regularly travels abroad but this was the first time we had collectively dared to visit Germany. When we arrived our attitude was pure Basil Fawlty—"Don't mention the war!"—but we soon realised that the second world war had not gone unnoticed by our hosts. In the nave of the minster, for example, was a display entitled "Poland"—black and white photos of landscapes with old barbed wire and that sinister single track railway.

The trick is to learn from history without wallowing in it, and I thought the Germans had managed this better than we had. Tour guides mentioned the war matter-of-factly and newspapers reported Britain's VE celebrations. There, as here, the Queen Mother made the front page—in the British papers smiling radiantly, in the German ones dabbing her eyes with a hankie.

The English newspapers cast a warm glow over the war with purple prose written mainly by—and for—people who were not yet born when hostilities ended. My father never became sentimental about his army experience but my own generation was raised on war mythology created by comics and films. Inevitable, I suppose, but it is worrying that our children have been fed the same diet of xenophobic stereotypes, so familiar that they are now parodied in lager commercials.

The average British male somehow believes that his dad or grandad singlehandedly defeated Hitler (with a little help from the Yanks). His German counterpart has, I think, a more mature view: that Nazism destroyed itself by calling down on its head the justified wrath of the whole world from America (the good guys) to Russia (the bad guys).

My near death experience on those 768 steps made me see things clearly. Britain, I decided, is suffering from what Freudians would call a war fixation. Deep down, we want it always to be 1945. We refuse to develop beyond that stage. As the pain in my thighs subsided I saw that this explains everything—Euroscepticism, the Falklands, and all those nostalgic television series set in the 1950s.

During the rest of our trip we felt that we had things to teach our German colleagues—particularly about medical education—and they had things to teach us. For example, in the maternity hospital we visited, the consultant on call has to sleep in the building. British obstetricians accept that this change is inevitable but we know it won't happen here for many years. After all, in 1945 consultants didn't live in, did they?

## *The British Misery Association*

Hello! As a BMA politician I believe one must keep in touch with the grass roots at the coal face. This is why I have found time in my busy schedule to pen this message to each and every one of you. The BMA is seriously concerned that some doctors (very few, I grant you) are happy in their work, and it is my urgent task to stamp this out.

Much as I prefer hewing at the bread and butter of clinical work, it has fallen to me to fight your corner against Whitehall mandarins, Westminster apparatchiks, and Brussels bureaucrats. The one thing that unites these machiavellian moneygrubbers is their remorseless resolve to grind doctors' faces in the mud. I hear the Cabinet Office just took delivery of a consignment of dartboards, each decorated with the face of a BMA divisional secretary.

My first message is to the nation's junior doctors. Never forget: the government is out to get you. Its latest dirty trick is to try to reduce your working hours. Have you ever heard anything so despicable? No wonder you are all so utterly disillusioned and depressed. Recently a London consultant told me her hospital's juniors had become a shower of scruffy clockwatchers. Modestly, I said this achievement was not entirely due to us. The media have done their bit in giving you role models to live down to. But the BMA has steadily hammered home the message that being a junior is as much fun as cleaning toilets in Sarajevo. So I suppose we must take some credit for the fact that young doctors now see their first duty as making war on managers.

Next, a stern word to all you consultants. On the train the other day I overheard a consultant saying that life wasn't too bad. Admittedly he had drunk half a bottle of Chateau Intercity Cote de l'Est Privee but I did have to change my seat and reason with him. Careless talk costs salary increases, I told him, and the NHS Executive has spies everywhere, particularly on pullmans. My little talk must have had an effect, for when we arrived he stepped off the platform in front of the 21.53 to Glasgow. I was very upset, because his ill timed gesture missed the deadline for the evening news bulletins.

Finally, our troops in the trenches, the GPs. What a pleasure it is for me to be able to say, hand on heart, that there is not a single happy GP in the length and breadth of the country. The BMA has successfully demonised every Health Secretary since Bevan and rubbished all their initiatives, well intentioned or otherwise. Nevertheless, we cannot rest on our laurels. The moment we relax our vigilance, contentment may break out and spread like some foul contagion from practice to practice. This must not happen. We at the BMA are the leaders of Britain's GPs and your morale is in our hands. If it ever rises, it will be over our dead body.

## *Employees of the Year*

Lesser journals run annual contests to find Britain's best doctor or nurse. Nowadays the Nurse of the Year is chosen NOT for her looks but for—er—her caring personality. The doctor is chosen, as ever, for his research. Some day the nurse may be chosen for her research and the doctor for his caring personality, but not yet.

Our awards are not limited to medical and nursing staff.

*Kitchen assistant of the year*—We are not necessarily seeking the person with the loudest singing voice but the one with the most extensive repertoire from the great musicals of the 1950s, and the ability to drop large metal objects at irregular intervals out of time with the music. Last year there was no award: the winning voice was identified but despite an extensive search of the kitchens its owner could not be located.

*Publicist of the year*—We are looking for the hospital public relations officer who achieves the largest headlines from the most routine medical case. At the discretion of the judges an additional prize (the "St Bartholomew's medal") may be awarded if the PRO has also convinced the hospital staff to believe their own publicity.

*Manager of the year*—Clinical directors are disbarred from this award, as is anyone else who has spoken to a patient within the last calendar year. Eligibility is restricted to pure bred managers with large format filofaxes. The winner will be picked with a pin.

*Hospital cyclist of the year*—Because cycling is healthy, exponents feel empowered to walk around the hospital dressed like extras from Star Trek, glaring at people they suspect of being motorists. The prize will go to the cycle parked in the most outrageous place within the hospital grounds. (Last year's winner: inside the MRI scanner.)

*Trust chairman of the year*—The winner will be the one who, in the opinion of the judges, makes the most memorably derogatory public comments about a consultant or about doctors in general. Subsequent retraction, litigation, or resignation will not affect the award.

*Security man of the year*—The prize will be awarded NOT for the loudest walkie-talkie but for the most incomprehensible directions on how to get to the casualty department.

*Visitor of the year*—This hard fought competition will again require heats. Entry is restricted to visitors who park with ALL FOUR wheels actually ON the flower bed. The first heat will be based on the number of FULL polystyrene cups left in the lift, and the second on the most imaginative disposal of chewing gum.

*Editor of the year*—All hospitals now produce glossy news sheets intended to boost morale with headlines like "IN-HOUSE TEAM WINS CLEANING CONTRACT!" This year the prize will be awarded for the most unflattering picture of any board member.

*Switchboard of the year*—The winner will be the hospital with EITHER the most seductive muzak OR the most bewildering call transfer system. The judges are still holding for the winner of the 1994 competition.

## *Fags and Feminism*

Good weather brings the patients to the front door. After the ward round their pains abate and they wheel their drip stands into the lift. On armchairs dragged from the foyer they sit, in dressing gowns and antiembolism stockings, enjoying their first cigarette of the day.

The sight does not inspire their carers. We like to believe in the myth of the deserving patient who needs our protection. Instead we see self confident women with rhonchi, forsaking their £700-a-day beds for a drag and a gossip about the perceived inadequacies of the NHS.

If I'm having a bad day I grumble, gesticulating at the No Smoking signs and the sea of butts. They ask what right I have to tell them what to do and I list my credentials. I walk away feeling a complete nerd.

Why do I find the sight of a woman with a cigarette so repellent? It's the same whether she is a patient, a nurse, or the driver of the XR3i in my mirror. Is it the health risks that upset me or is there more to it? Are cigarettes a threatening symbol of female aggression?

The sophisticated response is to shrug and smile. It is uncool to feel strongly about smoking and cancer now. I suppose this is because the issue has been around for years—though that doesn't stop people feeling passionate about African famines or Balkan atrocities.

It's frustrating to be angry and to know that people find your anger amusing. When I lecture about women's health I show a slide of lung cancer death rates in Britain—falling among men but rising among women. Every time, I feel the adrenaline beginning to flow as I point to the 10000 women's deaths a year. The audience waits patiently for me to calm down and move on to something more appropriate, like cervical cancer, which kills fewer than 2000.

Cervix cancer and screening excite women and the media. Recently I asked my wife why lung cancer isn't also a feminist issue. Why should it be? she asked. I rehearsed the reasons. Death rates have almost doubled among women since 1970 and it now kills more women than any other malignancy except breast cancer.

Like cervical cancer, it can be blamed on men. Cigarettes are made by multinational companies run by men. Smoking is promoted by male-dominated advertising agencies, with ads targeted at women. Surely the issue is tailor made for the victim culture in which feminists enjoy wallowing?

Effortlessly my wife put her finger on why lung cancer doesn't interest female health activists. It's because men die of it too. Women's groups have always been not so much pro-women as anti-men. Problems shared by both sexes are of little interest to them.

So there are no acronymic pressure groups called "Girls Against Gaspers" or "Women Oppose Marlboro Brainwashing." I'm told there is one called INWAT (International Network of Women Against Tobacco). It's small and underfunded. Now I know why.

## *Settefonte*

Weaving through traffic on the road out of Bologna, our taxi driver kept turning round, looking mystified. My wife's evening-class Italian rose to the occasion. "My father-in-law has been shot," she explained, "nella la guerra, in the hills near Settefonte. My husband wants to visit the place." Satisfied, the driver lapsed into silence, perhaps trying to work out from her accent which side my father had been on.

There was no way of knowing where the incident had occurred. According to the regimental history, the Lovat Scouts had carried out patrols in the Monte Grande sector of the Apennines early in 1945, and on one of these Lieutenant Drife had been wounded. The book's style is proud and down to earth, in Scottish military tradition. On page 103 a Lieutenant Scroggie steps on a schu-mine:

"Are you all right, sir?" asks Sergeant Hopkinson.

"Yes, I'm all right, Hoppy, but I think I've lost the sight of both eyes."

As he is carried away a Scout tells him softly: "If I get it, sir, I hope I take it like you."

My father, a modest man with a sense of humour, claimed that he himself was much less heroic. In the fifties we children did not think it unusual that our gentle dad, a bank manager and kirk elder, had been trained to kill with a knife. "The important thing," he remarked once, "is to ensure that your man doesn't make a noise as he falls."

It was his enthusiasm for silence that got him into trouble. Whispering his password inaudibly, he was shot by his own sentry. I suppose it was a high-velocity bullet, for it passed through his thorax and caused not death but haemoptysis.

He rarely mentioned the incident but if pressed he described it hilariously, commenting that he was far from silent as he fell. Uppermost in his mind was the thought that he was going to drown in his own blood. His comrades (embarrassed, I hope) transported him to hospital, where he met my mother, a physiotherapist. They had over forty years together.

I don't know what I expected to find in Settefonte. Foxholes and cartridge cases? It turned out to be rural and unexpectedly academic. The quiet hillside is now part of the University of Bologna, with rows of neatly labelled plants guarded by "keep off" signs.

An occasional car climbed up the narrow road from the plain, the occupants staring at us - a middle aged couple in city clothes, carrying umbrellas. One dusty Fiat stopped suddenly in the middle of the road. Its driver, a very old lady, leaned across and peered hard at me. She started to speak, changed her mind, and clattered off up the hill.

The rain almost held off as we strolled past peaceful clumps of bamboo and bullrushes and caught a bus back to the city. Our hotel had become busy. It was full of musicians taking part in a charity concert for the children of Bosnia.

## *Evidence Farm*

Dobbin the horse was the hardestworking animal on the farm. All day he pulled his cart and produced manure. He took both jobs seriously. He read the British Cart-Pulling Journal every week and subscribed to Manure Monthly.

He was respected by all the animals except the dogs, who rarely spoke to him. He wondered if they disliked him or felt intimidated because he was stronger than they were. One day the dogs came to see him.

"You will have to change the way you pull the cart," they said. Dobbin replied that he had pulled it for years and had managed pretty well. He had recently modified his technique after reading a paper in the BCPJ.

The dogs looked at one another and smiled superior smiles. They explained that they had read all papers on cart-pulling ever published. Noticing Dobbin's expression they admitted that they hadn't read them personally but they knew dogs who had.

"The evidence is clear," they said. "It is more efficient to push the cart than to pull it. You've been doing it wrong all these years, Dobbin."

To their surprise, Dobbin acquiesced. "All right, from now on I shall push my cart up and down the hills."

"No," replied the dogs, "the evidence applies only to pushing the cart downhill. There is no evidence about pushing it uphill."

Nor, it transpired, was there evidence about pushing it in the wind, or in snow, or around corners. This did not worry the dogs. They always brought discussion back to their Downhill Study. Their tongues hung out with pleasure as they told all the animals that Dobbin had been doing it wrong.

Dobbin waited for the Uphill and Round the Corner Studies but the dogs began to lose interest in cart-pulling. Their next evidence showed that the hens were laying their eggs wrongly. (When questioned, they admitted that this evidence applied only to brown eggs: there was no evidence about white ones.)

Dobbin asked if he could gather evidence himself. "Of course, old chap," they replied. "All you will need is a year's sabbatical, a team of computer programmers (who will be dogs, of course) and enough money to buy two tons of Pedigree Chum."

The dogs were not good communicators. They preferred to talk about evidence than about carts and they spent most of their time visiting distant farms. This gave them authority; the more time they spent away from farm work, the more confident they became. Some of them had once pulled little carts themselves, but they had not liked it as much as producing evidence.

They were very proud of their evidence although they pretended not to be. "Please criticise it," they said, but Dobbin knew they didn't really mean this. Somehow the evidence usually proved what the dogs wanted it to prove.

After their last meeting with Dobbin the dogs hurried away murmuring, "We are the horses now!"

"Oh no you're not," muttered Dobbin, straining forward with another heavy load.

## *Quangoholics Anonymous*

This is the story of an ordinary doctor. Like you or me. Let us call him Jack, though that is not his real name. A few years ago Jack was a useful member of our profession, with a wife, children, and a respected position. Life was good. Then someone—Jack can't remember who—offered him his first quango.

It seemed a small thing at the time. A few papers to read. The occasional trip to London. Where was the harm in that? After all, he had been working a little too hard recently. He felt he was getting into a rut and craved the extra thrill that a quango promised. Oh, Jack! If only someone had been there to guide you away from the downhill path. Your loving wife or an older, wiser colleague. But no. You accepted that first quango of your own free will.

At first Jack found the quango boring. Then he began to enjoy it. The relaxed atmosphere, the urbane company, the respectful secretariat, the freshly sharpened pencils. They all made him feel he was somebody. How different, how very different, from his other life in the NHS.

Inevitably, one quango led to another. And another. Jack began to find he couldn't do without them. When one quango ended (which happened infrequently) he would twitch and sweat. Then came the horrors as he envisaged life without quangos. But there was always another.

Jack lost his free will. He would say ruefully, "I have to go to London," and he believed it. He saw less and less of his family. Quangos became the most important thing in his life. Jack longed to escape but knew that if someone offered him another quango he wouldn't, or couldn't, refuse.

Then, one evening, as he carried his loaded briefcase back to his hotel he saw an open door and a beckoning light. What fateful hand guided him to that little hall Jack will never know. But he went in, to his first meeting of Quangoholics Anonymous.

There Jack learned that quangoholism is rife behind the frosted windows of Britain's consulting rooms. In one royal college 10% of the British members are on at least one committee. Jack felt better knowing that he was not alone. After listening to the testimony of several distinguished looking men and women, he made up his mind. He stood up and said in a clear voice, "My name is Jack and I am a quangoholic...."

Do not confuse Quangoholics Anonymous with the British Quangoholics Society, the National Working Party on Quangoholism, the Royal College of Quangoholics, the European Association of Quangoholics, or the Federation Internationale de Quangoholiques. QA has no council and no office bearers. If any member suggests this the others beat him senseless with lead-filled recorded delivery packages.

Jack now works as a doctor and has never been happier. But many stories end in misery. QA offers these wretches hope. It needs your support. Remember, these are ordinary doctors just like you. Or me.

## *The Secret Diary of James Drife, aged 48¼*

*January 1*—Gosh. The first day of my 25th year in the NHS! Today is a holiday so I watched a film called Reach for the Sky on TV. The best bit was when Kenneth More took over a demoralised unit and telegraphed Whitehall: THIS SQUADRON IS NOT OPERATIONAL, REPEAT NOT OPERATIONAL. The "brass hats" were angry but they gave him equipment. Then his men admired him and became moralised again.

*January 2*—Today 18 old ladies were sent to our ward from the medical unit. There are no beds on their proper ward. This is nostalgic. When I was a houseman in 1971 we had 18 old ladies blocking our beds. But that was a medical ward. Now I am Professor of Gynaecology and the old ladies have followed me!

*January 3*—Sister was upset because she has no room for our gynaecology patients. She said I should do something. I replied in my Stern Voice: "Who do you think I am, Sister? Kenneth More?" She should be used to this because it happens every January.

*January 4*—I heard Sister telling a Social Worker that a hospital bed costs £200 a day but a nursing home costs £200 a week. Some of our old ladies could go but Social Services have no money. Sister said it all comes from the same taxes. Then she said something about the government that I shall not put in my diary.

*January 5*—Our Important Meeting To Sort Out The Bed Crisis is traditionally held on Twelfth Night. This year was different because it was early and we did not shout at each other. Nobody cried, though one doctor and one manager looked as if they might. We blamed the government for not knowing there are lots of old ladies in Britain.

*January 9*—Beds are in the news! On TV Mr Gerry Malone said there are enough beds and it is all our fault. Although he has a Scottish accent I did not believe him. My Friend The Manager says Mr Malone does not know what is happening because his advisers are afraid to tell him the truth in case he sacks them. And he does not listen to doctors because they went on strike in 1975.

*January 10*—Mr Stephen Dorrell told us on TV about a hospital that has lots of beds because it has an Acute Ward beside the Casualty Department. That cannot be us because we have an Acute Ward but also we have No Beds. I used to trust Mr Dorrell. He looks like a doctor because he has bags under his eyes. But now he is beginning to sound like Mrs Virginia Bottomley.

*January 11*—Our Trust Board met. Strange. For years it has agreed with the government that we must work harder. Now it is wondering why the government is not helping us. My friends on other Boards are asking the same question.

*January 12*—Today is exactly 13 years and 6 months since Kenneth More died, unfortunately.

## How to be Scottish

English doctors sometimes remark that British medicine is run by a Scottish mafia (a Macfia, perhaps). I reply that English medicine should count itself lucky and the conversation usually ends there. National pride on both our parts prevents me explaining that anyone can be Scottish if they really want to be.

Some people, of course, are born Scottish but aspirants should not let this deter them. Nowadays congenital Scots are rarely tall, bony, or red haired and many have a sense of humour. In fact, they seem just like everyone else until they start to speak.

Achieving Scottishness, like any worthwhile endeavour, requires effort but you need to work at only two things. One is attitude. The Scots and English have different approaches to life. England has never managed to shake off feudalism but Scotland, like many northern nations, is oddly egalitarian. The two contrasting characteristics—Scots practicality and English self confidence—complement each other perfectly. This is why the empire did so well. In former colonies the streets are named after Scotsmen and the statues are of Englishmen.

Medicine, however, requires mainly Scottish qualities, particularly nowadays. Couthiness in a doctor is preferable to coolness and dour logic is now valued more than insouciance. The NHS is a typically Celtic idea. Most Scots view Harley Street with mixed amusement and incomprehension.

Don't despair, however, if developing a Scottish outlook seems beyond you. The real reason that Scots can stay aloof from the English caste system is that they speak in a funny accent. This is their defining characteristic and is all you actually need to be Scottish. As any English-educated Scot will confirm, birth, ancestry, and indeed attitude count for nothing without the brogue.

Strangers attempting a Scots accent for the first time usually sound like a cow with bronchitis. To develop the correct cadences you should listen to a native speaker—ideally, an expatriate, as the Scots accent becomes more pronounced the further its owner is from home. When I meet groups of compatriots abroad I keep being surprised at how we all sound like Sir Harry Lauder.

Foreigners rarely realise that within Scotland, as in North America, there is more than one accent. Some are best avoided even by the native. Rab C Nesbitt does not enhance the caring image, though if used judiciously it can resolve deadlock in difficult committee meetings.

Aim at a mid-Scottish burr. An Aberdeen accent is too introspective, Glasgow too amused, Edinburgh too refined, and a Hebridean lilt too unworldly. Try, however, to avoid the bland homogenate used for voiceovers in Scottish television commercials. Your accent should be individual but should sound as if you are doing your best to disguise it.

Personal tuition from an expatriate doctor would probably embarrass you both. So start by studying videotapes of Sean Connery ("My name's Bond. Doctor Bond.") and then try to synthesise an amalgam of your personal favourites—a mixture of, say, Malcolm Rifkind and Billy Connolly. You'll be surprised by the effect on your career.

## *We Know Why They Die*

Last month I was photographed in front of the Taj Mahal. All British tourists pose soulfully on Princess Di's bench, but our giggles were soon stifled by the beauty of the building. It commemorates a queen who, in 1630, died in childbirth. In 1996 over 100000 Indian women will do the same.

Later, in a Delhi conference hall filled with obstetricians, a small Indian doctor in a green sari asked us to imagine a jumbo crashing every 30 hours. She pointed out that India has world class hospitals and many doctors. The problem of maternal mortality lies in primary care.

About 40% of the deaths occur at home, mainly from sepsis and bleeding. About half could be prevented by an adequate system of referral and transport. In one study of 140 women moribund on admission to hospital, 97 arrived by bus. Some came by bullock cart and only 12 by ambulance.

There have been many studies. In the decade since the World Health Organisation, with touching optimism, announced its target of halving maternal mortality worldwide by the year 2000, the causes have been researched to death. As one woman speaker remarked, "we know why they die." We do indeed, and the knowledge is hard to live with.

It is of course the poor who die. The problem, however, is not resources. Maternal death rates are related not to each state's income but to its rate of female literacy. This shifts responsibility to teachers but offers cold comfort to doctors. It suggests that poor women have no effective advocates. Only when they can speak up for themselves do matters improve.

In 1935 Britain's and India's maternal mortality rates were similar. The reason ours fell was only partly antibiotics. More importantly, people got angry about it. Remember that scene in Lawrence of Arabia where a blimpish medical officer finds prisoners dying of thirst in hospital? Furious, he stalks around shouting, "Outrageous!" This is the only civilised reaction to a medical disgrace.

Although the Delhi conference committee had highlighted the problem, what was chilling was the lack of anger in the hall. The speakers had lived with this for years and seemed to be going through the motions, their passion almost spent. The Europeans felt upset: these were not our patients but how could we ignore them?

The rest of the audience was blasé. While one speaker, formerly a consultant in England, spoke about his new job training primary care workers in Bangladesh there was a small, steady exodus of expensively dressed lady obstetricians. Later that day the organisers shrewdly chose the smallest hall for the safe motherhood seminar. Afterwards its chairs were taken to pack the largest hall for the session on in vitro fertilisation.

Perhaps it is patronising to visit a country for a few days and then write about its troubles. It would be worse not to. Besides, they are not so far from home. In the NHS we are already seeing how public indignation about inadequate services can be silenced by financial arguments. Any nation without the will to get angry is a pitiful place.

## *To all Doctors in Britain*

Dear Doctor, You may be aware of articles in a Sunday newspaper alleging that doctors in some countries of the European Community continue to practise after they have died. The paper suggests that in parts of Europe posthumous practice is a common way of exploiting tax loopholes. Indeed, it claims to have found group practices in which only one of the names outside the surgery belonged to a living doctor.

Following these articles, the General Medical Council received letters from patients' organisations and members of parliament asking what measures are in place to ensure that this does not happen here.

The Council has been unable to verify the newspaper's claims. Regulatory authorities in the relevant countries have failed to identify the doctors, the towns, or indeed the mountain ranges named in the articles.

Nevertheless, the Council is mindful of the disquiet caused by these allegations, and of the profession's need to retain the full confidence of the public. The Council wishes to state unequivocally that medical practice should be undertaken only by doctors who are alive. This is implied (though admittedly not stated explicitly) in the Council's guidance, *Duties of a Doctor.*

At present in Britain when a doctor dies, relatives or colleagues inform the Council, which then removes the doctor's name from the Register. There is, however, no statutory duty on them to do so and the system is open to potential abuse. New guidelines are therefore being introduced as a matter of urgency to comply with European regulations.

All doctors will be required forthwith to provide the Council with documentary proof that they are alive. According to legal advice obtained by the Council this must be done in two stages. First, the practitioner must furnish proof that he or she has been born. You are therefore requested to supply the Council with your birth certificate. A photocopy is not acceptable.

As the checking of these documents has to be undertaken without an increase in staff, the workload on the Council's office will be considerable. We are sending out these requests in tranches based on alphabetical order. Please do not send us your birth certificate until we ask for it.

Second, you will be required to furnish proof that you have not died. The exact form that this proof should take is still the subject of discussion between the Council and the European Commission. Detailed instructions will be issued shortly.

It is likely, however, that you will be asked to supply a recent passport size photograph in which you are holding in one hand a copy of the Times, folded so that the date is visible, and in the other hand a glass of water (or similar fluid) to prove that you were in the upright position when the photograph was taken.

On the reverse the statement "This is a true likeness of Dr [your name]" must be signed by a Justice of the Peace, a clerk from the hospital personnel department, or a person of similar standing. The signature of a doctor is not acceptable, for obvious reasons.

## *Another Glossy Flyer*

Parasitic Productions, in association with the National Association of Health Authorities and Trusts, invites you to its annual conference on the NHS. It is for opinion leaders, including non-executive board members like you – people who are moulding the NHS for the next millennium.

This month's annual conference is different from last month's annual conference, which was designed to facilitate medium term thinking in small Trusts. This one is designed to facilitate long term thinking in medium sized Trusts. It will also be relevant to large and small Trusts and to medium and short term strategic thinking.

You will hear outstanding speakers whose colour pictures are reproduced in this brochure. They include the doyen of US health management gurus, Reggie P Errin, author of *Health Thru Work!,*

*Work Thru Health!* and the worldwide bestseller, *Thru Work, Health!* In what promises to be an inspirational presentation, Reggie will unveil some of the revolutionary concepts from his forthcoming book, video, and interactive CD, *Work Health Thru!*

The programme includes keynote addresses by leading politicians. Delegates to past conferences will confirm that on several occasions one of the advertised politicians has actually turned up–a tribute to the high-level regard for these meetings. As a lighthearted inducement, we shall enter the names of the first 500 registrants in a sweepstake based on exactly how late the politician will be.

For many, the highlight will be the debate, "Whither healthcare?" This will be an absorbing clash of deeply held principles between a fairly right wing health economist and a very right wing health economist. It will be insightfully chaired by one of the BBC's respected team of weather forecasters with a lifelong interest in healthcare matters.

The underlying purpose of this conference is to recover the "feelgood factor" which our research tells us is missing from so many Trust boards. We have therefore made strenuous efforts to exclude as far as possible any talks by practising members of the medical profession.

Nevertheless, we recognise the prime importance of ensuring that discussions are evidence based and relevant to the care of individual patients. This is why we ask you, when filling in your registration form, to give details of any medical procedures which you (or a close relative) have undergone during the past ten years. The information will remain confidential but will be used in our computerised system to enhance networking among delegates. Research has shown that this is by far the most important factor in top level NHS decision making.

In 1996 the NHS is facing its most potentially historic changes since 1995. These involve not only slogans but also letterheads and the job titles of many senior managers. You, like us, have a vested interest in promoting change, while at the same time ensuring that the people who deliver the service are left alone to do their jobs, and that the NHS's finite resources are used wisely.

The registration fee (£800 including coffee) can be reclaimed from your Finance Director. Parasitic Productions is an Investor In People.

## *Old Men and Young Girls*

Nine months on from last year's pill scare, the labour ward is groaning and the staff are full of wisecracks about the Committee on Safety of Medicines. Should the boys be named after the chairman? Are there any women members?

Unintended pregnancy has always been a source of humour, provided it goes to term. Abortion is different—a reason for censuring women, but not serious enough for high profile prevention. Teenagers' use of condoms increased sharply after anti-AIDS campaigns aimed at men. We don't try so hard to help girls avoid abortions.

In the early 1990s nearly half the 20 year old women in England were on the pill. How many stopped it last October? We don't know. The most recent abortion statistics, published in June, relate to the quarter ending December 1995. They reveal a slow fall over the past six years. The next figures, due in October, will show whether young girls managed to resist the old men who produced the scare.

To a 19 year old (the age at highest risk of abortion) everyone over 40 is old. I suppose we are, if the criterion is that we cannot, or will not, communicate with the young.

Last October's scary headlines resulted from rivalry between two groups of wrinklies—doctors and newspaper subeditors. I imagine subeditors as worldly men with Scottish accents, fond of puns and whisky. Not unlike ourselves, perhaps—but we never talk to them. We doctors send news to one another secretly and the newspapers try to intercept it. If they succeed and a scare ensues, we tell ourselves it was only because our system failed.

The reasons for pill scares are much more Freudian: prurience, a fear that pleasure brings retribution, dislike of drug firms, and epidemiological hype. And now, tradition — the cycle of scares and abortions has become so familiar that we feel nothing can stop it.

If we want it to end we should stop treating young women as bimbos. Men look at girls with mixed emotions: paternalism usually predominates and respect for their intelligence is low on the list. That is why, when a pill scare breaks, nobody talks sensibly to the people who have chosen to use it. Subeditors aim headlines at their parents.

The Committee on Safety of Medicines tells them to see their general practitioners.

This is laziness. It is easy for the committee to send doctors a mishmash of odds ratios and ask us to reassure people. When pronouncing on contraception the committee should talk directly to the public. It cannot marginalise doctors more than it has done already and it might show more self discipline if it did not have us to hide behind. How long did it take us, last year, to realise that we were discussing one-in-a-million risks of death?

My daughter and her friends are 18 year olds. They are dauntingly perceptive and they are not patients. Come the next scare, they will want information, not platitudes. Can the Committee on Safety of Medicines and the subeditors work together or is this an old man's fantasy?

## *Flaming August*

With our children leaving school I have taken to working through August. After two years patterns seem to be emerging. A summary may be helpful to people thinking of doing the same.

Early in August you notice that your senior house officer has moved on. Thanks to the new partial shift system a series of unfamiliar young doctors begins to appear in your clinics. Each spends a little too much time staring at you, searching for clues to your character and mood.

Suddenly self conscious, you decide to lose weight and start using the stairs. Your office on the top floor of the hospital has by now become stiflingly hot (the airconditioning does not react until September because the sensor is in the basement). Throughout August there is a film of sweat over your unseasonal pallor.

The outpatients become more and more tanned. They all reply: "No, in the back garden, actually." Default rates are low because holiday makers have rearranged their appointments and those who are left are pleased to have something to do.

In the first half of August there is a sharp increase in emergency telephone calls. These are due not to the juniors' changeover but to people inviting you to give a lecture some time next year. You wonder why their voices sound so urgent. Then you realise they are finishing off their list of "must dos" before going on holiday. Guiltily, you remember making the same kind of calls, often from the departure lounge.

Proper emergencies occur too. "You do know you are covering today?" Er, yes. "Can you come immediately?" Of course. Any change in the on call rota usually means that you will preside over something spectacular. August provides good opportunities to discover how acute medicine has advanced since last summer. This year I spent a Saturday afternoon marvelling at the gadgetry in the magnetic resonance imaging suite: I emerged with renewed respect for the radiologist and the finance director.

For clinical academics the university's long vacation is no more than a student-free fortnight. Nevertheless, up till July you nurse a hope that in the summer you will catch up on your writing if not on your thinking. In late August seasonal depression sets in as the extent of your overoptimism becomes clear.

The telephone is even more useless than usual. The nation is in the grip of ansaphones: in desperation you actually begin to talk to them. You wonder uneasily if by some statistical quirk all the doctors in England have gone to gites in the Dordogne simultaneously. When at last you find a human being you cling to each other, unwilling to hang up.

August's coup de grace is its last weekend. The hospital could almost survive a one day bank holiday but the NHS takes two days. The reason is unclear—something to do with chaos theory, perhaps. Clinics and operating lists are rearranged and woe betide Friday's admissions: their investigations will be delayed for a week. Still, by then it will be September.

## *Memo from a Marketing Consultant*

Now that the NHS is Britain's largest provider of private health care, it should start running television commercials. It is unfair that your competitors advertise nationally while you do not. The campaign should promote the NHS as a whole. Sainsbury's stores don't advertise individually, do they?

Commercials aim at creating a positive image in the public mind. A few organisations, like Marks & Spencer, thought that they could do without this but are now changing their minds. The NHS certainly needs help. The media aren't continually telling potential customers that Marks & Spencer is a shambles.

Advertising also promotes self confidence among employees. About a million people work in the NHS and each of them reads the newspapers' knocking copy every day. Your staff are motivated by the Dunkirk spirit. Potential recruits are not. No wonder so few young people want to become nurses.

The NHS has no visual identity or corporate logo. This is deliberate: the government's policy is to fragment the NHS until it no longer exists. Commercial logic, however, demands strong national branding. Your competitors have cheekily appropriated familiar images into their logos—an electrocardiogram, for example, or a cathedral spire. You might go further and personalise the NHS with trusted faces. This worked well for Ben and Jerry's ice cream. What about your chief medical and nursing officers?

Television commercials fall into a few standard types, most of which could easily be adapted for the NHS. I'll run a few ideas into a jar for you to dipstick.

*The sexist ad:* It is now normal practice for commercials to portray women as cool and commanding and men as buffoons. As most of its staff are women, the NHS is tailor made for this ad style. We would take care to avoid the *"incompetent male"* image rubbing off on consultants or senior managers.

*The xenophobic ad*: The NHS is a very British institution but jingoism needs careful handling. We mainly use xenophobia to sell products that are fundamentally un-English, like lager. How about a series of ads with a suave British holidaymaker in awful foreign hospitals? Do Bavarian doctors wear leather shorts? Are there pan-European libel laws?

*The teaser*: The latest trend is not to mention the product until the last moment. In current BUPA commercials a string of athletic images ends with the slogan: "You're amazing. We want you to stay that way." What about an NHS parody? "You're solvent. We want you to stay that way." But your message would be that you actually treat ill people. How about this, after the watershed? Bedroom: cool woman seducing middle-aged man. As things get really steamy he collapses, clutching his chest. Cue logo and soothing voiceover: "The NHS. When you need us, we're here."

*The hurry! hurry! hurry! ad*: Some commercials still cram as many words as possible into ten seconds, usually when a carpet warehouse is closing down. An NHS version could appear in March, when purchasers find they still have cash that must be spent by 1 April.

Advertise or die. You know it makes sense.

## *Obstetrician's Distress*

Charlotte and Arthur had been married for seven years when they attended my clinic because Charlotte was still virgo intacta. I have given them Bronte pseudonyms but in Yorkshire sexual medicine is much the same as elsewhere in Britain. Few clients live up to the strong, silent stereotype: "You're frowning, Heathcliff. Would you like to share your anger with us?"

Treatment began with "sensate focus." According to the standard texts, this involves the couple going home, getting naked, and relaxing together. They are advised to touch in a non-genital way and verbalise their feelings. I suspect this works better in California than in the Pennines. The British may have acquired central heating but they still retain their sense of humour.

Back in the clinic I suggested that Arthur put his finger on to his wife's hymen. He gamely did so, turned pale, and had to sit down. I wrote to their general practitioner that I thought treatment would take some time. I predicted that it would be successful "over about four or five months."

Two years later Charlotte became pregnant. After many visits and some imaginative counselling we had a good rapport and although she lived near her local hospital she asked to attend my antenatal clinic. I felt embarrassed by her making unnecessary journeys but it seemed churlish to refuse.

This was a low risk pregnancy and the clinic visits involved us beaming at each other and chatting. Then, a month from term, Charlotte telephoned to say the baby wasn't moving much. She came straight to hospital. The monitor showed a normal fetal heart rate but the trace was "suboptimal." The registrar decided that labour should be induced next morning: was this all right with me?

It is a cliché in our specialty that we can cope with fetal distress and maternal distress but by far the most dangerous condition is obstetrician's distress. I told myself that there is no such thing as a "precious pregnancy" and that I was too close to this patient to be objective. Looking back it is hard to say why I decided on immediate caesarean section but I think any consultant obstetrician would have done the same.

Baby Jane was delivered almost dead, with a pH of 7.01 and a haemoglobin of 4.9 g/litre. There had been a massive fetomaternal haemorrhage. Jane made what the neonatal senior house officer's discharge summary described as "an exceptionally good recovery." Charlotte wrote a nice letter and I never saw her again.

The point of this little anecdote is its political incorrectness. Our sexual medicine clinic is now at the bottom of our cash strapped purchaser's list of priorities. Consultant involvement in routine antenatal care is currently as unfashionable as plus fours (though I sense the pendulum starting its swing again). Routine fetal movement counting is on the list of interventions that "appear promising but require further evaluation." Rising caesarean section rates are causing national concern. And obstetricians are no longer practising anecdote based medicine. Or if we are we certainly aren't writing about it.

## *Burns Night Do's and Don'ts*

Today, 25 January, is the anniversary of Robert Burns's birth. You may be feeling apprehensive because a Scottish colleague has invited you to a Burns Supper. Here, just in time, is your non-Scotspersons' guide to Caledonian etiquette.

Do accept the invitation. You will enjoy yourself. In southern Britain formal dinners are expected to be boring but in the north people go to be entertained. Burns Night comes along just as the Scots regain their taste for gracious living after the New Year hangover.

Don't expect to be home before midnight. The great northern festivals–St Andrew's Night, Hogmanay, and Burns Night–take place at monthly intervals in the depth of winter and one of their purposes is to defy the dark. This also means defying public transport timetables. It is customary to hire a minibus, so only one person in 30 needs to avoid alcohol.

Do wear a kilt. This is not compulsory but the Scots are happy to sell or hire a kilt to anyone with ready money. Don't worry about unwittingly taking sides in an ancient clan feud. Our local Caledonian Society was delighted when the mayor turned up in what he claimed was the MacLiebowitz tartan. Nevertheless, he should have been warned that the hemline is normally above mid-calf and that large hairy sporrans are for outdoors.

Don't be alarmed by the whisky. There will be a bottle on each table. You are not obliged to drink any of it unless you are playing the bagpipes. Bagpiping does occur but it will be brief and afterwards the instrumentalist is expected to down a glass of whisky at a draught. He may have several engagements in one evening but try not to worry about him. All pipers wear that glassy expression.

Do remember that the format is enshrined in tradition. The evening's raison d'etre is the gap left when John Knox abolished the frippery of Christmas. The Scots, like everyone else, need a quasireligious ceremony once in a while. Burns Night is our equivalent of the Festival of Nine Lessons and Carols.

Don't expect to hear anything original. The order of poems, speeches, and songs is fixed, from "Tae a Haggis" to "Auld Lang Syne." The main speaker knows what is expected and Burns will not be debunked. The romantic lyrics, heard only once a year, will surprise you with their freshness.

Do look interested when your host explains things. Early on you will be told the difference between Scottish and Scotch. Later you will be given an approximate recipe for haggis. Finally you will be reminded with some asperity who invented the steam engine, television and penicillin. Affect ignorance and avoid wisecracks.

Don't try to understand the poetry. I was brought up in Ayrshire and the Doric has always baffled me. They say that when stuck for a rhyme Burns cheerfully invented the odd Scotticism. Perhaps he even wrote the scholarly footnotes. By all accounts, he was a man with a lively sense of humour.

## *The Gynaecologist in Winter*

One of the saddest sights in the natural world at this time of year is that of little groups of bedraggled gynaecologists with nothing to do. Up and down the country these normally busy, elegant creatures have been forced to stop working until April. Ever mindful of doctors' morale, the NHS Executive has set up a working party to suggest ways of filling their time. Here are some of its recommendations:

Teach undergraduates: Medical schools should concentrate all gynaecological teaching into semester two (formerly the "spring term"). Doctors may object that clinical teaching is impossible without patients but this outdated view is countered by educationalists, who have shown convincingly that people with real diseases merely confuse students. Actresses provide a more consistent educational experience and do not consume scarce NHS resources.

Attend an in-depth briefing on government thinking about the future of hospital services in Britain: Assuming a ten o'clock start, a long coffee break, and an early lunch, this could occupy almost a full morning if generous time is allowed for discussion.

Go on holiday: All health economists who gave evidence to us agreed that it is much cheaper to pay doctors to do nothing than to treat patients. Several trusts are actively considering sending their gynaecologists to Gstaad for four months' skiing but the working party found this idea totally unacceptable. An option appraisal by management consultants showed that the most cost effective option is Bulgaria.

Catch up on your reading: It is a well known fact that a six month old medical journal is always more interesting than the current issue. Editors should be encouraged to publish all their copies in the summer with biodegradable wrapping that spontaneously disintegrates after six months.

Write medicolegal reports: It is estimated that by the year 2000 the average consultant gynaecologist will spend half of his or her time providing patient care and the other half writing reports on care provided by colleagues. The working party, however, foresaw difficulties in confining the latter work to the winter months. Medicolegal reports fall into two groups: those required by the end of the decade and those required by the end of the week. Persuading lawyers to organise their timetables more than a fortnight in advance is likely to prove impossible.

Retrain: Female opinion leaders unanimously advised us that most, if not all, gynaecology is completely unnecessary anyway. They had no sympathy with their weaker sisters who collude with gynaecologists by complaining of reproductive ailments. The working party endorsed this view but before it can be adopted as NHS policy a programme of public re-education will be necessary. This is already under way.

Do private practice: Meanwhile, official policy remains that elective gynaecology should move wholly into the private sector as soon as possible. Stopping NHS work in the winter, on various pretexts, has been a highly successful first step in this process. If the "winter" is extended by one month each year, gynaecology will be eliminated from NHS hospitals by 2005, at considerable saving to the taxpayer.

# PART 2

## *Words and Music*

As a senior house officer I performed with youthful colleagues for six nights on the Edinburgh Festival Fringe. According to a personal view that I wrote in 1974, it was an exhilarating but stressful experience and "one that we are keen to avoid repeating for quite some time." Twenty three years on, we are preparing to try again.

Our first revue, though scrupulously non-medical, seemed to set a trend, and junior doctors became a familiar sight on the Fringe. The urge to perform, however, dies at registrar level. Indeed, for most doctors it ends much earlier. All candidates for medical school play a musical instrument but few do so after entry. Medical students still produce revues but the postgraduate hospital show is now a rarity.

As we become more senior, performance art is sublimated into medical practice. The lengthy lecture, the assertive scientific presentation, the medicopolitical oration, the histrionic grand round, the clash of titans over trivia in committees–all these are manifestations of unfulfilled urges to play the trombone or dance the paso doble.

How much healthier it would be for our patients and profession if, like the Victorians, we held musical soirées in which these desires could be harmlessly indulged to the applause of admiring friends. Doctors could then practise medicine with appropriate modesty, paradoxically improving their standing with patients and colleagues alike.

My collaborator and I write our own material, and we are discovering that the work has changed over 20 years. Technically it is much easier now. I fax him my lyrics and he plays his music into a gizmo which instantly prints out a score. Psychologically, however, it is more difficult.

Songwriters traditionally come from underprivileged backgrounds and are motivated either by hunger for security or by a need to protest–which is why medical students still organise revues. These driving forces lose their impetus when lyricist and composer live in detached houses and own reliable cars.

Time is another problem. To be creative you need to be slightly bored, but doctors have a pathological desire to make the day job as busy as possible. Worst of all, medicine is interesting, and we have little need of extra stimulation in the evenings.

Nevertheless, there are tricks for forcing the muse. One is to start selling tickets. This is a powerful incentive to finish the songs. Another is to share the show with a professional singer-songwriter. Listening to his immaculate performances on compact disc has a disturbing effect on the adrenals.

So why bother? Why do famous actors or comedians keep working into old age? I used to assume it was because they had received bad investment advice, but now the explanation seems more innocent. Performing is enjoyable because (if all goes well) you are sharing pleasure with the audience. Entertaining in a theatre feels more honest than speaking after dinner: people have paid to listen, and many of them are sober. And doing it in a Scottish royal college may add a veneer of respectability.

## *The Last Examiner*

Hong Kong University's steeply sloping campus is crammed with buildings and ingeniously engineered roads. Its guest house has trees, a fishpond, and distant harbour views, and the shirtsleeved visitors come mainly from China or North America. One, with white beard and shorts, might have come from a Tintin book. As for me, I wore my college bow tie and jetlagged suit, as befits a British external examiner.

The final MBBS examination in obstetrics and gynaecology was 49 days before handover, according to the countdown in the local paper. The students would be the first to graduate under Chinese rule. Hong Kong is Britain's only sizeable colony so, unless someone builds a medical school in the Falklands I shall be the last external examiner of the British Empire.

Instead of a sedan chair, each morning a punctual Volvo swept me to the hospital– named, like several landmarks, after British royalty. "Welcome to Queen Mary Hospital," smiled a doctor. "Perhaps after July it will be 'People's Hospital Number One.'" A translator murmured as candidates took histories but stars and strugglers look the same in any country. I wondered if the students should get extra marks for eliciting symptoms in Cantonese and presenting them in another language.

When I asked if they spoke English at home my hosts smiled: "Even we don't do that." The University of Hong Kong has decided, however, that all lessons will continue in English. In the Chinese University, too, the faculties of medicine and engineering will teach in English. Indeed, I was told that English is the language of the leading medical schools in China itself.

I feel grateful for England's linguistic imperialism. It should see me out, if history is any guide. Sixteen centuries after the Romans left Scotland I graduated BACCALAVREI IN MEDICINA ET BACCALAVREI IN CHIRVRGIA. But mine was the last generation of schoolchildren to learn Latin, so perhaps the lingua franca will change by AD 3500.

In a few days' time Britannia will sail past the guest house towards the sunset, bearing the Prince of Wales and the Governor General. Then, back at the harbour, the firework display. People were already planning where to watch it. How will they feel? Their realism was best articulated by the delightful junior doctors who took me to lunch after our mock viva: "We can do nothing about it, so we carry on as usual."

My reactions to the handover will include embarrassment. We British gained Hong Kong by fighting to protect our iniquitous opium trade. During my visit the young expatriates in the kitsch British pub seemed unnecessarily pink and foul mouthed. It feels right to give way to people who work on Saturdays and enjoy life without alcohol.

But my predominant emotions will be affection and pride. As a child I first heard of Hong Kong when an uncle became a judge there. I had another uncle in Tunbridge Wells and both place names seemed equally familiar and exotic. The handover will bring a lump to my throat, like being a relative at a graduation.

## *Professional Highs*

Now that students are cared for by personal tutors, house officers by postgraduate deans, and registrars by college advisers, we consultants should demand someone to watch over us and help us look on the bright side. At the very least we want annual visits from a person with a clipboard, who will smile encouragingly and ask us to think of things we enjoy about our work. I have already prepared my list.

*Assisted delivery:* The interview must be confidential because it is politically unacceptable for obstetricians to admit that they take pleasure in practising their craft. Soon, I expect, every forceps delivery will be followed by counselling—optional for the patient but compulsory for the doctor. Nevertheless, in truth it is deeply satisfying to demonstrate dexterity, even to oneself. The presence of a wide eyed junior detracts from this as the consultants wonder whether modern training means that their skills will die with them.

*Draping up:* Unfolding the green drapes before an operation gives a surgeon a feeling of security. With the patient safely anaesthetised it is no longer possible for the managers to cancel the procedure. There is pleasure in having only one job to do and being able to ignore distractions. An operating theatre is one of the few places where you can tell someone what to do with a mobile phone.

*Outpatient clinics:* Tyros in surgical specialties regard clinics as the price they must pay for the pleasure of operating. The first sign of aging in surgeons is when they start to enjoy talking to patients and the last is when they enjoy listening to them. Even senior consultants, however, dare not risk losing face by admitting to looking forward to the clinic. They give themselves away on retirement by continuing to consult in private.

*Teamwork:* As army commercials keep pointing out, working in a team brings a sense of fulfilment. Like mushrooms, comradeship grows best during the night and when the manure is deep, but even so, bonding is a slow process. It takes about five years before a team decides that it can trust a new consultant. It then signals its confidence through non-verbal communication. This is why we are so dismissive of artificial team building exercises involving awaydays or paintballing.

*Making a difference:* I asked a colleague what he would put on this list and he said, "Changing a woman's life." Dramatic, but I know what he means. The feeling is most obvious in the fertility clinic, but other routine work can also transform patients. The buzz is not immediate—it comes with the follow up visit or the misspelt thank you card—but it is strong. Not strong enough, though, to transmit itself to purchasers who keep asking for written evidence that we are doing something useful.

*Getting paid:* With the trust's finances as parlous as those of the Russian army, the arrival of the payslip brings a monthly sense of relief, but the thrill is only partly financial. It is good to get positive feedback, even from the finance department's computer.

## *Separate Development*

During August my journey to work is faster than usual. In term time the route is cluttered with schoolchildren. Near my home, pupils of both genders walk to a state school. Near the hospital a line of upmarket cars disgorges grammar schoolboys who are visibly different, mainly because they wear their shirt tails inside their trousers.

Halfway between home and work a group of Muslim schoolgirls in white head-dresses waits to be bussed to yet another school. The sight always depresses me. I wonder which form of educational apartheid I dislike most—separate development by gender, by social class, or by religion? For me, religious segregation wins.

The little Scottish village where I grew up had two schools. In ours, railings no longer separated the boys' and girls' playgrounds, but still there was one school for us and another for the Catholics. The same applied at senior schools in the nearby town. All Catholic schools were named after saints, so bigots needed to ask only one question or to glance at the first page of a curriculum vitae.

Scotland tries to play down its sectarianism and is surprisingly successful in disguising its snobbery. As a smug expatriate I boast that my old non-Catholic school did at least admit all strata of society. Privately, however, I know that it was the exception rather than the rule and that its liberalism owed more to geography than to principle.

England, by contrast, revels in class divisions. When one of my children decided on a sixth form at a public school, I felt apprehensive. What would the other parents be like? Aristocrats? Flash Del Boys? I discovered that most were professional people and many were doctors.

Two years later I had a more balanced view of the English public school. Its strength is that it aims to educate leaders. Grammar schools train pupils to compete, but public schools assume their pupils will win and teach them what to do with success. Their weakness is social isolation. The local state schoolboys (known as "Kevins") were alien beings.

Most entrants to medicine come from grammar schools, with the result that doctors are good at competing with one another but bad at knowing what to do with the position they achieve. Medical schools ignore leadership skills, teaching students increasingly to follow rules rather than make them.

Looking back, I think my old Scottish academy achieved the right balance. It avoided divisions because everyone attended the same institution. It anticipated success by streaming the high fliers, who knew they were the leaders of the future. The French lycée, with its atheism and equality, does the same.

As I inch through the traffic on my way to work, I know that nothing will change. The opportunity seized by the French a century ago has been missed forever. Our new government may use its huge majority to stop me driving to work, but from my guided bus I shall still watch the haves, the have nots, and the Muslim schoolgirls going their separate ways.

## *This Month's New Journals*

We are often told that 20,000 medical journals are published every year. Presumably we are expected to feel guilty for not having read them. Most doctors use their intelligence and ignore 19,998 of the titles, but publishers still find it profitable to keep starting up new ones. In case you were wondering what you are missing, here is my selection from those that have appeared since the summer holidays.

*Journal of the Blindingly Obvious:* "We seek," say the editors, "to publish well designed trials, preferably those which have used large sums of public money, proving what everybody already knows." Competition for space is keen. A recent landmark paper ("An international study of doctors' attitudes") concluded that patient satisfaction scores are significantly higher if doctors smile at patients than if they throw books, instruments, or paperweights at them. Prepublication fast tracking of this paper to the NHS Executive has already led to an official guideline entitled: "Kneeing your patients in the groin: evidence from a large multicentre study."

*Journal of Scandinavian Salami:* Research in Nordic countries is carried out during the summer months and researchers spend the long northern winter seeing how many separate papers they can produce from each project. According to the Guinness Book of Medical Records a questionnaire sent to 2000 randomly selected names produced forty-three papers and abstracts, including: "Smoking habits among Scandinavian women," "The prevalence of smoking among young Scandinavian manual workers," "Chronic cough and smoking in premenopausal women in Scandinavia," and "Urinary incontinence among elderly Scandinavian female smokers."

*Journal of the Latest Fad:* Each of medicine's technical advances is marked by the formation of a society of enthusiasts. All office bearers write papers at frequent intervals, citing all the other office bearers' papers as references. These provoke heated correspondence from non-office bearers. Thus the JLF, which is well supported by advertisements for new equipment, has a staggeringly high impact factor and an ethos of vigorous, if incomprehensible, debate.

*British Journal of Thumb-Twiddling:* In a ground-breaking venture, the British Journal of Surgery will in future be published only from April to November, and subscribers will receive the BJTT for the rest of the year. Forthcoming papers include "Electromyographic studies on rotator pollicis" and "A comparison of the directionality of thumb-twiddling in Britain and Australia."

*Health and Efficiency*: A new title replacing eleven other management journals, including Health in the Community and Efficiency in Hospital. The publishers have been surprised by its success, which they attribute to its radical stance on information technology.

*Evidence!* This exciting journal is spearheading a campaign to reintroduce the exclamation mark into academic writing. Subscribers also receive an interactive CD, a bumper sticker ("Honk if you think I'm significant!"), and much glossy advertising.

*Journal of Clinical Information:* Published electronically, this replaces the Journal of Clinical Knowledge, which, incidentally, took the place of the long defunct Journal of Clinical Wisdom.

## *Public Accountability*

Every year, around the autumnal equinox, our trust holds its annual general meeting. For weeks beforehand posters in exotic languages appear beside the lifts. I wonder what we would do if non-English speaking members of, say, the Thai community actually turned up. We could give them a synopsis of our report to read. "Last year we treated more patients than ever before" probably sounds quite fresh in Thai.

Before the meeting the board gathers for a briefing on possible googlies. Some members are shaking their heads. For the past five years our AGM has passed off bloodlessly, but this time things will be different. In this postelection year our deficit will not be quietly massaged away and cuts in services have been trailed.

The podium in our lecture theatre is not quite long enough to accommodate the board with dignity. We shuffle chairs and the chap on the end looks apprehensive. Lined up behind the draped table like a low budget party conference, we gaze impassively at the public.

The same faces as last year gaze back. This is an annual reunion, with everyone in their traditional places. In the front rows is the Hard of Hearing Club. In the aisle are the guide dogs, and to our right are a few familiar members of the community health council. Behind them rise row after row of trust employees and, standing at the back, men who don't want the commitment of a long term seated relationship.

We look up expectantly. Where is he? Our usual latecomer arrives at the last minute—a short, bearded man with pebble glasses and a pointed woolly hat, like a myopic Big Ears. At question time he always asks excitedly if there are any MPs present and then complains that he has not seen the meeting advertised. His accent defies location. Bolivia? Kazakhstan? Lancashire?

One of the standees keeps leaning accidentally on the dimmer switch. The chief executive reports that our major purchaser is underfunded and we cannot go on treating patients for free. The finance director's report is aimed at the person on the Cleckheaton omnibus. Even I can understand it. Our deficit is clearly illustrated with a computer graphic. The plan for financial recovery involves doing less work.

The chairman invites questions. Two hundred people fall silent, depressed by the Powerpoint graph. The patients' advocates tell us kindly that we are doing the best we can in the circumstances. After years of listening to self serving economists they really believe the mantra that the demand for health care is limitless. The MPs, of course, have moved on. Goodbye Aneurin Bevan, hello Gordon Gecko.

The few sparks come from the hard of hearing, well organised and grumbling through their sign language interpreter about acoustically insensitive architecture. As we leave the blood-free auditorium we smile grimly. We get the message. The public is bored with the NHS. The only able bodied people who wanted to protest were trapped on the podium, staring at the stoical yeomanry, and waiting for angry shouts that never came.

## *Fear God and Work Hard*

According to the plinth, David Livingstone's statue beside the Zambesi was "UNVEILED BY HIS EXCELLENCY THE RIGHT HONORABLE THE LORD LLEWELLIN, GBE, MC, TD, DL, GOVERNOR GENERAL OF THE FEDERATION OF RHODESIA AND NYASALAND, AND DEDICATED BY HIS GRACE THE LORD ARCHBISHOP OF CENTRAL AFRICA, EDWARD FRANCIS PAGET, ON 16 NOVEMBER 1955."

Today the inscription seems older than its 42 years but the sculpture itself is ageless, with its resolute chin, gormless moustache, and trouser legs tied with ploughman's "nicky tams"—more useful as anti-creepy-crawly devices in Zimbabwe than in Lanarkshire.

Visiting Scots cannot help swelling with proprietorial pride. Livingstone's five word motto— "Fear God and work hard" —sums up our national ethic and his life is a legend in our Sunday schools. A mill boy at ten years old, he learnt Latin by night and decided to be a missionary. He went to London, studied theology, zoology, botany, and astronomy and walked the wards of Charing Cross Hospital before leaving for South Africa. There he dissociated himself from the British community and learned the local language.

His writings about the Arab slave trade in Africa are forgotten, but his description of the effects of endorphins is memorable. A lion broke his arm and "shook me as a terrier dog does a rat. The shock ... caused a sort of dreaminess in which there was no sense of pain nor feeling of terror, though quite conscious of all that was happening. It was like what patients partly under the influence of chloroform describe, who see all the operation but feel not the knife."

He claimed that he survived without sepsis because of Scots tailoring. "I had on a tartan jacket ... and I believe that it wiped off all the virus from the teeth that pierced the flesh."

When he died in 1873 the Lancet called him "a man whom we are proud to identify as belonging to our profession," setting aside earlier doubts about his sketchy medical training. His remains, respectfully disembowelled, salted, and cut into portable pieces by his African companions, were identified by the false joint in the humerus and buried in Westminster Abbey.

Standing in the spray of the Victoria Falls, we asked our guide, Messiah, what he thought of the Doctor. He pointed out gently that African people had known about the Falls before Livingstone discovered them. But they were grateful to him for telling the world. No, they didn't mind still calling them "Victoria." There were various names: the famous one, Mosi-oa-Tunya —"the smoke that thunders," had actually been synthesised by Livingstone.

Messiah had graduated in French from Harare and most of his work involved looking after Francophone visitors, but many European firms sent out employees as part of incentive schemes. "I organise team building events like tug of war. Then we cruise on the river and in the dusk Livingstone appears in a canoe. I have two white men who are excellent lookalikes." Sic transit, I thought—but can they really do the accent?

## *Disappearing Willies*

When Mrs Thatcher said, "Every prime minister needs a Willie," she was talking about her senior adviser, William Whitelaw. He was in his 60s, seven years her elder, and, although it was mainly his character that made him a valued counsellor, his experience must have helped.

A consultant, even one as tough as the Iron Lady, sometimes needs to talk to an older colleague. So do GPs, and a general practice should have its Dr Whitelaw as well as its Dr Wunderkind. Our medical Willies, however, are disappearing. In my specialty, most consultants plan to retire before 60. Colleagues tell me this is part of modern life. They draw comparisons with accountants and policemen. If I were an accountant or a policeman I would welcome retirement, but medicine is a stimulating profession, like law and the church. Judges and priests linger as long as they can.

Retired consultants always say that they are busier than ever. Why then did they stop work? It is not as if they are bored with medicine as they often continue private practice and medicolegal pontification. They all claim that the reason they retired was NHS bureaucracy but I think what actually got them down was the job. A consultant post does not change or develop. A doctor, after 35 years of upward progression through education and training, suddenly reaches a level playing field. He or she is expected to do the same things, week in, week out, for 30 years and is officially equal to all other consultants.

This is against nature. Humans are programmed to be hierarchical and doctors are naturally competitive. With no more rungs on the job ladder, we create our own organisations—colleges, committees and, now, academies—to let us continue discreetly locking antlers. The dominant males or females are rewarded, not by droit de seigneur, but by distinction awards. Do A holders retire later on average than C holders or is that just my clinical impression?

This amiably old fashioned system cannot continue. Surgeons appointed because of a special skill should not be ignominiously forced out when they develop presybopia. Consultants in acute specialties should be able to relinquish night work without guilt and acrimonious negotiation. These needs will soon become pressing as hospitals move towards consultant based services. Yet we cling to a pattern that has not changed since 1948. The staunchest defender of the post-war status quo has been the BMA, which welcomes early retirement schemes and opposes non-consultant career grades.

Recognising how difficult it is for us to accept a career structure for consultants may I suggest starting gently? We should introduce the title of consultant emeritus, not as an honour on retirement but as a salaried post for which application is invited from suitably qualified practitioners. The job descriptions will vary. Some emeriti will teach. Others will serve on national bodies without being sniped at by local managers. Others will see patients and give legal opinions. Colleagues and patients will benefit from their experience. Everybody needs a Willie.

## *My Last Car, I Promise*

*Dear Colleagues,*

A hospital is like a goldfish bowl and you have all noticed that I am driving a new car. Mindful of my accountability as medical director, I am writing to explain why.

Some people have suggested that I changed surreptitiously. They point out that this car has the same maker, colour, and number plate as my old one, and say that if I had just resisted the temptation to wash 'n' wax for the first time in seven years nobody would have noticed. I deny this. If I had wanted to deceive you I would have worked out how to open the window before greeting the car park attendant (sorry for spraying you with wiper fluid, George) and found out in advance how to switch off the alarm, which I agree is oversensitive.

The car is mine, not the trust's. Perhaps I was tactless to take delivery at a time when our purchasers have run out of funds and operating is curtailed, but it is simplistic to suggest that if I had kept my old car we could treat more patients.

The professor of social medicine has urged me to cycle. May I point out that we live in Yorkshire, not Holland, and it is uphill all the way home. I know the warehouse opposite is being converted to executive apartments, but I thought he disapproved of doing business with property developers and anyway my wife enjoys gardening. Like everyone else, I shall give up driving when gridlock comes, but not before.

Several colleagues have remarked that although my last car was eleven years old it never gave any trouble. I wish to inform them that the handbrake warning light had remained on since 1991 and that there was this really annoying rattle when I turned left. There comes a time when a car is too old to be reliable and too young to be classic and it needs replacing. This applies to everything in life except NHS equipment.

I believe that my new car has raised morale throughout the hospital and particularly in the academic department. It is depressing for everyone when the professor keeps being mistaken for a client of the social work department. The lecturers look much happier now that I have joined the gleaming concourse of NHS consultants.

Contrary to rumour, my new car is only 15 mm wider than my old one. It was not my decision to reorganise the car park to provide more spaces for visitors (most of whom are visiting the shops in town). The fact that our doctors and nurses are being urged to use public transport is nothing to do with the size of my car.

Some of you who have peered through its windows (often setting off the alarm) have made slighting comments about the walnut effect fascia. Well, it helps me relax, as does the fact that I can now receive Radio 3. By avoiding John Humphrys in the morning I arrive calm and refreshed, with obvious benefits to patient care.

## *Pray Silence*

Humorous cartoons sometimes feature notices saying "Quiet please—hospital." Such signs once existed in real life. When I was a boy there was one outside our local infirmary, though it was not a success. Buses and lorries did not freewheel, pedestrians did not tiptoe, and delivery boys continued to whistle.

Its rationale, I suppose, was a feeling of respect. You lower your voice near a sickroom. Now that hospitals are perceived as processing plants dealing with waiting lists, this instinct has faded. Occasionally I remind raucous visitors that there are ill people in the wards, and they look at me with incredulity.

The idea that quietness is therapeutic is not evidence based. There have been no randomised controlled trials of noisy versus silent hospitals. If institutions under the flight path into Heathrow were compared with those in the shires there would be confounding variables. And what outcomes would be measured—death rates, length of stay, or staff turnover?

The main impediment to such research, however, would be that it is impossible to find a quiet hospital. One of the ways we providers demonstrate our value to the community is through conspicuous activity. Ambulances hee haw to (and, less explicably, from) the casualty department. We test our fire alarms with deafening thoroughness. Some of us now have helicopter pads—though, mercifully, no helicopters.

Once inside, a blindfolded person can recognise a hospital not, these days, with the nose but with the ears. The yellow waste bags are collected in a barrow that sounds like a Schoenberg symphony. Security men, walkie talkies dangling from their belts, stalk malefactors amid a roar of static. Painters, decorating the corridors, cannot function without a transistor radio tuned to Radio One.

Catering staff, amid a cacophony of stainless steel, enjoy fearsome blasts of hilarity. Nurses develop an enviable ability to ignore ringing phones, presumably because answering them is not one of the duties of a modern all graduate profession. Junior doctors' bleeps keep up metallic conversations consisting mainly of numbers.

Consultants feel left out. Some tried mobile phones but are discarding them as the mobiles' image goes down market. In the street their most visible users are drug dealers and accountants, and in hospital "Mobile phones may interfere with sensitive equipment." Only hospitals and aeroplanes issue these warnings, which actually mean "Mobile phones irritate us beyond endurance."

Why some noises are annoying is mysterious. Why is a laptop more intrusive than a typewriter? Freud might know. Do I dislike the din made by other staff because it challenges my status? As a would-be dominant male, perhaps my primordial urge is to put my head close to the ground and roar, or drum my back legs on the lino.

Or perhaps my irritation is due to age. Young people can study with a Walkman and registrars like to operate to canned music. As a postmenopausal surgeon I prefer the sigh of the ventilator. Enjoying quietness is a lost art. Silence means reflection, and hospitals are not good at that.

## *Valedictory Lecture*

The second world war flattened most of Nijmegen, but spared some of St Steven's Kerk, a fifteenth century gothic building in the town centre overlooking a branch of the Rhine. When I was in the restored church last month people were uncertain about whether it is Catholic or Protestant and seemed to wonder why I was asking. Not for the first time I thought we can learn from the Dutch.

It was a Friday afternoon and the bells were ringing to announce a public lecture. A local professor was retiring and several foreigners had been invited to join the procession. I am not sure if this was the first overseas trip for my MD gown. It was given to me by the widow of an eminent Scottish doctor after I wrote an article about the annual trauma of the graduation ceremony. Having his name on the label is strangely comforting.

As we robed in the chapter house my stand-up collar and white bow tie were outshone by united colours of Europe. A Spaniard in yellow and purple, with a fringed hat, looked like a mediaeval pontiff. Two Swedes in dark shirts and top hats might have stepped from an Ingmar Bergman film. Doctors from the low countries were in Calvinist black with discreet ostentation— emerald edging, touches of embroidery, and luxurious velvet collars—and some, in bavettes and round hats, looked like judges from the European court.

My own cap, a kind of floppy mortar board, has never impressed me but it was, I realised, in the local style. Of course: Edinburgh medical school was founded by doctors who had studied in the Netherlands. I remarked artlessly to a woman beside me that I had only just realised that Scottish academics wear Dutch caps. Suddenly blushing, I eyed her warily, but her smile gave no clue as to whether our lingua franca extended to double entendres.

The lecture itself was delivered from the pulpit while we followed an elegantly printed translation. It was about the role of homocysteine in preventing birth defects. The high, whitewashed nave had chandeliers but no projection facilities so the talk was illustrated by a molecular model, held up by the lecturer's little granddaughter and then propped in a side aisle. I looked at it regretfully. One carbon atom too many for jokes about the cysteine chapel.

This was a grand occasion for a particularly distinguished man, but public valedictory lectures are normal in the Netherlands, like inaugural lectures here. I like the idea. It could be criticised for encouraging excessive respect for seniority—an affliction among doctors in mainland Europe. Nevertheless, there is something fitting about requiring a chairholder to stand up in front of the people and give an account of his or her stewardship.

We should try it. It might counterbalance that current British fad, excessive respect for middle age. People should retire with a bang, not a whimper, and ought to dress up for it. All professors are peacocks at heart.

## *Dead Hospitals*

Britain's hospital services are being restructured and everywhere the talk is of mergers and hub and spoke configurations. Doctors generally like the prospect of better facilities and we negotiate with enthusiasm for new offices, more teaching space, and patient-free loos. When moving day comes we look forward, not back.

Although there are "Save our Hospital" campaigns they have the defiant but defeated air of the Titfield Thunderbolt or Arthur Scargill. Local sensitivities are soothed by name changes. When St Swithin's Hospital closes, Loamshire Royal Infirmary acquires a St Swithin's Wing. The prewar support of the Swithin's Penny-a-week Club is commemorated by a plaque awkwardly resited near the hospital shop.

But what happens to St Swithin's itself? Legally, an empty building must be made safe but there is no law that it must be used. Near our own unit an erstwhile maternity hospital stands empty, unchanged apart from general decay since 1983 when the last mother left. Its history runs from its foundation stone: "Laid in 1928 by The Princess Mary," through a newer notice: "Keep clear for deliveries," to a final, depressing: "No entry – asbestos within." The ground floor windows are bricked up, the upper windows are broken, and the roof lantern has disintegrated.

Thinking back over the hospitals where I trained, I realise that a disconcerting number are closed though none has been demolished.

The buildings which saw my first caesarean sections and my first hysterectomies are now homes for the elderly. The theatres in which I assisted at my first operations and carried out my first oocyte retrievals are boarded up. I feel vague nostalgia but nothing stronger. After all, I have other patients to look after now.

A hospital is a repository of personal memories for the staff but more so for the patients and their relatives. In a way, they are the real owners of the property. When I heard recently of the closure of a labour ward in Scotland I felt a keen sense of loss not because of the deliveries I had conducted there but because my own son and daughter were born in Room One and Room Three.

Bereavement brings an even stronger sense of ownership. I wonder if anyone who lost a baby there ever makes a pilgrimage to that derelict maternity unit up the road? I hope not. From my 30 years in hospitals, the room I remember most clearly is the one in which I spent a few minutes with my father, touching his cheek to make sure he was really dead. That was in a new hospital mortuary, presumably still several years away from being locked and ignored.

A few organisations are obliged to tidy up after themselves. British Coal, for example, turns its spoil tips into grassy knolls. Others can do what they like. Property developers leave lifeless office blocks in our town centres for years on end but a dead hospital is more than an empty building. It is an affront to anyone with a little bit of imagination.

## *A Very British Congress*

Normally I am cynical about spas and large congresses. Both have something a little too artificial about them for my taste. Nevertheless, at the end of June there I was in our local watering place, wearing a name badge with a long ribbon marked "chairman," and awaiting the arrival of a thousand obstetricians.

Four years ago, it had seemed a good idea. The British Congress last came to Leeds in 1952, when (according to his Lancet obituary) one of my predecessors presided over it with grace and charm. That sounded fun, and anyway my colleagues and I thought that after forty-six years of enjoying other people's hospitality it was only polite to invite them back.

For three years and eleven months the congress loomed over us, distant but inevitable, like a postgraduate exam. Our first planning meetings were relaxed and expansive. A floodlit concert at Fountains Abbey? A talk from Betty Boothroyd? Then we realised that the trick was to blend imagination and practicality.

In the final weeks, things became eerily quiet. Most of the stress was falling on the professional organiser, who responded with more grace and charm than I could muster. When she told me that an eminent speaker had had a serious accident, I telephoned his secretary. "Are you quite sure he can't stand up? What if we ..." A distinguished and understanding replacement performed brilliantly.

At 17.50 on day zero I joined the line to greet the royal couple who were to open the proceedings. What we had not realised was that the ceremony would coincide with the England and Argentina match in the World Cup, and that one of the couple was a keen football supporter. The congress was opened with dignity, warmth, and a minimum of delay. The royals departed for their stately home and everyone else crowded round hastily erected screens in the exhibition hall. Apart from the disallowed goal the highlight for me was negotiating with the football-hating hall manager as the game went to extra time

For the next three days I carried a dysfunctional walkie talkie and operated on a need to know basis. There was nothing I could do about strike-hit railways or the spontaneous combustion of the van carrying the abstract books. What a chairman is useful for, I discovered, is reasoning with people who try to talk their way in without paying.

Surprisingly, my cynicism about congresses evaporated. Of the thousand people, nearly half were active contributors and all of them—from student stewards to jet setters—were on their mettle and anxious to do well. For the first time I realised just how much creative energy goes into these meetings.

It ended as it began amid sporting gloom, caused, this time, by Tim Henman's defeat at Wimbledon. The damage to the national psyche did not affect the bar of the Majestic Hotel, where stragglers rendered some impromptu Gilbert and Sullivan. An overseas speaker remarked that this was a very British congress and I could see what he meant.

## *NPD Blues*

High summer is the time for rites of passage. Like weddings, graduations are attended by generations of relatives and a sense of awe. Entering medical school or full registration are arguably more momentous events, but we have no admission ball or registration ball. Graduation is the big one.

The degree ceremony has a quasi-religious quality. Like ordination, it separates aspirants once and for all from the laity. On a secular level it gives them life membership of the club and permanent licence to call themselves "Doctor," whether or not they ever see a patient. Oddly, the public is comfortable with this.

Well informed people are often surprised that I see patients. They assume that the pressures of writing and speaking about medical practice do not leave any time for practising medicine. This attitude irritates me intensely. Without clinical responsibilities, how could I look students or colleagues in the eye?

Not all medical graduates have such precious feelings. The profession is well supplied with non-practising doctors (NPDs) who feel qualified not just to look colleagues in the eye but to tell us how to do our jobs. The most familiar example is the medicolegal expert who makes a comfortable living telling lawyers how impeccably he managed cases before he gave up clinical practice.

More recently we have become used to the way NPD scientists, NPD editors, and NPD journalists influence our practice. They like to go straight to the public or the government with their results, reminiscences, and opinions. This allows them to exploit lay respect for doctors, and to avoid submitting their pronouncements to peer review.

Now, with clinical governance, a new network is being created to control medicine. National quangos with ridiculous acronyms are going to issue guidelines, which will be based in part on the work of NPD researchers. Clinicians may be involved but they are busy people and clinical governance will be a fine opportunity for NPDs to extend their influence.

Most NPDs respect clinicians but they face subtle pressures from the laity. In committee and on camera they realise that they can gain credibility, if not by criticising their colleagues, at least by failing to defend them against stereotyping. Some NPDs like to accuse clinicians of arrogance. This is the supreme irony. Clinical work is what keeps doctors' feet on the ground but for NPDs, free of this humbling influence, arrogance is hard to avoid.

Could NPDs be differentiated from clinicians? Like midwives, practising doctors could reregister every few years but the criteria would be minimal and after all, graduation is for life. We could add a figure to our name on the medical register signifying how many years it is since our last night on call, but double figures look more impressive than zeros.

All I can suggest is vigilance. Clinicians must remember that in medicine the shop floor has a higher status than the boardroom. NPDs must remember that the public values clinical ability more than skills in politics and public relations. Occasional reminders like this one might help.

## *Letter from America*

In Atlanta, Georgia, you can visit the house where Margaret Mitchell wrote *Gone with the Wind*. The actual typewriter, marked with her nail varnish, is in a glass case. You learn that in her original manuscript the heroine was called Pansy. When an editor questioned this she chose Scarlett. Well, gee whizz. Was Rhett originally named Rab, I wonder?

Pansy was not the only one in Georgia to benefit from an inspired change of name. In the 1850s Atlanta itself was called Terminus. The Mitchell house is one of few old buildings in the city, which has followed a cycle of self destruction and rebirth ever since the civil war.

Down the road in Savannah things are different. Its founder, James Oglethorpe, left England in 1732 with a town plan in search of a site, but mercifully did not give the place his name. His street pattern now forms the historic district, preserved by seven ladies (as women are called in the south), who stopped its mindless demolition in the 1950s. Sadly, they never came to Britain.

Savannah is currently experiencing a visitor boom because of a book called *Midnight in the Garden of Good and Evil.* John Berendt, a New York journalist, talked to the townsfolk and wove their gossip into a best selling narrative. One bizarre result is an incestuous tourist trail, with bookish people trying to identify buildings where Berendt himself stayed while he was writing.

The English are regarded amiably here. In fact, the only group which suffers nationalist stereotyping is the Yankees. There are a few pubs, one of which was transported lock, stock, and barrels from England. The sign outside has Sir Winston Churchill's face beside a dartboard. Lese-majesty, I thought, but the old boy was a bit of a poseur and might well have approved.

Inside, people are playing darts and a television screen above the bar is showing a baseball game. As we settle down to an authentic pint, a baseball player wearing a red jersey hits the ball over the boundary wall and begins an increasingly triumphant lap of honour. By luck, we have witnessed what the media will hail as a defining moment in American history. Mark McGwire has scored his 62nd home run of the season, passing a record that has stood for 37 years and eclipsing the total of 60 "homers" achieved by the legendary Babe Ruth.

Commentators choke back the tears. On screen, men hug one another. The Dow Jones had already risen sharply when McGwire's tally reached 61. As important as the record itself is the way it has been achieved. By all accounts McGwire has behaved throughout the season with exemplary sportsmanship. America, with its political leader mired in scandal, is rediscovering its self respect.

My wife and I stare in wonder at the screen. Most of the other customers are unmoved, but a few minutes later they suddenly begin a-hollerin' and a-whoopin'. The electric scoreboards flanking the dartboard show that one of the teams has scored 301.

## *Winter Draws On*

Years ago a snowy haired anatomy lecturer used to make us cringe with his double entendres. Smutty jokes can be funny if they have a touch of wit but once they lose their freshness they are just embarrassing, even to preclinical students.

That sad old man is gone now but his spirit lives on in the British advertising industry. The latest blitz from behind the admen's bicycle sheds is promoting brown bread, of all things. "Butter me up and I'll go down a treat," said a poster as I drove to work. As I was supposed to, I felt guilty for imagining sexual undertones but further on the message was more explicit: "Let's play hide the sausage."

Our city centres now have wall to wall urological innuendo. Billboards promoting a television show tempted us with "Cox out in Greece." In the Renault advertisements, Papa and Nicole have given way to: "Size matters. It's what you do with it that counts." Cigarettes are "longer than John's." And of course French Connection UK has its initials everywhere.

If a poster shows a nipple there is an outcry but these slogans are like Rorschach blots. Some people see nothing in them, and the rest of us keep quiet for fear of being accused of seeing sex everywhere. We remember the ridicule heaped on the BBC's old Blue Book, which cited "winter draws on" as the type of joke that could give radio a bad name.

I like saucy British humour, in its place. Every time I see a chihuahua I remember Max Miller. I sit happily through the dregs of the Carry On series on late night television. But the art of innuendo lies in knowing how far to go, and I think bus shelters full of schoolchildren are a nudge too far.

The young provide an easy excuse for my indignation. The girls in my clinic with unwanted pregnancies are little older than those tittering at the posters, and every week I become more exasperated at the British way of treating sex with fourth form sniggers rather than education.

But really, I just don't like tat in public places. Do we need billboards at all—even those in good taste? They are ugly, a hazard to road safety, and commercially unnecessary in our television age. Get them down, if you'll pardon the expression.

## *Friday the 13th*

The breathing trouble had begun on Monday with an unusually poor showing in the Railtrack sprint. Then came difficulty going upstairs. Just a virus, said I, but on Friday the 13th I had unilateral calf pain and breathlessness going downstairs too.

Words like "barndoor" spring to mind but I had just proof read the latest maternal mortality report, with its sharp increase in pulmonary embolism and its comments on doctors who ignore the signs. When I developed a full house myself I naturally thought it was my imagination.

Finally in theatre, dyspnoea on scrubbing made me call a physician. He seemed impressed. So were the staff when the professor, still in surgeon's pyjamas but now with an oxygen mask, was wheeled out on a trolley. Surely the operation had not been that difficult? My first emotion was relief that this was not hypochondria. The next was gratitude—to the porter who knew where in the reorganised hospital the computed tomography scanner was, to the nurse who stayed with me until my wife arrived, and to the radiographer who warned me that contrast medium produces strange feelings in the perineum.

In an emergency, carers communicate by body language. You can feel the team working together and you want to play your part, albeit horizontally. All my questions were put on hold except the big one: who would give tonight's after dinner speech?

After years in obstetrics, I feared I would be given a choice of treatment options. Thank goodness, these were proper doctors. A young consultant told me that I would get streptokinase. OK? Yup. Later the cardiothoracic surgeon dropped by, watchful and impressive, neither fazed nor wistful about the chance of operating on a member of the General Medical Council.

Wired up on the ward, I had time to reflect. I should not have worn those new long socks during a week of non-stop travel. Is that pump really working? The link to my arm seemed so fragile. Something steam driven with brass tubes would inspire more confidence. What would I like to be called, asked the nurse. In Tony Blair's new Britain it had to be Jim.

I watched the clock. The annual dinner would be nearly over. On balance, it had been a lucky day, but I would feel happier when Saturday the 14th arrived.

## *Egosurfing*

Looking yourself up on the internet— arguably the naffest way of coping with boredom—is known by computer buffs as egosurfing. Celebrities with websites can count their visitors. BMJ contributors can check responses to their articles. It is by no means guaranteed to boost morale.

Another method is to search the web for your name. "Smith" has almost five million entries. James Young Simpson has 674 789, but only the first 20 are about the obstetrician. The next hundred are about contemporary Americans called James Young, and the rest about OJ, Homer, and Bart. "Drife" has 136 entries. Some are misprints, though this may become clear only well into the story when someone revs a roadster and drifes away.

Egosurfing has expanded my horizons. I might never have known that "drife" is an old Saxon word, though I still have no idea what it means. The net gives the impression that I have coauthored Aelfric's Colloquy, Elene, and a ballad about the Sultan of Babylon. Saxon poetry is incomprehensible and scanning it on screen made me nervous. What if it is obscene? The university is strict about accessing pornography and might want to make an example of me.

The net has introduced me to the Rife family, whose members—at least those with the initial D—are high achievers. One gave his name to an alumnus house in Shippensburg University, Pennsylvania, and another is a member of the Southern California Association of Violin Makers. The most active D Rife is a meteorologist who forecasts for Puget Sound, Washington.

Thanks to the University of California's British Women Romantic Poets project, the web now includes the work of Janet Little, "the Scotch milkmaid," a contemporary of Robert Burns. Spurred on by the possibility that she—or even he—might be an ancestor I eventually found the poem that includes my surname. It romantically compared a young man's beauty with that of the River Drife in Dumfriesshire.

Some entries were indeed papers of mine. There were a few Soundings, mysteriously entitled "Diabetes," and a long forgotten review listed under "Aphrodisiacs." Egosurfing strengthened my belief that the world is not quite ready to do without paper. Nevertheless, universities could be making plans to judge academics on their internet hits and the response rate. Perhaps I should issue some hoax gale warnings for Seattle.

## *Guest Faculty*

Southern California is often portrayed as being on another planet, so it came as a surprise, at a meeting there recently, to find that the doctors did not arrive on roller blades, wearing fluorescent shades.

Lecturing abroad is straightforward if you have invented a new technique like transspecies fertilisation or minimal access caesarean section. If, however, the purpose of the meeting is local postgraduate education the guest faculty becomes uneasy and asks itself thoughtful questions.

Just how international is medicine? Global journals and research networks would have us believe it is universal and that the results of trials conducted in South America or Africa are applicable in London or Yorkshire. I am unconvinced, but I find it hard to explain why. It is not just my concerns about informed consent given by people who cannot read but more a feeling that there may be confounding factors which I cannot discern from a distance.

Colleagues overseas could apply the latter reservation to research here, so is British experience useful to doctors abroad? Are results in our hospital system of trainee based medicine relevant to places where senior obstetricians sleep near the delivery suite? American speakers on the faculty seemed to think so. They cited United Kingdom studies with gratifying frequency, though with a bit more emphasis on our mavericks than on our mainstream opinions. The "gee whizz" attitude is hard to avoid, whichever direction you look across the Atlantic.

I thought that my postgraduate education was benefiting more than my hosts' was. I had not known that obstetricians on the east coast of the United States use forceps while those on the west coast dare not for fear of litigation. Nor had I realised how much pressure they all feel to reduce caesarean section rates, sometimes against their clinical judgment. Or that many American women use their gynaecologist as their primary care doctor.

Some of the differences between Leeds and Los Angeles were more spectacular. Our menopause clinic does not as yet offer complementary therapy by a robed and turbaned doctor with a waist length beard. Experience in Beverly Hills suggests that this would be hugely successful and that the practitioner could be caucasian. Whether or not therapeutic efficacy would be altered by a Scottish accent remains to be tested.

## *Spin Doctor*

I used to enjoy firing off letters to newspapers. If they were published they produced no discernible results apart from occasional postcards from long lost relatives. Nevertheless, I felt that the papers were trying to help.

Now, recently installed as press officer to a royal college, how do I feel about the media? Uncomfortable when they focus on medicine's shortcomings. Stimulated when journalists ask incisive questions. Paranoid? No, surprisingly. The media rarely seem to be out to get us for no reason.

In an era of government by focus group, even the most altruistic college needs to work on public opinion if it wants to improve care. But it is hard to influence the media's agenda. They are today's control freaks.

Should we become a pressure group? Last week, when launching recommendations for safer labour ward care, should we have suggested that at present things are really dangerous? Or wheeled out a couple who have lost a baby? Certainly not, I thought, but part of me mourned the lost opportunity.

Next day, it was easy to persuade myself that I could do more for womankind by broadcasting on national radio than by attending my antenatal clinic. When I reached our local studios an apologetic receptionist told me that my interview had been cancelled because America's leading femme fatale—Monica Lewinsky—had turned up at the BBC.

Such setbacks are understandable, but occasionally I get the feeling that the media are being devious. Take this month's number one obstetrical issue—the millennium baby. The first questions were factual. When should a couple make love to schedule delivery on 1 January 2000? The reporters did not want to hear about odds or biological variation. They wanted understandable physiology.

The next questions were on the advisability of elective caesarean section at 00 01 on a public holiday. That would be unwise, said I, because of possible staff shortages, unpredictable emergencies, and the millennium bug.

The third wave was trickier. Would the college regard such an operation as unethical? Say the woman had enough money to pay privately for all the staff that she could possibly need? I began to suspect that my questioner's ethical stance would depend on whether it is his paper or a rival which is financing the stunt. I think that I am losing my innocence.

## *Arise, Sir Lancelot*

Greying beard, dark suit, middle age spread, consultant status. Coincidence, or have I been subconsciously working on my image? Anyone over 50 feels like a youngster in an ageing body, but for a few of us, Simon Sparrow is trapped inside Lancelot Spratt.

*Doctor in the House* was published in 1952, when I was 4 years old. The film was produced in 1954 by Betty Box, who died recently. Sir Lancelot was played by James Robertson Justice, who died 24 years ago. The images, however, live on, giving the book's last words a prophetic quality: "From now on it was always going to be like this."

With screen doctors spanning the alphabet from Cameron through Gillespie to Zhivago, why should Spratt remain the most recognisable? One reason is the brilliant portrayal. James Robertson Justice (a name impossible to shorten) was a former naturalist and journalist and his intelligence showed. Today's directors prefer senior consultants to be played by cardboard actors with untwinkling eyes.

The main reason, though, is that Sir Lancelot is like Santa Claus. Deep down, everyone wants to believe that he exists. Richard Gordon's creation was humane beneath his bluster, but what still attracts us is his armour plated self assurance. He is the embodiment of what zoologists call the dominant male. As Desmond Morris keeps reminding us, humans are little different from our cousins the apes. Like them, we are programmed to be part of a hierarchy. The leader may be challenged but nobody likes to see him bleed.

Nowadays, however, an unreconstructed Sir Lancelot would last about 48 hours before a whistleblower reported his bad attitude. This sets a problem for his successors. Can we reconcile the primordial need for leadership with the current distaste for medical authoritarianism?

The quandary was brought home to me recently during a meeting which included some routine doctor bashing from consumer representatives. The medical profession, they said, is still as arrogant as it was in 1952. Silence would have meant assent but taking offence reinforced the irascible stereotype.

We usually cope by agreeing, finding scapegoats, and looking for leadership from outside medicine. Better, I think, to rediscover our self confidence. We can banish paternalism from the individual consultation without completely abrogating our collective authority.

## *New England Journal*

*Sunday*: United States immigration officials are scary. In my student days they sniffed my toothpaste—or was it the Customs? The huge shoulder badges still intimidate me, even here in Shannon airport where the lady with the stamp tries to inject world weary gruffness into her west of Ireland brogue.

*Monday*: "Grand rounds" suggests big processions from bed to bed, or a series of cases with obscure Bostonian diagnoses to challenge the visiting professor. It actually means a lecture. What is grand is that at 7 30 am people actually turn up. Interns in theatre pyjamas munch takeaway bagels. Should a talk be different at this hour, I wonder, like the morning's laid back weather forecast compared with the evening's?

*Tuesday:* Going to Harvard the taxi driver speaks in Russian into a mobile phone. "Where are you from?" we ask. "St Petersburg," he replies sadly. "Very beautiful," we say. Long pause. "Yes," he murmurs. Chekovian despair fills the cab.

*Wednesday:* Boston has umpteen centres of excellence. I express envy, and a local doctor smiles wryly. "I think of us," he says, "as a care centre for people who are still trying to prove something to their mothers."

*Thursday:* Another state, another bagel. I've adjusted to early rising—or remained on British summer time. And I've learnt that jokes are acceptable over breakfast. American medicine, unlike ours, still has a sense of humour.

*Friday:* Downtime. In Newport, Rhode Island, near the church where the Kennedys were married, is a street of empty chateaux. A lady from the Preservation Society shows visitors the marbled opulence built by Gatsby-style fortunes. "Before unions," mutters a man in a check shirt.

*Saturday:* Salem's tourist industry is based mainly on hick witchcraft, with palmists and models of crones on broomsticks. A judge in the 1692 trials is buried here and on adjacent ground is a memorial to the people he hanged. There is a posy on each of 19 stones, and carved quotations: "O Lord, help me. I am wholly innocent." The surrounding tackiness makes it all the more moving. Arthur Miller compared the Salem witch hunts to McCarthyism, but each generation makes the same mistake in a different way. Ours has its own martyrs to political correctness. I suppose we should be pleased we have not hanged them.

## *St Mark's Guidelines*

Dear Chaplain, It has been brought to the attention of the trust guidelines committee that you are distributing a booklet entitled *The Gospel According to St Mark*. The committee has obtained a copy and has requested comments from the relevant departments. Several concerns have been raised.

1. In the title, "gospel" should be changed to "guideline." "Gospel" implies inflexibility. With a guideline, however, adherence is closely monitored and persistent deviation results in this committee providing supportive counselling for the deviant.

2. In chapter 3 the selection criteria for disciples are unclear. The human resources director has pointed out that no person specification was available. This is likely to generate adverse comment in relation to the lack of gender and ethnic mix. Were these posts properly advertised and were structured interviews carried out?
3. The feeding of the five thousand (chapter 6) produced a positive response from the contract caterers, but the research director raised several questions. He advises that the subjects should have been randomised using sealed envelopes into two groups of two and a half thousand, one of which could have received five loaves and the other two fishes.
4. In chapter 2 a patient is instructed, "Arise, and take up thy bed, and walk." This caused considerable concern to both the physiotherapy department and the trust equipment manager. The patient should have been advised to turn on his left side and put his feet to the floor before arising. The guideline should also say, "Even if thou feelest well, thou shouldst not arise unless accompanied by a nurse or health care assistant. Thy walking will be assessed by the occupational therapist. Thy bed should be left for the next patient."
5. Finally, after a computerised literature search using the keyword "gospel" the committee's research assistant identified three other publications not referenced in your guideline. Please check if any further gospels have been published as abstracts or conference proceedings. We would ask you to combine the four published gospels (plus any unpublished ones) by formal meta-analysis.

We look forward to receiving a revised draft which can be distributed with the full authority of this committee.

## *Luvvies Guide*

Damon Seerewijf is a renaissance doctor. His exhibition of abstract medical art opened recently at the Galerie La Vage in Paris, but his day job is professor of molecular umbiloscopy at the University of Palm Beach. Author of more than 200 papers and a syndicated column, he recently converted to Buddhism.

*Who was your most influential teacher?* Hippocrates. Everybody knows his name, but only a few of us have read him in the original Greek. I love his sly sense of irony.

*Which event has had most effect on your work?* The birth of my daughter. Suddenly, life clicked. I think of that moment every time I email a paper to a journal. And I take the video whenever I travel.

*What would be your advice to a newly qualified doctor?* Forget everything they taught you. Look, live, paint, weep, think.

*How do you relax?* I swim with a friend who happens to be a dolphin

*What is your favourite film?* "A Night at the Opera." I see myself as a fusion of Groucho and Harpo, while Margaret Dumont personifies the medical establishment.

*What is your greatest fear?* Losing my humility.

*What are you currently reading?* Nietzsche's Die Geburt der Tragödie, Unzeitgemässe Betrachtungen and Menschliches, Allzumenschliches.

*What is your greatest regret?* Not learning German.

*What alternative therapies have you tried? Did they work?* I regularly practise yoga but I see it as mainstream For me, aspirin is alternative. I tried it and it didn't work.

*What is the greatest love of your life?* After my daughter, the Angkor Wat in Cambodia—its serenity started me on the road to Zen. My wife will kill me for that answer but I'll be reincarnated as her husband.

*What is your worst habit?* Quoting too much from Jackson Pollock when I lecture on molecular medicine. Audiences just don't get it.

*How would you like to die?* There's no need to threaten me. If you don't like pretentiousness just turn the page.

## *Society Column*

September is the conference month. For politicians this means soundbites by the sea but health workers are less ostentatious. Across the country university halls of residence are almost—but not quite—cleared of drawing pins, bits of adhesive putty, and peremptory notices before being filled by carers with name badges.

Everyone agrees that the most useful part of any conference is the social interaction. No organiser, however, carries this to its logical conclusion by dispensing with talks and simply keeping the bar open day and night. A formal programme is necessary and this means speakers. We academics cheerfully help. We understand. We were meetings secretaries ourselves once.

What surprises us is the diversity. Every subspecialty, every part of the body, and almost every practical procedure now has a society. Those whose members use expensive equipment meet in posh hotels. Some societies are exclusively medical but many include scientists and nurses. In general, the smaller the proportion of doctors, the jollier the society.

Some are female with only an occasional male accompanying person. Compared with men's the speeches of female chairpersons are shorter, friendlier, more poised, and better prepared. All-female societies are happy to hire a discotheque for the sheer pleasure of dancing together after dinner. In my experience, all-male societies have reservations about this.

We outside speakers need podium savvy. When asked to fax the chairman a curriculum vitae, we keep it as brief as possible, remembering times when the full version was read out verbatim.

Though we prepare carefully, reality becomes apparent only on the day. Outside the venue, yellow AA signs give us mild tachycardia. Inside, we assess the atmosphere. Sometimes it is evangelical and we recognise how to evoke either hisses or murmurs of approval. We then have to decide whether to stir things up or opt for a quiet life.

Sometimes we are invited to stay and be amusing after dinner. This is challenging. Humour is based on shared experience and the speaker is an outsider. Many societies have a guru—a senior figure, perhaps even a founder. Members pulling his or her leg are met with general hilarity and a tolerant smile from the guru but no visitor should attempt this. Rely on self deprecation if you want to be asked back.

## *The Lords Medical*

I liked the House of Lords with its families of accidental legislators. Hereditary peers were motivated by the unfashionable principle of noblesse oblige. Without them, all parliamentarians are driven by personal ambition, just like the rest of us.

The upper house still has twenty-six Lords Spiritual and a similar number of Law Lords. The third great profession, medicine, is underrepresented. There are noble doctors but they have been selected by the prime minister for their excellent personal qualities—despite (you feel) rather than because of their medical backgrounds. By contrast, bishops arrive in the house by "achieving seniority."

When the chamber is finally democratised, medicine, too, should be represented as of right. It consistently outscores other professions in terms of public respect. More importantly, doctors, even senior ones, still talk face to face with the people.

Law Lords interact with commoners through the medium of other lawyers. Bishops communicate mainly with their coreligionists. Only doctors talk on a daily basis with a wide range of people about the things that the people really care about. This is reflected by the fact that when members of the House of Commons go back to their constituencies they hold "surgeries." They do not hold court or preach.

With so many lawyers in the lower house, the upper chamber should practise positive discrimination to include other professions. A starting point would be twenty-six elected Lords Medical. Nowadays, over half of medical graduates are women, so this group should have the correct gender balance.

Election would not be straightforward. Unfettered self-nomination and alphabetism, as favoured by the General Medical Council, are undesirable. There should be an electoral college with lay people, some medical editors perhaps, and representatives from the mêlée of organisations which currently fail so dismally to give a single coherent voice to our profession.

The only rule regarding election of the lords medical would be that they should be aged under forty-five when they begin their single twelve year term. This means that none of the medical grandees who could champion this change would benefit from it. A fatal weakness, perhaps, but it is still an idea worth archiving.

## *Publish and be Praised*

It is the distinction awards season. All over Britain hospital doctors are hand delivering envelopes marked "Strictly private and confidential." Inside are computer generated forms that never quite manage to position themselves correctly on the page.

The completed forms contain lists of achievements, something of which most people would be proud. Doctors, however, are oddly furtive about them. We sidle up to one another like Michelle of the Resistance, "Listen carefully, I shall photocopy this only once."

But this is not a subject for levity. Merit awards, like natural functions, should not be discussed in public. Writing this is a breach of protocol. It is un-British, like analysing the honours system.

I should say that I am not one of the decision makers. In this era of open.gov.uk it is probably easy to find out who sits on the important committees, but most of us rely on hearsay. We take the process seriously but not that seriously. Nevertheless, I have seen many completed forms over the years. It is quite a feat to compress a lifetime of service into two sides of A4, even using font size 8. A tiny typeface gets in more information but may be unwise, considering the seniority of the people who have to read it.

What always strikes me is how little doctors know about one another—even close colleagues. Reading other people's CVs is a humbling experience. All those publications. All those committees.

There is something illogical about a system that expects doctors to work flat out all week and then rewards those who do more. Nevertheless, it is popular among doctors, who are naturally competitive, and among health economists, who know it is cost effective. So much medical advice for the NHS, most of it free at the point of use. Patients may be less impressed with a system that encourages overwork. "Busy doctor" and "busy hospital" are popular cliches with NHS staff. Patients might prefer "relaxed, easy going doctors" and "quiet, efficiently run hospitals."

Whatever you think of the system, it does provide extra motivation to type A personalities. Its flaw is its secrecy. The names of award holders are published but their completed CV forms should be too. That would be an effective riposte to accusations of nepotism, and I think that the public would be impressed.

## *How to Party*

At an academic dinner recently two professors remarked that their grown up children had advised them to get a life. This advice had been given in all seriousness and, in one case, had been reinforced by a postcard saying, "WORK is for people who don't know how to party." "It's true," the professor added sadly, "I really don't."

Such ignorance is new. Older professors always used the word "fun" in their retirement speeches, usually when referring to the second world war or academic life in the 1960s. Sooner or later medical schools will realise that those bon viveurs were actually more productive than their workaholic successors.

When this happens, partying will come back into fashion. Indeed, it will become compulsory. We shall have a national RAE (Revelry Assessment Exercise) involving detailed questionnaires on party quality and quantity. We shall agonise about how many parties to declare.

We shall need published guidelines. At present there is no basis for evidence based partying. What follows is a draft for consultation.

*The invitation*: Email is boring. Have your invitation sung by a stripping lab technician or encoded on a genetic fingerprint.

*The venue*: Be original. Choose somewhere that will be stimulatingly unfamiliar to academics—the outpatient clinic, for example. Inexpensive decorations can be made from bunches of used airline tickets.

*Games:* Academics love to see themselves as Machiavellian plotters. Get things going with a box of rubber daggers. Everyone has to stab everyone else in the back and when stabbed has to writhe in agony on the floor. (Keep an eye on the stilettos to make sure that nobody slips in a real one.)

*The food:* Bring back memories of your days as a junior. Install a hospital vending machine with sinister looking pasties. And why not retune the microwave to sound like a mobile phone?

*The music:* Hip disc jockeys with strange names and huge loudspeakers can be easily hired. Most are medical students but a few are ear, nose, and throat surgeons drumming up trade.

*The drugs:* Having trouble recruiting volunteers for your latest phase III trial? Make sure your doormen have a good supply of consent forms.

Remember, these are only guidelines. Enjoy.

## *Seven Guidelines of Wisdom*

Doctors are expected to be wise. Nowadays people can access knowledge without our help. They want more from us than just correct decision making, and we expect wisdom of one another. The commonest complaint about doctors in trouble is that they lack insight.

Yet we receive no training in wisdom. We assume that it is randomly distributed and partly genetic, like musical ability. Over the past six years the BMJ has published only thirteen papers with "wisdom" in the title or abstract. Three of them were about teeth.

Here at last are some guidelines.

1. *Mix the generations:* In modern Britain the only time that the generations mingle is at weddings. In hospital, consultants teach registrars, registrars teach juniors, and students teach one another. Intergenerational discourse should be reintroduced. Don't assume the flow of wisdom will be one way.
2. *Take time for reflection:* "Reflective practice" is a cliché in nursing journals but not in ours. If anyone passing my door sees me sitting and thinking I feel guilty. The only place where you could stare thoughtfully through the window used to be the train, but modern electronics have stopped even that.
3. *Converse with lay people:* This is hard. Many lay people have fixed attitudes to our profession, ranging from awe to resentment. Many doctors encourage these feelings. Concealing your calling is no help. We must converse as equals.

4. *Dare to be unoriginal:* Today's NHS is constantly seeking novelty. Its jargon has a six week shelf life. In this context it takes nerve to point out the obvious. Wisdom is old fashioned though it can be repackaged under a snappy title like "clinical governance."
5. *Move around:* This is increasingly difficult. Long ago undergraduates could move around Europe, but medical schools' seamless curricula now make this impossible. Regions are doing the same for specialist registrars. And consultants stay put.
6. *Keep your sense of humour:* Seriousness belongs in the consulting room. Outside, be a jester, whose job is to deflate pomposity. Good jokes depend on insight. Think of all the books called The wit and wisdom of....
7. *Stop reading articles with "guidelines" in the title:* Whoever heard of a wise person reading numbered guidelines? Or writing them?

## *Student Feedback*

The medics' revue is a tradition that does not stand still. Compared with our own efforts as students, today's shows have more sophisticated backing tracks, more gender equality, and much more bumping and grinding (all of it from the male members of the cast). The comparison is memory based, however, not evidence based. Ours was a pre-video generation—something that causes me mingled regret and relief.

Today's performers seem so confident, with their synchronised dance routines involving all four limbs and their benign responses to heckling colleagues. The targets hardly change but the satire can still be original. This year an offstage voice announced a preclinical lecture: a Chinese student stood gravely at a lectern and spoke in fluent Cantonese, with the occasional insertion of "*immunology ... T cell ... cytokine ...*"

As a senior member of staff you enjoy the obvious jokes, like the dean's face on the sun rising above the Meditubbies, but you sense that others are passing you by. Young teachers whom you regard as rather trendy are lampooned because their clothes are out of fashion. You smile uneasily.

But it goes deeper than dress sense. The students are cool. The Ali G lookalike appeared last year but not this year. The humour is post-ironic and post-stereotyping: "Aren't you from Ethiopia?" "No, I'm from Sri Lanka. It's just that I've shaved my head." What on earth must these knowing undergraduates think of our clumsy attempts to teach them correct attitudes?

For the staff, the revue provides better feedback than a sackful of questionnaires. This comes less from the scripts than from audience reaction, as some remarks are greeted with a roar of the laughter of recognition. It tells you a lot about other people's teaching styles, though the most spectacular response is when female students name a would-be Don Juan.

An annual jab of disrespect should be compulsory for everyone, particularly those of us whom overconfidence could otherwise lead into danger. The BMA would benefit—but who would put on the show?

I left happy, and not just because I had been sung about by a bowtie-bedecked chorus. There is something life affirming about people putting heart and soul into doing a thing well. And about a virtuoso trumpeter. As Ali G might say, it gives you hope for da future and dat's good, man, innit?

## *Happy Birthday, Ma'am*

The Queen Mother is patron of our royal college and we were among the 300-odd organisations invited to join a parade celebrating her 100th birthday. Envisaging something dignified, like Armistice Day, we decided that our council would process in academic robes, preceded by the college mace.

When the written briefing arrived, it sounded a different note. "Please bring a large sense of humour (you might need it) ... There are a large number of animals in the parade including corgis, chickens, camels, and winkles." All, apparently, "walking with a 23 inch pace at 112 paces a minute (so you have to get a move on)."

At the dress rehearsal we were marshalled by young guardsmen exuding effortless authority, even in green shirts and berets. "How will we know when to start?" I asked one. "Remember the sixties, sir," he replied, without a flicker of irony, "and go with the flow."

When the flow ended, Horse Guards Parade was full and all 5000 of us were being urged through a loudspeaker to march more quickly next time. As we looked around, we gained a deeper understanding of the British character. In mainland Europe there would be giant creations of papier maché. In South America there would be sexy costumes inspired by tropical birds. Here in England some of our neighbours were wearing knotted handkerchiefs and woolly jerseys.

After the rehearsal, sweltering in our robes, we had arranged to take tea and fruitcake in a quiet oasis in Pall Mall. We still had our official signboard saying "Royal College of Obstetricians and Gynaecologists," and the only way to carry it through the thickening crowds of royal watchers was to hold it high. In the current climate of media opinion, we developed sudden misgivings.

The public's reaction was unexpected and reassuring. Some women smiled quietly before averting their eyes. One called out, "Thank you—I owe you so much." One kissed a beaming past president. Then, as good humoured police stopped the traffic while we crossed the Mall, the spectators broke into a round of applause.

Two hours later, our brisk progress past the royal dais was upstaged by the Red Arrows. We called, "Hello, Ma'am," as instructed in the briefing, and gave her a cheery wave, but everyone was gazing upwards. Happy birthday, anyway.

## *My Hero*

It is uncool for a grown man to admit to having a hero. My generation—and, worryingly, its successors—are cynics. Nevertheless, here goes. My hero is Mahmoud Fathalla, professor of obstetrics and gynaecology in Assiut, 375 km south of Cairo.

In Egypt, maternal mortality is still high. In Sudan, female genital mutilation is endemic. A doctor can tackle these problems locally, but Fathalla saw the bigger picture. Worldwide, over half a million women die in childbirth annually. Millions of children are left uneducated or even deprived of food because they are female.

Global statistics are so overwhelming that personal action seems pointless. Most of us content ourselves with short-lasting indignation.

We blame governments and tell ourselves that over the coming century female literacy should improve and things may start to get better.

Professor Fathalla did more. Well respected in Egypt, he became president of the International Federation of Obstetrics and Gynaecology—an organisation which used to pay lip service to the task of improving women's health in developing countries. Almost singlehandedly, he focused it.

In 1988 in Rio, his lecture on "medicine's seven deadly sins" produced a standing ovation. Last month in Washington DC he received another, after telling a thousand doctors "how you can make a difference." The difference he had made was that in 2000 his message was being repeated throughout the meeting and people were no longer smiling.

This took persistence. He must be a highly effective committee man and lobbyist. Organisations such as the World Bank are now trying to help save women's lives. But Fathalla understands that you need to win individual hearts as well as corporate minds.

Close up, he is charming and modest. On a podium, he is inspirational, using not demagoguery but wisdom. He stands still, choosing words from global English and ideas that cross cultures. Speaking just after Labor Day, he mused on the political and obstetric connotations of the word "labour": "What a pity the world's women have not unionised."

John Lennon, almost a hero for us boomers, wrote, "We all wanna change the world." He meant it ironically. Last month in Washington, as we heard of new partnerships between countries north and south, we began to believe we could.

## *Auntie Pat*

As a medical student you have to develop an understanding of what is common and what is rare. "Look out of the window," our teachers would say with elaborate sarcasm. "Is that a sparrow or a lesser sulphur-crested cockatoo?"

Knowing what was normal was especially hard in the trendy 1960s. For those of us who clung to our tweed jackets, there was the medical students' society. In Edinburgh, it had a royal charter. Enterprising predecessors had petitioned George III, and, ever since, the Royal Medical Society had flourished quietly, with small numbers of members electing large numbers of office bearers.

After centuries of people donating books, the society had a valuable collection but nowhere dry to keep it. The decision to sell was difficult but meant that we could buy our own premises and hire a permanent secretary. Legend has it that most of the candidates appeared for interview in miniskirts. All the more surprising that the new secretary was a woman of uncertain age with a no-nonsense hairstyle, a throaty laugh, and children almost ready for university themselves.

Mrs Strong became Auntie Pat and then "AP," moving with the society from a tiny basement to purpose built rooms on campus. Her glass-fronted office became its politically incorrect heart, with AP enjoying regular ciggies, and one of the white pillars decorated with a filter tip.

Not everyone likes students. Those of us who do still find it difficult to relax without trying too hard to be young or taking refuge in age and experience. For AP it came naturally. She had her likes and dislikes, and she never patronised. She took her job and her young colleagues seriously but was always ready for a joke.

Last summer there was a party celebrating her three decades in post and her 80th birthday. Among the presents was an album with photographs of her 31 student presidents. She laughed about her age, commenting that the cigarettes had not got her yet.

When she died recently of a smoking related illness, her handwritten invitations to the annual dinner were in the post. For those of us who left Edinburgh years ago, the sense of bereavement is strangely acute. The end of a matter-of-fact relationship always catches you by surprise. This one, we now realise, was not so much rare as unique.

## *Say Noinety-Noine*

As every television presenter knows, credibility in the new millennium means having an accent. This varies with the target audience. For the young, Essex is the linguistic place to be. The middle aged prefer Ireland, Wales, or Barnsley. Traditional BBC English is aimed at the over 70s.

The public is being conditioned to mistrust upper class speech, not just in Britain, where it is mocked, but worldwide. The archetypal villain in a Hollywood movie sounds like George Sanders. The baddie in The Lion King was suavely voiced by Jeremy Irons. Bob the builder, by contrast, is the laddish Neil Morrissey.

Our politicians understand this. The health secretary keeps his speech just this side of Paul Gascoigne and even the prime minister affects vaguely regional consonants. Imagine how well the Social Democrats might have done if Lord Jenkins had remained a boyo from the valleys and Lord Owen had retained his Devon burr.

Medicine has always been a way for clever people of humble origins to better themselves, and one of the first things we did was to learn to talk proper. Sadly, we have overdone it. Nowadays the popular stereotype of the hospital consultant is someone who talks like a 1950s government information film.

We need to rethink our vocal image. This includes the Scots, I'm afraid. People are wising up to the fact that Educated Scottish is the equivalent of Oxford English. Edinburgh graduates are starting to pretend they come from Glasgow. They sit up and take notice whenever Sir Alex Ferguson gives a soundbite.

There are limits, of course. The Queen may have famously toned down her cut-glass accent over a lifetime of Christmas broadcasts but she has not yet become an eastender. The medical profession, to regain the top spot in public esteem, needs to relocate from Harley Street but no further than the North Circular Road.

Our leaders should start practising their glottal stops before their next meeting with those influential government advisers. And when they talk to the media, the aim should be to sound fractionally more downmarket than the interviewer. What about the rest of us, and our patients? No worries, mate. According to all the evidence, patients are far too busy reading our body language to care about our vowels.

## *How to be a Health Secretary*

So the general election is over and you are the new secretary of state for health. Welcome to the best job in the cabinet. You will be advised by some of Britain's brightest young sociology graduates, who will help you draw up your plan for revolutionising health care.

Other cabinet posts carry responsibilities. Defence secretaries, for example, have been known to resign over mistakes. With health, however, like transport and prisons, public expectations are so low that this question does not arise.

A major part of your job is to keep them low. Health economists will help you do this. You need not talk to them. Nobody else does. Just let them continue telling everyone that the demand for health care is infinite, so nobody—least of all you—can be expected to supply it.

Never suggest that hospitals adopt rational business practices, such as planned replacement of equipment. On no account talk to people who see patients. Instead, praise them with half-hearted platitudes. This always unnerves them.

Never criticise nurses, midwives, or porters. Take every opportunity to refer, in sentimental but non-sexist language, to their selfless dedication. This creates the right conditions to underpay them.

Never underestimate the tolerance of the public. Voters who readily give money to famine and earthquake relief in developing countries will not raise a murmur in protest when you strip those countries of doctors and nurses.

Criticise senior doctors as much as you like. This is a tradition started by Aneurin Bevan. Indeed, it is the only tradition of his that you are expected to maintain. Don't worry about the profession's response. At any given moment it has at least three dozen leaders, all of whom dislike one another much more than they dislike you.

People are always interested in their health, and the healthier they are, the more they complain. You are their spokesperson. Let's face it: nobody really expects you to know anything about the health service.

A country in which half a million people die each year (mostly of old age) provides lots of human tragedies, many of which you can exploit for political ends. With skill, you could be the first health secretary in decades to advance your political career. Good luck.

## *The European Leisure Time Directive*

The European Working Time Directive, currently causing chaos in the NHS, puts a 48 hour limit on the working week. This is difficult for doctors as most of us warm up only after 48 hours. Indeed, we are starting to panic about how to fill the other 120. Fortunately, help is at hand in the form of the European Leisure Time Directive.

Research has shown that leisure is beneficial to health and therefore, like seat belts, it is being made compulsory. This is not as easy as it sounds. Academics, for example, are paid to think but if they do so beyond the limit, their employer will incur financial penalties. The traditional decerebrant, alcohol, is also unhealthy, so universities are introducing intensive tenpin bowling and snooker.

Unlike the Working Time Directive, which puts doctors on a par with shelf stackers, the European Leisure Time Directive (ELTD) treats medicine as a special case. It also acknowledges that Britain is not like other countries, leisurewise.

Britain's favourite relaxation is watching television drama. Nowadays this consists entirely of psychologically damaged people being aggressive to one another. As doctors spend much of their time listening to psychologically damaged people being aggressive, soap operas—particularly EastEnders—will not count as medical leisure activity (MLA) under European law.

The country's second leisure activity is eating out. This raises problems of definition as working meals become more common. The ELTD requires the buffet to be weighed before and after a meal and the difference divided by the number of doctors present. A working breakfast is defined as up to 75g of croissant, 100g of muesli or 50g of yoghurt per head.

Our third relaxation is sport. The gym is classed as MLA although it involves more calorific output than work. Boxing and tae kwon do are acceptable MLA for geriatricians but not for casualty officers, for whom they are normal working activities. Coarse fishing involves sitting around for long periods staring into space and waiting for the chance to do something, so it does not count as MLA for NHS surgeons in winter.

Fourth is complaining about the state of the NHS. The ELTD recognises reality and allows this as leisure activity for doctors as for everyone else.

## *Secretaries for PRHOs*

My son the trainee solicitor, in his first salaried post after five years at university, is the equivalent, I suppose, of a preregistration house officer (PRHO). Nevertheless, he has his own telephone and an answering machine that suggests to callers that they either leave a message or speak to his secretary.

As a houseman I had no secretary. I filled in my own forms, delivered samples, and found films deep in the X-ray stores. On teaching rounds, my main worry was that I had left some administrative task undone.

That was in 1971, but things have not changed. In a 1995 survey, administration occupied between 19% and 31% of PRHOs' time. Teaching occupied less than 1%. When I talk to PRHOs as a General Medical Council visitor, some are happy and some complain.

Strangely, they never complain about bleeps. The pager may have shrunk but it is still around, turning the house officer into everyone's skivvy and making mockeries of both postgraduate training and clinical practice. Surely its role as a status symbol must end now that every schoolchild has a mobile phone.

Hospitals have tried to ease the pressures on PRHOs by appointing phlebotomists. This is the wrong approach. Venepuncture is a skill to be practised until you are flawless. It would be better to follow the lawyers' example and give them secretaries.

Doctors will dismiss this idea as a joke. High and low, we all like the familiar hierarchy, and house officers should know their place. If pressed we will say, as we always do, that the NHS cannot afford it.

I wonder. It costs about £225,000 to train a student to PRHO level, so the proposed annual output of 6000 new doctors will cost the country over £1bn a year. Within seven years of graduation, however, 17% of young doctors are lost to the NHS. The cost of that wastage will be over £200m a year.

For much less money, one secretary could be allocated to every two PRHOs. The secretary would deal with paperwork, take telephone calls, and hold the bleeps during working hours. The PRHOs would see patients and attend teaching sessions. These bright and educated women and men would feel valued instead of being treated like children. They might even want to stay.

## *Language Unbecoming*

Early one morning I was almost the only passenger—sorry, customer—in the carriage as the train left Edinburgh. "I will look after you, sir," said the young steward with a faint accent. "I will keep serving complimentary coffee. When you are pissed off, let me know and I will stop."

Charmed, I hadn't the heart to explain that in first class we become "replete," not "pissed off." I assumed he was European—unlike most train staff, who are British, or most pub staff, who nowadays are Australian. One of the many good things about antipodean barpersons is they rarely swear at the clientele.

Our hospitals too used to be full of young Australians—but, increasingly, junior doctors are from mainland Europe. A nursing colleague commented that they were good clinicians and excellent record keepers. The only trouble was the swearing. She had recently had to rebuke one for using bad language in front of a patient.

I can sympathise with that doctor. Anyone coming here to learn colloquial English is likely to end up—how you say?—bloody confused. British bookshops are full of the works of Irvine Welsh. Our films, however frothy, are scattered with four-letter words, and even the BBC loses its gentility after 9 pm.

Foul language has spread from Billingsgate to Hampstead and from low tavern to smart bistro. I find it appalling to hear a well dressed woman effing into a mobile phone or—the other day in our hospital corridor—a dad chatting to his little daughter with throwaway obscenities.

Maybe it's being a gynaecologist that makes me so fastidious. Centuries ago, oaths used to be religious. "Cor blimey" ("God blind me") or "'Od's bodkins" (translation mercifully obscure) must once have had great shock value, carrying a real risk of damnation. Nowadays all our swear words relate to pelvic anatomy and physiology. Paradoxically, the only place guaranteed free of them is the gynaecology clinic.

Or perhaps it's my age. As an enfant terrible on committees I used to swear from time to time with what I imagined was telling effect. A grey beard makes this inappropriate, and looking back I doubt that it was ever necessary. Nowadays I have to do it alone in the car, like everyone else.

## *Paging Dr Parris*

August. High summer and mid silly season. With parliament in recess, Britain's heavyweight political commentators have gone on holiday and the media have turned to trivia. Newspaper readers, grateful at first, soon tire of pap. They begin to long for autumn, when the journalists will sharpen their knives again.

For medical politicians, however, autumn never comes. One of the delights of being on the General Medical Council or, I daresay, the BMA council is that press scrutiny of individual members is almost non-existent. The institutions themselves are subject to routine criticism, but the doctors who run them are largely ignored—or, worse, treated with respect. Even their presidents are spared the cartoonist's pen.

I have never met Tony Blair and I glimpsed Gordon Brown only once, years ago in the students' union. But I know them as well as I know, say, Prince Charles or President Bush, because they are regularly dissected by well-informed writers. When they face important decisions, their options are discussed, the electorate is informed, and the politicians can gauge public opinion.

The medical electorate, by contrast, relies on glossies produced by its official organisations, or on trade newspapers written by lay people. There is no medical Matthew Parris waspishly observing which medical quangoholics are pompous windbags, or Blair toadies, or Trappist monks, or barking mad. Or, maybe, sensible and constructive.

And yet, at intervals, Britain's doctors—all 0.1 million of them—are sent a list of names, unknown or vaguely familiar, and asked to vote. Without feedback from the fourth estate, democracy is a farce. Some like it that way. Years ago, when the GMC discussed regional representation, a member told me, "We can't have this. Nobody who knows me would vote for me." He was not joking, just stating a fact.

Sadly, "Dr Parris" is pie in the sky. No reader would be willing to pay for a journal devoted to professional politics. And no medical writer would want the job. Parliamentary sketchwriters are already struggling to make Westminster's cloned legislators seem interesting. Medical politicians would be an impossible challenge.

Dr Parris dot com? Perhaps the internet is the answer, but for me the words "heavyweight" and "web" are incompatible.

## *Cruising*

Only a month ago, I had never seen the Crimea and my longest sea voyage had been on the ferry to Brittany. Now I am one of the growing number of doctors who cruise. Specialist societies are probably already being formed—the British and European College of Ancient Medical Mariners, perhaps, or the Medical Association of Sea Travellers.

Most of the people on our ship were not doctors, but there were enough of us to cause comment. Why so many medics? One reason, I think, is that on a cruise somebody else does the driving. If your job is making decisions and implementing them yourself, a holiday means abrogating responsibility.

Those of us still working felt rather conspicuous, but retired people are good company and fine role models. They show enviable economy of movement. They enjoy jokes without convulsing. They can fill a dining room within seconds of its opening, without apparent effort. After nightfall, they can dance the polka.

And they don't miss much. We found that in the Ukraine it is fashionable for women of all ages to wear almost nothing as they clamber over Roman remains. Our sea of panama hats did not flicker as we gazed at the ruins, but afterwards in the coach there were murmurings of refined surprise.

On board, we had educational lectures. Go on—ask me a question about Byzantine church architecture. Some facts are oddly satisfying, like finding the missing piece of a jigsaw. Did you know that the Black Sea is so called because to the ancient Turks, north was "black" and south was "white"?

Tourism in the former Soviet bloc has its depressing side. In Yalta we bought a watercolour sketch from an unemployed architect. In Odessa an old lady begging at the top of the Potemkin Steps said she was a paediatrician. At the bottom of the steps we found a sign saying "Chicken McNuggets" in Cyrillic script. Go on—ask me who Cyril was.

On a brighter note, each Ukrainian port had its own brass band. Nearly 150 years after the Light Brigade we left Sevastopol to the strains of Glenn Miller. We lined the rail, smiling and waving (in an energy efficient way) before turning and heading for the dining room.

## *Consultants' Hootenanny*

Doctors gather in large numbers rarely and only for serious reasons—political, educational, or funereal. Our purely social occasions tend to be segregated by specialty or age, or to invoke a sense of duty. Most of us would be wryly amused at the thought of colleagues massing simply to have a good time.

Imagine my feelings, then, at being appointed, in my absence, social convener for the senior staff committee and asked to organise a morale boosting event for the consultants of our recently merged mega-trust. For years the driving force in each constituent hospital had been antipathy towards the others. Now we no longer squabbled. None of us knew enough colleagues to quarrel with.

The idea of a hootenanny emerged from discussion with my son, a socially skilled twentysomething. The committee greeted the idea with acclaim and suggested hiring Leeds Town Hall, scene of hospital tea dances in more spacious days. The consultant body responded enthusiastically to a mailshot. Only later did they admit that nobody knew what a hootenanny was.

Officially it is "a party with folk singing and sometimes dancing, esp an informal concert with folk music (N Am colloq)." Recently it was the title of a Jools Holland television show with several bands and an audience in one big studio. Surely a trust with more than four hundred consultants could produce half a dozen musical groups.

Most medical school applicants can play an instrument. Almost all give up on acceptance, but a few maintain their skills into mid-life. These are wonderful people. Not only are they willing to stand up and be counted, but also they can persuade non-medical fellow musicians to turn up in return for a free supper.

The evening was magic. It started with an orthopaedic bagpiper on the steps and a professorial Dixieland band onstage. Female vocalists accompanied dinner with electric jazz and later a long haired Blues Brother played sax as he shuffled among the dancers. Volunteers in the gallery shone spotlights on the Soul Surgeons, swaying in a riot of colour. As midnight approached, an anaesthetist stood on a table and pumped out lead guitar. Man, the place was jumping.

Afterwards the committee agreed that our morale had indeed been boosted. Certainly, with a rock band at full volume nobody can hear you whinge.

## *Missing Christmas*

A month ago the chaplain's secretary phoned. Would I read a lesson on Christmas morning? Normally I agree and wait to see if I am the warm-up man with Isaiah chapter 9, or top of the bill with Luke chapter 2. This time I stammered an apology. After an unbroken run since 1971 I would not—barring accidents—be in hospital this Christmas.

Nor would most of my colleagues. In our consultants' dining room there would be mince pies and a dwindling band of doctors—some reminiscing about Christmas Past when the ward sister sipped an unaccustomed sherry and the senior consultant, in a funny hat, carved the turkey. Neither she nor he would have dreamed of taking Christmas off.

My medical generation experienced the end of an era stretching back to Dickens' time, when the festive season lasted only a day or two. In A Christmas Carol, Fezziwig's clerks worked normally on 24 December. Not until 7 pm did their boss give the signal to roll up the carpet and start the dancing. And they were back in the office on Boxing Day. Nowadays parties begin in early December, and the 25th is a blessed relief for everyone except the very young.

Our family stoutly maintained the old tradition. From an early age, our children took it for granted that after Santa had called, you went to hospital to show your toys to the midwives. Later, as students home for the holidays, they automatically woke up, programmed to walk the wards.

In recent years skeleton staffs of nurses began to look puzzled by our presence, and patients became fewer and iller. The lord mayor, the Salvation Army band, and our family followed one another around, hoping to find a patient who could speak or a Christmas mum who could smile while holding on to her caesarean stitches.

This year both children spent the winter abroad—trying, perhaps, to let us down gently and break a 26 year habit. My wife and I decided that rather than buy a tiny turkey and one cracker we too would leave town.

The chaplain was understanding. The nurses chided me, not for going, but for returning early and missing a pagan Hogmanay in Edinburgh. Please, anything is better than that, even Isaiah.

## *Fire Down Below*

Someone somewhere must have been the first to compare reorganising the NHS with rearranging the deckchairs on the Titanic. The joke does not bear analysis—the health service is not about to capsize—but "rearranging the deckchairs" entered the language because it catches the real feeling in the engine room about activities on the bridge.

The only people who go up and down the ladder between the two are doctors. A few of us spend part of the week in London on the medical equivalent of the promenade deck and part of it back home working in the galley.

Or rather, this week, not working. I am writing in January and elective surgery in our hospital has been cancelled, as it was last year and the year before that and the year …

Below deck, your reaction is fury. You are the person who saw the patients and shared their pain and anxiety. You are the person who will see them when they are finally admitted. Your fury is only increased by knowing that they will not blame you or anyone else for the failures of the NHS.

Above deck, you are all urbanity. You nibble a custard cream, comment on the second draft of a discussion document, and check your diary for dates for the next meeting. If yesterday's anger intrudes into your conversation you feel foolish. Your colleagues smile and advise you not to let it get to you. After a while you think they are right.

Your upper deck friends are talented and committed people. They may not feel raw rage when the service breaks down but they do want to improve things. The problem is that the higher people are in the NHS ship, the less is the fire in their belly. And on the bridge are the politicians, cold as ice and ignorant about everything except politics.

It may be mythology but I like to think that the NHS was brought into being by combining Beveridge's cool brain and Bevan's hot blood. According to his biographer, Michael Foot, Aneurin Bevan was "a man of passion and compassion." Those are exactly the qualities missing from the politicians who are steering the ship today. Those, and knowledge about life below deck.

## *Lawyers are from Mars, Doctors are from Venus*

Perhaps you disagree with the title. That's OK. You may say, "Hey, lawyers talk a lot, and that's a Venusian characteristic. And doctors (especially surgeons) do things, which is Martian." I respect you for saying that, and up to a point you're right. But let's look at it another way.

Which profession is the more confident and doesn't care what the other thinks of it? Which profession imposes its way of working on the other? Which profession cannot tolerate uncertainty and says, "Come along, doctor, answer yes or no"? Which profession is the one that worries? Which profession can't make a major decision without asking the other's opinion? Which practitioners keep wondering, "What might the lawyers make of this?"

To the rest of the world, they look and sound alike. They're both middle class achievers. Both sets of mothers are equally proud of them. But they come from different planets.

On Mars, life is lawyer centred. Cases wait for years without anyone complaining—least of all the government, which is composed of lawyers. Aggression, a male characteristic throughout the solar system, is channelled into writing unpleasant letters or fighting each other in court. And victors get promoted.

On Venus, patients come first. Empathy is feminine. Doctors work late but blame themselves for not working even harder. They acquiesce to being treated like other healthcare workers. And they lose their sense of humour.

Here on Earth, doctors and lawyers have to get along. This is where I, an experienced relationship counsellor, can help. In my hugely popular seminars I say, "OK, now you've hugged one another, let's talk. Tell me honestly, where would you rather be? Mars or Venus?"

Guess what? Nobody wants to go to Venus, unless they're ill. But many doctors envy the Martian lifestyle. They like going to court because it's the only place they're allowed to fight any more.

As a therapist, my job is to help professions get along. I can't like one more than the other. But I'll tell you something. In any long term relationship the partners have to feel equal. Doctors have a problem, not with lawyers but with their own self confidence. Boy, do they need therapy.

## *Postmenopausal Doctors*

The medical menopause affects doctors of both sexes. It normally occurs in the mid 50s but its basis is controversial. Those who believe in a hormonal cause say it is the end result of decades of disturbed circadian rhythm combined with bursts of excessive adrenalin secretion. Others argue that it is psychological, triggered by reaching the horizontal phase of medicine's 30 year learning curve.

In many cultures it is welcomed and the postmenopausal doctor (PMD) is valued for his or her wisdom. In Britain and the United States, however, attitudes are ambivalent. PMDs are appreciated by patients but not by healthcare systems. One of the features of the medical menopause is disinhibition, and the NHS has difficulty in relating to professionals who speak their minds.

Self medication for the condition has been used for centuries but modern sufferers are particularly hard hit. In the early part of their careers they worked long hours to maintain the service while their seniors had a pleasant lifestyle. Now they work long hours to maintain the service while their juniors enjoy a pleasant lifestyle.

In Britain, today's PMDs have worked throughout their careers in a severely underfunded service. When they pointed this out they were ignored. Indeed, the public was told that if only the doctors would work harder, the NHS would be fine. The recently announced cash boost will produce improvements shortly after these PMDs retire.

Pharmacological treatments remain inadequately researched. Clinical opinion is divided between Highland and Islay malts on the one hand and claret and burgundy on the other. The most effective remedy, however, is surgical. Cutting oneself off from the NHS produces immediate and lasting relief of symptoms. Sleep and temper improve, the will to live returns, and the doctor alarms his or her friends by becoming cheerful again.

The NHS, having previously encouraged such surgery, is now beginning to question the high rates. Britain needs more doctors and its major suppliers—developing countries—may not be able to cope. Stopping the haemorrhage of PMDs would help but cannot be achieved unless the system recognises and manages this treatable condition.

## *Respect: a Journalist's Guide*

According to a recent poll of radio listeners, doctors are the most respected profession in the United Kingdom. The least respected are MPs, estate agents, government ministers, lawyers, and—fifth from bottom—journalists.

Doctors are not ones to gloat or to advise those 12,000 *Today* listeners to get a life. Instead, our hearts go out to the poor journalists, who have put so much effort into advising everyone else how to do their jobs that they have neglected themselves. Time for them to benefit from our wisdom, for a change. Here is a quick 'n' easy, cut-out-and-keep guide to earning respect.

*Think substance, not spin.* When doctors went through a tough time image-wise, we didn't hire Max Clifford. We took a hard look at ourselves and changed the bits that weren't right. Like, if I may say so, the arrogance.

*Respect the public.* Medicine now has lay people on most major committees and we listen to them, as well as to individual patients. Journalists, however, treat the public like children. The contrast between a television journalist talking off camera and on camera has to be heard to be believed.

*Don't talk yourselves down.* We've realised that if you say, "I'm only a simple surgeon" often enough, people believe it. Journalists have called themselves "hacks" for so long that they believe it themselves.

*Teach your juniors respect.* Treating patients as equals is now at the core of undergraduate and postgraduate medical education. By contrast, trainee journalists are told that the public has a reading age of 8 and the attention span of a hypomanic gnat. Medicine has smartened up while the media have dumbed down.

*Provide a consultant based service.* The NHS is moving away from dependence on trainees. But when doctors are interviewed for newspapers or news programmes, it is usually by people half their age. They are charming, yes, but perceptive? No.

*Believe in something.* People sense that most of us in the NHS—doctors, nurses, secretaries—stay with it because we believe in it. Legendary journalists covered their idealism with a veneer of cynicism, but their successors have copied the wrong layer. They should try being like us. The public respects sincerity.

## *Graduation for Oldies*

Happier than funerals, less fraught than christenings, and cheaper than weddings, graduations are the most enjoyable of family milestones. They are also the most exclusive. With only two tickets per graduand and no black market, most of the family has to be content with the official video.

After years of gazing impassively over the audience as one of the gowned academics on the platform, it comes as a mild shock to find yourself in your Sunday best among the mums and dads. You have noticed that all parents somehow act alike on these occasions and, when your turn comes, you effortlessly follow the pattern.

Your basic instinct is to whoop and whistle at the climactic moment and to accost passers by throughout the day and tell them what a smart kid you've got. Your superego tells you this would be a mistake. New graduates are perceptive and tolerant, but there are limits.

Moreover, says your superego sternly, remember this is our kid's day and you are supporting cast. Hence the dad's characteristic air of controlled pride. He carries his smallest camera and tries to snap discreetly. There is also a tinge of anxiety. Will his choice of restaurant impress the new generation?

Graduations are of two types—at the alma mater and elsewhere. At the University of Elsewhere you expect to get lost so you turn up too early and then try to look casual among the bustling Elsewherians.

At the alma mater you think you know your way around. Big mistake. How can so many one way systems and office blocks appear in only 30 years? Once inside the hall the nostalgia is overwhelming. The first time you were here was as a fresher, waiting in a long queue for the mass chest x ray. When did they decide that tuberculosis was no longer a problem?

No matter where the ceremony, medical or not, you bump into old friends. Once you have exhausted the main topic of conversation (retirement dates) you fall silent and watch the happy graduates—mainly women now, whatever the profession.

It is an odd feeling, being one of the grey brigade. Passing on the baton, what? As we leave the hall, the organ music ends in a huge crescendo. Nobody seems to notice. We're heading for the Pimms.

## *She's Bleeding Again*

Obstetric haemorrhage is frightening, at least for the obstetrician. The woman's partner, however, views it calmly through his video camera. He knows there is always a lot of blood. When the norm is exceeded it is the professionals who sweat.

Life threatening haemorrhage occurs after one in a thousand births, so each NHS obstetrician should see a case every year or two. Not so. The play of chance means that in each hospital one consultant sees them all. The rest of us feel quietly smug, as if our good luck were of our own making. Then the wheel of fortune rotates and it's your turn.

An obstetrician's day job consists of balancing one small risk against another and trying to avoid both. Saving babies has become a matter of applying protocols. So when you help save a mother's life you feel liberated, but only briefly. Even while you are checking the drip and catheter, the partner is asking whether all this could have been prevented.

Emergencies have a way of telescoping your memory. You remember the last time and the time before that, as if they were yesterday. You hear yourself telling the trainee what the old prof did when you were a registrar. Then you realise that you are the old prof now.

These days there are courses that create the adrenaline rush under controlled conditions, so new consultants are well prepared. Still, some lessons only come through experience. Always empty your bladder, for example, and, however urgent the dash to theatre, never leave your credit cards in the changing room.

Immediately afterwards, there is a high. It has little to do with altruism. It comes from being part of a team and confronting something real. During an emergency there is no pretence. The team's rapport is instinctive. They read one another's body language. They tolerate foibles and feeble wisecracks but not indecision. And when the worst is over, they become phlegmatic.

The worst? That is when you have done everything and someone says, "She's bleeding again." At this moment, I recommend the Tarrant manoeuvre—phone a friend. On call or not, colleagues won't mind. They will offer to come in but all you want is a reassuring voice. Believe me, it helps. Take the word of an old prof.

## *The Turn of the Screw*

Paedophilia is an unusual subject for opera. Librettists normally stick to a more wholesome diet of murder, consumption, and suicide. Composer Benjamin Britten's adaptation of Henry James's *The Turn of the Screw* had its premiere in 1954, when child molestation was thought to be rare. Even today, scholars try to reject the obvious interpretation of James's enigmatic story about two haunted children.

In Sydney Opera House a few weeks ago, evil seemed far away. Outside, ferries hurried back and forth across the harbour, and even inside the auditorium we were conscious of the beauty of the famous sails above our heads. Somewhere in the city, however, an archbishop was facing accusations of interfering with (as people used to say) an altar boy 40 years ago. And I was thinking of the gynaecology clinic back home.

The children in the opera are a boy and a girl. The boy is the centre of attention, perhaps because of Britten's own sexuality, or perhaps because a treble among grown-up singers makes the audience nervous. He dies dramatically in the last act. The girl lives on, and I bet she presents to her doctor twenty years later with chronic pelvic pain.

After three decades in gynaecology I'm starting—I think—to develop an instinct for taking an adequate history from patients with thick case notes. Those whose sex lives began after puberty never take offence at matter of fact questioning. With the others, responses vary.

Some simply tell you, just as matter of factly, about their experience of abuse. If you are the first person to have asked, you cannot suppress a feeling of diagnostic satisfaction, like solving a cryptic crossword. It doesn't last long. Unlike in the movies, catharsis cures nothing—at least, not straight away. But at least you understand.

The difficult cases are those who deny it while instinct tells you differently. I don't believe in suppressed memories but I do know that patients choose when to talk. Sometimes they phone up out of the blue. You wish they had done so years earlier, before losing so many organs to well intentioned surgery.

Their stories can be chilling, even forty years after the events. The worst aspect, though, is that for some the aftermath of abuse has been not so much chronic disease as a life sentence.

## *Feel Free to Ululate*

In Pretoria a few weeks ago the jacaranda trees were blooming. The highway near the airport was lined with the offices of multinational companies, gleaming in the sunshine. As we reached Johannesburg the nation's health problems intruded. An advertising gantry read: " 'I only do skin to skin' John (18) … 'Wrap it or zip it' Zena (17)."

We were visiting the national college. In Britain, medical royal colleges are regrettably independent from one another but The Colleges of Medicine of South Africa have a single senate, a common admission ceremony, and one shared base in each city. Johannesburg's low-rise building is surrounded by roses as well as railings and in the foyer is an unexpected portrait of Lord Lister.

It became clear that the senate, like his lordship, was white, male, and no longer youthful, but this was about to change. At the annual general meeting the next day, the old senate was retiring, to be replaced by one which included "previously disadvantaged groups"—non-whites and women. It had not been easy to organise the transition but the outgoing senators were proud that it had been achieved.

At sunset we headed for the admission ceremony in a nearby auditorium. We lined up outside in academic robes, while on stage a choir, gowned and smiling, swayed to and fro in rich harmony. "We have the best music in the world," murmured an outgoing senator in the darkness.

The new president, whose wife has written a textbook about the Xhosa language, was bonhomie personified. "This is a joyful occasion," he told the audience. "When your relatives receive their diplomas, feel free to clap or ululate." (He and his wife were white—does it matter?)

Applause from a large hall is a potentially cruel gauge of opinion. This multiracial audience did not snub or patronise but simply enjoyed the success of a long line of doctors of all specialties and races. There was indeed sporadic ululation. Honorary fellows from abroad, black or white, were welcomed equally.

South Africa has ways of bringing a lump to your throat, whether at the thought of Nelson Mandela's 27 years on Robben Island, or those long lines of people waiting patiently to vote in the first integrated election. In October it was at the sound of that African choir singing Gaudeamus igitur as our procession left.

## *Gadgets for Consultants*

Calling all consultants! We know you don't buy executive toys but just take a look at our 2003 range of useful gadgets.

*Blow-up chaperone:* Remember when clinics had enough nurses? Nowadays the healthcare assistant cannot be in every room at once. So use our blow-up chaperone, attached by Velcro to the consultant's side. With caring expression, realistic hand for the patient to hold, and sound system to make reassuring noises. "Better than the real thing!" (Miss A).

*Parking preserver:* Scared to leave the hospital for fear of losing your parking slot? Now you can boldly go to that midday meeting at the PCT. Simply put our flatpack under your car. On your departure it expands into a cardboard box stamped "Beware MRSA" in luminous letters. Deluxe version oozes slime (refills available).

*Hospital positioning system:* With constant reorganisations, are you finding yourself lost in your own hospital? Our satellite-based hospital positioning system (HPS) can guide you to within 1 ft (30 cm) of your destination. "I even found the clinical governance office!" (Dr B).

*Political corrector:* Nothing destroys a consultant's credibility more quickly than referring to doctors as "he" and nurses as "she." Our voice-activated corrector immediately adds "or she" when you say "he," "or hers" when you say "his," and so on. Absolutely undetectable. Includes deactivating button for use in church when the vicar announces the next hymn.

*Portable complaints department:* Fill those idle moments when your work is cancelled at short notice through lack of beds, juniors, etc. Just carry your latest batch of complaining letters and our individualised portable complaints department. It consists of two rubber stamps. The Standard prints: "And the same to you." The Super prints two words of your choice.

*Serenity suit:* Upset by constant criticism? Unsure of your role? Recapture the old certainties by wearing our all-in-one serenity suit. Bright green, it commands instant respect, confers self-assurance, and tells the world that you are a trained professional.

Interested? Gadgets for consultants are classed as "medical equipment" so they cost twenty times as much as identical gadgets sold to the public. But we think you'll agree they're worth it.

## *The King and I*

For many of my colleagues, junior or senior, a winter break means a spot of skiing. You can tell when a trip is in the offing. They look thoughtful and you catch them doing quadriceps exercises. Afterwards you notice their facial tans and sense of relief at surviving intact. Or occasionally you hear them praising the efficiency of Alpine casualty departments.

Why don't I join in? I pretend it is inherent mistrust of quick-release bindings, or unwillingness to dress like a fluorescent Teletubby, but the real reason is that skiers are readily classifiable. There are "black run bombers," there are the merely competent, and then there are those who spend most of their time upside down in a snowdrift. I know which I am.

Nevertheless the urge to migrate in winter is infectious and is no longer restricted to the rich. Most patients over a certain age seem to head for the sun when the New Year holiday is over. My wife and I, stern Scots who believe that getting warm in January would be cheating, stick to European cities.

Madrid, due south but 635 metres above sea level, was sufficiently bracing last month to keep our consciences clear but not cold enough to stop Andean buskers playing drums and pan pipes. The city's cultural diversity included the national ballet providing its own accompaniment with handclaps and voices, and *Harry Potter and the Chamber of Secrets* dubbed into Spanish.

Luxury is visiting an art gallery knowing you can return tomorrow. Some paintings take your breath away when you see them for real, however familiar the image. Picasso's Guernica is no longer behind glass but still has two guards. It produces a visceral revulsion against war in general and air raids in particular. Some might want to throw acid. I wanted to send a postcard of it to Downing Street.

Outside the Palacio Real, we came across a crowd. Over in the courtyard were guards on horseback, men in suits, watchful police, and dozens of white-gloved motorcyclists. We waited. Headlights appeared and then an accelerating line of Mercedes. Fleetingly, there was the king of Spain, and the queen's hand waving out of a just-open car window. Strange, isn't it, that an unplanned glimpse should prove as memorable as a roomful of Goyas.

## *Walking the walk*

Since January each consultant obstetrician in our hospital has been spending a week at a time in the delivery suite. The days of the senior registrar are long gone and now there aren't enough registrars. After years of preaching the need for a consultant based service, I could hardly refuse to join the rota.

I had not done routine labour ward sessions since my lecturer days. For 20 years it had been emergencies only, often at the end of a phone. Of course I had written and lectured about intrapartum care and pontificated as an expert witness. I could talk the talk. Now I had to walk the walk.

Cancelling other commitments proved surprisingly easy. The rota is published a year in advance. There is quiet pleasure in sending apologies to committees on the grounds of clinical indispensability.

In the delivery suite office, reality reigns. The midwives huddle over shift rotas in their free moments, ingeniously working out how to keep the place staffed. On the board is a list of the region's neonatal nurseries, each permanently marked "closed." What matters is which ones are "very closed."

The bells, the bells. At the locked front door are streams of relatives. On the phones are endless queries that can rarely be answered by either the hard pressed ward clerk or the professor.

Some things have changed. A computer gives instant access to evidence. Applying it remains an art, however, and the final arbiter is still the midwife's gut feeling. The biggest transformation is in anaesthesia. In this epidural era, shrieks are rare. At caesarean section a radio plays while the woman chats to her partner.

Some things stay the same. Just before an instrumental delivery there is still that moment when you feel alone with the baby, knowing a mistake is not an option.

Hands-on work is immensely satisfying. You end the week with a frontline soldier's contempt for the generals. Then you remember that you are one, or a brigadier at least. Next week you will talk about the midwives' dedication and it will sound like platitudes. You will complain about national understaffing and people will shrug. Talking the talk could make a difference if only you could get it right. You suspect that you are not as good at it as you thought.

## *Reader's Consent*

To help you decide whether or not to read this article, there are certain things we need to tell you. You should think about them and share them with your family, close friends, or chatroom. This will empower you to give—or withhold—your consent to reading this column.

In the past, like other journals, we relied on "implied consent." By opening the BMJ, turning it the right way up and finding the back pages you were deemed to agree to read *Soundings*. This is no longer adequate.

Thanks to consumer organisations like ARMA (Action for Readers of Medical Articles) we now know what trauma may affect unprepared readers. At special risk are recently retired doctors who, never having unwrapped the BMJ for 30 years, go to the back pages expecting advertisements for holiday cottages. Several have recovered substantial damages for stress caused by magical realism or in your face opinions.

Please be advised, therefore, that reading *Soundings* may cause these unintended side effects:

*Laughter:* Claims that "laughter is the best medicine" are not evidence based. On the contrary, it may seriously damage your health. Do not read *Soundings* while eating pretzels or drinking soup from those deceptively cool polystyrene cups. From January 2005 the European Reading Time Directive (ERTD) will prohibit solitary reading or reading with a full bladder.

*Tears:* Sad stories can distress those of a sensitive disposition. We have set up a 24 hour helpline to provide counselling for people upset by these articles. This in no way affects your legal rights.

*Anger:* Under the ERTD, before reading this column you must have undergone a course of anger management. Such courses are provided online at bmj.com/areyoulookingatme?

*Drowsiness:* In certain circumstances *Soundings* may cause you to fall asleep. Therefore you must not read it while driving, operating machinery, giving (or receiving) psychotherapy, or assisting at laparoscopic surgery.

*Confusion:* People with anhumoria (congenital inability to see the joke) may become seriously disoriented. If you have been told that you have this condition, stop reading immediately and turn to any article with "guidelines" in the title.

If you are comfortable with this information and wish to proceed, please sign below in the presence of a witness. Happy (and safe) reading!

## *Honorary Woman*

More than half the UK medical graduates starting their first jobs this week are women. They'll say: so what? More than half the babies born are girls. It's no big deal.

Historically, though, it is. After being excluded from medicine for 500 years, women will soon form the majority. The change is fastest in my specialty, where 74% of UK career senior house officers are women. An American journal recently asked, under a picture of a woolly mammoth and a man in a white coat: "Are male ob/gyns headed for extinction?" Silly question. Of course we are. Hardly any male students now consider a career in obstetrics and gynaecology. Last week on our medical campus I noticed a summer school full of male postgraduates—aspiring surgeons, of course. To an obstetrician this was an unfamiliar sight.

How do you face extinction with dignity? We fifty-something obstetricians started our careers in an era of small quotas of female students, when sexism and schoolboy jokes were common (though by no means universal) among our teachers. We understand the anger of contemporaries who had to fight old fashioned prejudice, or who gave up the battle.

But we've been caught in the crossfire for 20 years now. The backlash against male obstetricians has taken the form, not of frontal assault, but of surreptitious jokes. Newsletters of maternity consumer groups peddle the image of uncaring male consultants. Radical midwives brief politicians against us. And the new generation of women obstetricians cannot resist the odd jibe.

All we can do is join in with humorous self deprecation. Twenty years of apologising, however, is enough. We're leaving. In 2001 the average retirement age of obstetricians was 57. They gave all sorts of excuses, including the ageism endemic in the NHS, but I think they would have stayed if they felt appreciated.

It's time for the victors in medicine's battle of the sexes to show some magnanimity. For me, the process started last month when a group of distinguished female colleagues made me an Honorary Woman. No surgery or hormones, you understand, and no paperwork—only a feeling of liberation. Enough to write this article, at least. I shall wait a few more years before setting up the Medical Men's Federation, dedicated to promoting the interests of the new minority.

## *Brava at Fountains*

In August, during the heatwave, we went to our first open air opera. We had no idea what to expect. We had heard about Aida at Verona but this was La Bohème in Yorkshire. Would we be convinced that Mimi's tiny hand was frozen?

Fountains Abbey is a long way from a Parisian garret, but the opera's underlying theme, tuberculosis, was closer to home. In Haworth, a few miles away, Patrick Brontë had lost three of his children to consumption in a single year. Anne, Bramwell, and Emily were 29, 30, and 31 respectively. It must have been unbearable.

That was in 1849, the year that Henri Murger's novel, *Scènes de la Vie de Bohème*, was published. When Puccini adapted it for his opera nearly 50 years later, Mycobacterium tuberculosis had been identified, but effective drugs did not appear until my lifetime. I was two years old when George Orwell died and as a child I remember people lowering their voices when mentioning "TB."

"In case of wet weather the event will go ahead," said the tickets, and sure enough there were canopies over the little stage and grand piano. And no microphones. One audience member arrived in black tie, which he hastily removed, but most of us dressed for the dales. This, I realised, was Glastonbury for grown ups.

Everyone turned up early with a picnic. Most brought folding chairs and some had tables and tablecloths. Those of us with rugs were ushered to a groundsheet at the front. Trying to look cool, I realised that I am no longer capable of lying down, drinking cava, looking up at the stage, and keeping control of my Scotch egg all at the same time. So it's chairs for us in future.

As the sun set, the walls of the famous ruin were picked out by floodlights and the grassy amphitheatre was dotted with the audience's lanterns. In the distance a baritone was warming up. An owl screeched in the nearby woods. A page turner appeared and then a pianist in full evening dress. The small company, Opera Brava, was indeed totally convincing. Mimi sang her heart out and as she died in Rodolfo's arms, tears were running down my cheeks. Were they for her, the Brontës, Orwell, or victims everywhere? Hey, man, no. It was the music.

## *Who Cleans the Clogs?*

Surgeons have an image of being control freaks, but today's operating theatres are more democratic than you think. Few of us surgeons enjoy sitting in a circle and sharing our thoughts in an egalitarian way, but then nor do the rest of the team. Each member—nurse, technician, anaesthetist—is proud of his or her role and knows that the rest do not fully understand it.

Nevertheless, most decisions are shared. Patient and surgeon together decide whether an operation is needed. Others in the NHS determine whether it goes ahead and when it can start. Almost the only decision left to the surgeon is to say when it is finished.

How the operation is done is increasingly determined by distant bodies. Centralised packs contain standard instruments. More and more items are disposable. Curiously shaped plastic devices appear, presumably to protect patient or staff. You learn not to ask about the evidence base for these changes. Rules are rules—they have been made by someone else's professional body or by an important-sounding committee. Clinical governance means unquestioning obedience.

Despite all the bureaucracy, you feel that nobody is really in charge. When you are called to an unfamiliar theatre the technicians address you as "mate." On home ground your team may consist of a nurse from an agency, a locum registrar (European working hours, you know), and whichever senior house officer is on that shift. All anonymous in theatre "blues." Symbols of rank would be discriminatory.

In the changing rooms are bloodstained clogs. It is the same throughout the country, according to an informal survey of colleagues. A distant body has decreed that everyone now cleans their own. Unenforceable, particularly in large operating suites, but hey, it's democratic.

My first job in hospital, as a student clerk in 1968, was cleaning the surgeons' boots. I was supervised by the chief orderly, a former soldier. Clean boots symbolised a well run army and we were proud that our surgeons could expect the same when they entered our theatre.

Why does the passing of this tradition upset me so much? I should be grateful that I am now paid a six figure salary to clean my own boots. And that nobody expects me to care about the others. Not your job, mate.

## *Student Selected Caesareans*

2004 is my fortieth year in medical education, as student or teacher. Back in 1964 our class was special—the first to experience the New Curriculum. The idea had been to reduce factual learning and make the course more integrated. I now know that reducing factual learning is a tradition stretching back to the 19th century. Each generation of educators discovers that designing a fully integrated and really challenging course is fun. It certainly beats teaching.

Our last new curriculum in Leeds had special study modules (SSMs). Our current one has student selected components (SSCs). When I asked about these damn fool initials, I was told they came from the General Medical Council (GMC). Ah yes. Back in Hallam Street it had seemed a good idea to let students choose subjects for in-depth study.

When the Leeds ethics theme team asked for topics for a third year SSC, I suggested: "Should women be allowed to choose caesarean section?" Later the emails started arriving, asking: "When can we meet?" That's when the magic started. After decades of force-feeding students the basics I had five lively undergraduates talking to me by choice.

Never having done obstetrics, they soaked up background information about indications and risks. I tried (but not too hard) to disguise my own opinion that a well-informed woman can choose how to have her baby. Then off they went to surf the literature. Most of the stuff on the internet is written by people who believe that pushing a baby through your pelvic floor is a harmless and fulfilling experience. The students, rather pro-choice to begin with, were persuaded that caesarean section is risky, bad for bonding, and too expensive for the NHS. People who like it don't say so on the web.

The climax of the SSC was dramatised presentations. Emily wore a pregnancy belly with an umbilical ring. Hinaa was the NHS obstetrician and Imran the hospital manager. David played the suave Brazilian husband and Aysha provided the commentary. They wrote the script but let me direct. "Now, luvvies, let's do the moves. Autonomy here… Beneficence here… Marvellous, darlings!" I got a text message when they were about to start. They were terrific. I went home a happy medical academic. Now that is new.

## *Hank at the Shed*

I liked Hank Wangford even before I met him. His name, perfect for a country and western singer, suggests deadpan mischief. It's made up, of course. In real life, he is a London doctor. He mentions this on stage but doesn't make a big thing of it. I liked The Shed before I saw it, too. A tiny venue on the edge of the north Yorkshire moors, its gigs include poetry readings on Radio 4 and an improvised bingo and percussion show. On its website (http://www.theshed.co.uk/) are detailed instructions on how to knit your own Elvis wig.

The last time I had met Hank was at the Royal Society of Medicine. We had chatted about contraception and then he told me about falling angels. Kicked out of heaven along with Satan, they were still falling and causing trouble. He thought the idea might make a good song.

Now, on the moors in December, a lad with a lantern directed us to the village hall. Crammed in were 70 seats and little candlelit tables. In the kitchen Simon, the friendly but pensive impresario, was helping to sell drinks. Hank and his band, the Lonesome Cowboys, were changing in the toilet but would be signing CDs later.

The packed audience included men with pullovers and women with pink Stetsons. Hank told us that he, like everyone else, had once considered country music naffer than naff. Then, one life-changing day 20 years ago, he met one of the genre's greats. Now, according to www.hankwangford.com, he has become its "troubled grubby soul… and walks the thin line between laughter and the dark."

He mournfully welcomed us to an evening of festive misery and sang songs about death and loneliness. They included a Johnny Cash number about a divorced man learning to fend for himself ("Beans for breakfast once again") with the exquisite line: "I ain't got no clean utensils." And a wonderful song about falling angels.

As we left, Simon was there in the darkness, handing out fliers for a forthcoming concert by an avant-garde string quartet from the Netherlands. Britain was experiencing a meteorite shower and on the long drive back to Leeds the sky was full of shooting stars. Angels? On this surreal night, I could believe it.

## *Pedalling up the Amazon*

I have been subscribing to a local fitness centre for years but have not lost any weight at all. Sometimes my wife suggests that I ought to go and at least look at the place. She says it is delightful, full of slim people of both genders.

That's the trouble. What I want to kick-start my personal struggle against cuddliness is a gymnasium where I don't stick out. I resemble the "before" part of the advertisements and I feel conspicuous. More muscle would be nice, certainly, but what I really need is nerve.

My opportunity came on our last cruise. Like most people these days we take a winter holiday but we are non-skiers. This year, South America was as far off-piste as we could get. The routine history at booking, at least with this cruise company, is: "Are you a wheelchair user?" No. "Will you be bringing your own oxygen?" No. "Do you require syringes and needles?" Certainly not. By the time you put the phone down you feel years younger.

On board, the fitness centre was on deck 9 at the front—near the internet cafe. My wife radiated silent approval of my trips for'ard until, two days out from Recife, she caught me among the workaholics logging in to the office email.

Shortly afterwards I was in the gym, blending in with other first timers as Katie, the youthful instructor, explained which piece of apparatus trains what. She related well to wrinklies. She made jokes, avoided looking at our bodies, and knew about cardiopulmonary resuscitation. It was my kind of place, I decided.

Pedalling against resistance with a pulse rate of 120, I waited for the endorphin surge. Katie had said you had to break sweat. The last time I was in a gym, back in 1964, it was all wallbars, ropes, and beams. Now I had a digital display of calories burned and a button to press if I needed to go downhill.

Time to pump some iron. Adjust the peg to reduce the weight. The last user must have been some kind of a freak. Outside, the banks of the Amazon slid past. Inside, I was doing 3.6 mph on the running track. Feel the burn, man. Get some samba CDs for the Walkman and this just might change your life.

## *CAMRA shy?*

Gynaecologists are expected to enjoy gin and tonic and know about wine. Most of us manage the first without difficulty (off duty, of course) and bluff our way through the second. I have colleagues who really can tell their Pouilly Fuisse from their Pouilly Fumé, and jolly impressive they are too. It is like watching a table conjurer—entertaining but faintly irritating.

After a few decades in the specialty the time has come for me to admit, at least to myself, that when it comes to oenophily my heart isn't in it. Wine is pleasant enough but it makes me thirsty. Real men enjoy a draught on the back of the palate. I prefer beer.

I am the first to admit that this has its downside. Doctors do not drink at lunchtime so ale appreciation means entering public houses in the evening. In town, pubs with stripped out interiors and names like The Old Bank or The Old Library are full of youths with their shirts hanging out. Country pubs are either twee or funereal.

My wife and I have the perfect local. Unpretentious and English, its blackboard features Cajun chicken and Yorkshire pudding. Its amiable clientele materialises from a village that we have never actually found. I suspect that, like Brigadoon, it does not exist.

Once a year the inn is taken over by sinister but ageing motorcyclists. This Easter, as I edged past their leader, who was a large tattooed man with shaven head and a Genghis Khan moustache, I noticed that he was telling his leather-clad gang about his patio extension.

Last weekend, visiting Suffolk, we happened across a regional beer festival. Among the exotically named barrels was a stall selling T shirts: "BEER WARRIORS. RIP Oliver Reed, killed in action 1999" and "The liver is evil and must be destroyed." After years of living with health propaganda promoting the dubious attractions of longevity, I found the black humour liberating.

Nearby, the Campaign for Real Ale (CAMRA) was staffed by bearded enthusiasts whose silhouettes hinted at their hobby. In fact, they looked rather like me, except that each wore a large cardboard hat in the shape of a beer glass. My wife and I scarcely hesitated. We are now life members. Not that I shall rush to tell people. I am a gynaecologist, after all.

## *Saving Lives on the Silk Road*

Long haul flights are exciting but rarely scary nowadays. We British tend to go to countries that were once pink on the map. It is a new experience to fly to someone else's former empire, to places you had not heard of until recently. Kyrgyzstan lies between Kazakhstan and China. Tajikistan separates it from Afghanistan—only just, but enough to reassure the wimp in me. The Kyrgyz capital, Bishkek, was not in my atlas but according to the web it did exist. Until the Soviet Union broke up it was called Frunze.

At Bishkek airport you cannot help noticing the United States Air Force planes. Then, as your taxi turns east along the Silk Road, you see an endless range of snow capped mountains. When the sun begins to set, they turn pink. Gee whiz, this is a beautiful country.

The central Asian republics have convoluted borders said to have been drawn by Stalin to prevent their peoples uniting. Now their leading doctors and midwives were being brought together by the World Health Organization (WHO) to discuss how to reduce maternal mortality.

Their rates are good compared with some nearby countries. In Afghanistan mothers are dying in huge numbers. In Iraq, sanctions multiplied the maternal mortality rate more than tenfold, even before last year's invasion. Central Asia's rates—at least officially—are only four or five times those in Western Europe. One way to reduce them, we hope, is UK-style confidential inquiries.

Each delegation sat at a long table with a little flag. Everyone except the WHO visitors spoke Russian. You had to remember to remove your earpiece when answering questions, otherwise you heard yourself in Cyrillic.

I was prepared for disappointment. International meetings often generate only hot air. Soon, however, we were making delayed-action jokes through our interpreters and by the end there was an unmistakable air of resolve. We were all professionals who had seen women bleed. We got quite emotional.

The farewell party beside a moonlit lake involved toasts, a bonfire, a sheep's head (delicious), Moldovan brandy, communal Kazakh dancing, and a not entirely successful Scottish reel. I felt surprisingly at home, but then I come from a long line of shepherds.

## *The 57 Club*

I rarely feel moved to turn my birthday into a public celebration. That might have been a problem if I had been Queen, but as things are it has been easy to let my 30th, 40th, and 50th birthdays sidle past with some bubbly and a family meal. Soon my 57th will do the same.

Fifty-seven is a special age for male doctors. With statutory retirement at 65 we are into the last eight, in Olympic phraseology. It is a time when men behave unpredictably. Lifelong socialists, for example, quit their jobs and go into private health care.

For obstetricians it is even more significant. Recently, fifty-seven was our average age of retirement from the NHS. We baby boomers had our families earlier than they do today. With our kids gone, we are free agents. We have neither a war nor a gap year to look back on. It is time to have fun. To hell with the lump sum.

But the NHS needs us. We cannot leave yet, not with all our colleagues on maternity leave. We must encourage one another to carry on. A bit of bonding and peer pressure should do it. Which is why I have formed the 57 Club. Here is the format for our annual party.

*Catering:* With a name like "57," the buffet has to be an enormous bowl of baked beans, with spaghetti shapes for non-bean-eaters. Then, as in *Blazing Saddles*, we sit around a camp-fire passing wind and swapping tales of our days as senior registrars.

*Cabaret:* Fifty-seven year olds have a great sense of humour, but it takes a lot to make them laugh out loud. More effective than a conventional stand-up comedian is to invite someone from the human resources department to read excerpts from the European Working Time Directive.

*Guests:* We love talking to trainees but we rarely get the chance. Be sure to invite them to the party. Don't worry about the expense. Only one will turn up, with a long explanation about the rota. Try to look interested.

*Music:* By all means have Classic FM in the background, but we prefer to make our own music. We are word perfect with the LP of *Bridge Over Troubled Water* and we sing the tracks in the right order. But you try telling that to kids today.

## *Dear e-mail correspondent*

Thank you very much for writing. I hope that you will not think me discourteous if I respond with this generic reply. Despite my best efforts it has become impossible to write individually to everyone who is kind enough to get in touch with me by email. Unfortunately neither the NHS trust nor the university is willing to provide me with an electronic secretary and both are now urging me to take a little time away from my desk and undertake some clinical or educational activity.

Firstly, may I offer my condolences. It must have been a great shock to lose your relative in such tragic circumstances. It is indeed rare for a private jet to encounter a flock of ostriches at 10 000 feet over impenetrable jungle and it is desperately sad that your relative's $300m is languishing in the Bank of Chad instead of being distributed to the orphanages as he intended.

I must admit to feeling flattered that God has told you that I am the only person in the world honest enough to access this money and ensure that it reaches the orphans while keeping 15% for myself to cover administrative costs. I had no idea that God held me in such esteem. Normally I would, of course, defer to His commands, but on this occasion the only authority capable of challenging Him—the Inland Revenue—has, alas, forbidden me to do so.

Secondly, I appreciate your offer of unlimited supplies of sildafenil at low, low prices. Many thanks for letting me know about the new soft tablets (is this the best name for them, I wonder?). I was a little concerned that you and so many others are aware of my shortcomings, but I have talked things over with my wife and we both feel that we are already very busy, particularly now that we have joined our local golf club. Can you tell us whether Viagra might improve my swing?

Finally, thank you for the guidelines that your personal assistant has just cascaded to me. The one on modernising overshoe disposal was a particular delight and, if I may say so, your use of bullet points on page 72 was masterly. It is a great advance to receive such documents electronically. In the old days, opening envelopes wasted so much of our precious time.

## *Sudan in Winter*

The Khartoum Hilton, last month, was a comfortable pied-a-terre for an external examiner. Downstairs in the business centre I caught up on my emails. The Sunset Lounge had plenty of drinks, all non-alcoholic, and the lobby had a Christmas tree.

I felt surrounded by history. Along the Blue Nile was the palace where General Gordon died. Across the Nile itself were the Madhi's tomb and the Khalifa's house, now a museum, where a smiling guide showed me Kitchener's Gatling gun. Shock and awe, Victorian style. At Omdurman in 1898 the Anglo-Egyptians lost 43 dead, while the Mahdists' casualties were 27 000.

Incredibly, the conflict left no hard feelings but only mutual respect. The British built Gordon Memorial College in 1902 and the Kitchener Medical School in 1924. After independence in 1956 these became Khartoum University and its medical faculty, which now admits about 280 students annually.

Medical graduates do house jobs and military service, and then specialise. Young obstetricians may face spectacular pathology. I heard about a patient with a ruptured uterus who waited for days by the roadside for a lift to hospital. She survived. What right had I to examine these doctors, in English, at the end of their training?

My fellow examiners, from local centres, were keen to maintain standards. Many had done part of their training in the United Kingdom and spoke affectionately of their time there. As so often, I apologised for the loss of professorial power, which once facilitated overseas exchanges.

Was the trip worth while? For me, yes. The laughter and hospitality were wonderful. For Sudan? The nation got 26 more obstetricians and gynaecologists, most of whom, I gathered, would probably stay in Khartoum. Dispersing doctors around the country will have to await peace but hopes are high.

Although the hospital now has easy web access, personal contacts are prized. One professor described external examiners as "a straw connecting us to the world and letting us breathe."

At dinner the vice chancellor said he had heard that UK

consultants were retiring early. "They could do lots of good by spending short spells here. Fares and accommodation but no salary, I'm afraid." I said I was sure they would enjoy it and I would pass his request on.

## *Climate of Fear*

When it was part of the former Soviet Union, Moldova was called Moldavia. Now it prefers the Romanian version of its name. Most people have heard of it but, uniquely among European nations, nobody knows where it is. Go straight on past Transylvania and you can't miss it.

Of course I went by plane. Checking in for Chisinau, the capital, I saw my bag disappearing down the conveyer, apparently labelled for Kiev. There followed one of those embarrassing airport moments until I learned that KIV stands for Kisinev, the Russian name for the city. (Kiev's code is IEV.) Oh. Sorry.

The demise of the Soviet Union left Moldova with Soviet architecture, a fine opera company, and no money. And a medical system steeped in doublethink. On the one hand doctors are subject to meticulous centralised control. On the other hand their state salary is around £32 ($60; €46) a month, making a parallel economy inevitable.

We were there to advise local specialists about perinatal audit and confidential inquiries. In the United Kingdom, we told them, we depend on full and honest reports from doctors and midwives. In Moldova, they replied, things are different. People are punished. If a pregnant woman dies the Ministry reacts quickly, sending officials to identify the guilty employee, who is then fired. A climate of fear does not encourage constructive reflection, they said, any more than it fosters a culture of accurate and contemporaneous note keeping.

But, we reminded them cheerfully, you're free now. You're just like us. You can share problems with your managers and politicians and work together to make things better for patients. Our Moldovan colleagues looked unconvinced as we insisted this is how we do things in the United Kingdom.

I was unconvinced too. Does the British working doctor trust the medical politicians any more—let alone the party politicians? In which of the two countries do doctors have to prove to their employers that they are not mass murderers? Which nation, I wonder, has the scarier healthcare commission?

The temperature in Chisinau in January was below freezing but the Moldovans were used to it. They produce splendid wine and brandy and when work is over, in private people laugh. They don't long for early retirement. They know how to cope with the climate. We could learn a lot from them.

## *Good Morning Iraq*

The Hilton Resort Kuwait is posh. It has expensive shops, a palm-fringed beach, and electric buggies to ferry guests to their villas. Well out of the city centre, it feels secure. The guards at the fortified gate use mirrors to look under your taxi.

We were running a training course on obstetric emergencies and trauma. The ballroom was full of doctors from Kuwait and Iraq, some from places familiar from news bulletins. It hadn't been an easy drive, they told us, but clearly they felt it was worth the trouble.

You might think that doctors from a recent war zone had little to learn about trauma. Our young British team was part of an initiative that has raised emergency training to a new level (I learnt a lot) but perhaps the delegates had been attracted more by the chance to make contact with international medicine.

Our hand luggage had contained latex female torsos which, as it turned out, shortened the airport security checks. As the delegates sat round them in small groups, rapport came easily. They soon realised we had seen action in the labour ward and we realised they were academically gifted people.

During the 1990s maternal mortality in Iraq rose to medieval levels as a result of sanctions. Many women and babies died for want of drugs and transfusions. A hidden tragedy, as always. Maternal death, unlike bombing or gassing, never makes the front page.

The doctors were matter of fact about the war but critical of the failure to plan for its aftermath, though only when asked. Their conversation was courteous and guarded. Looking into their eyes you sensed a depth of life experience that you couldn't fully understand and didn't really want to.

There were surprises. Some Iraqi doctors were fluent in catch phrases from *Little Britain*. A sponsor had placed two gleaming Range Rovers beside the podium. The trip was organised by a charity, Baby Lifeline, and at the front desk the British ambassador's wife was helping out and selling her own marmalade to raise funds.

The delegates' hunger for knowledge was inspiring. Home again, the trainers began emailing one another about how to improve their manual. You don't often see pure altruism these days but when you do, it's a beautiful sight.

## Dangerous Places

Risky destinations bother me less as I get older. Uzbekistan, a few months ago, felt safe. I heard the president was autocratic but relatively restrained in comparison with his neighbour in Turkmenistan, who has closed all regional hospitals and renamed January after himself.

A British passport, a World Health Organization schedule, and a police checkpoint outside our hotel gave me a sense of reassurance. The only time I felt anxious in Tashkent was when the lobby filled up with GIs. Hey, with y'all here, we're a target.

Nepal, several weeks later, was equally undemocratic. The king had seized power, apparently exasperated by parliament's failure to quell Maoist insurgency. Outside the royal palace, wary sentries crouched behind sandbags. On the streets, one blown-out shop was being repaired but otherwise life was normal. We checked our email in internet cabins to the sound of traffic tooting outside.

These two countries, north and south of the mountains, had much in common. Each had once been part of an empire whose influence could still be felt. In Tashkent we lectured through Russian translators. In Kathmandu schoolchildren wore English-style uniforms, and the local radio, playing requests, broke into "Happy Birthday."

Both places inspire heartache in the visitor. Uzbekistan has ancient, evocative architecture and markets almost unchanged since

Marco Polo's day. Nepal has the Himalayas: the tourist flights at dawn are stunning, I'm told. These timeless countries could be magnets for visitors. Instead, men shoot one another.

Doctors in both places are wonderfully hospitable, but their official salaries are too small to live on. Compromises have to be made, and the rural poor lose out on medical care. Slowly you realise that this is normal across much of the world.

Neither country is in fact dangerous for foreigners. It is the natives who are at risk, especially the women. In Nepal one in 135 pregnancies ends in the mother's death.

When you check on the internet you can easily find data on a nation's population, economics, and oil reserves. Webmasters could help by making the maternal mortality rate a headline statistic. It is a clear indicator of how civilised a country is. Who knows, it might shame some autocrats into action.

## *Music of the Mountains*

Armenia once stretched from the Black Sea to the Caspian, but these days it is small, high, and landlocked. Its capital, Yerevan, looks wistfully across a valley to Mount Ararat, last resting place of Noah's Ark and now part of Turkey. "But only temporarily," they say in Yerevan's marketplace.

The country's population is three million, but with its troubled history there are more Armenians in the diaspora. Many of them are musical. Charles Aznavour was born Charles Aznavourian in Paris. Cher, famed for her minimalist gowns, began life as Cherilyn Sarkisian in California. Aram Khachaturian, best known for his "Sabre Dance," lived in Moscow but Yerevan Opera House has an auditorium named after him.

Its favourite opera, Tigranyan's *Anoush*, is a story of doomed love in a mountain village. The male chorus wear shaggy coats and hats, and the heroine throws herself off a cliff in the last act. Just the thing, we thought, for pre-conference relaxation.

Opera-going in former Soviet countries is a family affair. We found ourselves sitting in front of middle aged mums who exchanged observations during most of the performance. They fell silent in the tenor's final scene—not when the poor man was fatally shot by the bass but when the crowd parted to reveal his mother. Behind us there was dead silence, then sniffles.

In front of us was a group from the diaspora, just flown in from the West and checking out their heritage.

After the conference, there was time for a short trip to a mountain monastery. Armenia adopted Christianity in 301 AD, and church building has been a national preoccupation ever since. This one nestled against a cliff and merged with a series of chambers hewn from the rock, complete with pillars that had survived several centuries and one major earthquake.

As we marvelled, the sound of a choir echoed around us. We lowered our digital cameras respectfully. The singing seemed to come from another world. Back at the altar we saw in the candlelight a young woman—head bowed, lips barely moving—murmuring a psalm. The mountain was supplying the harmonies. Nice to know that the diaspora does not have all the best tunes.

## *My Pelvis and I*

Medical student assessments (or "exams" as we used to call them) are like military exercises nowadays. "Examiners must rendezvous at 0800 hours sharp in the Sports Hall." This was the only academic building large enough to house objective structured clinical examinations for all 194 candidates in a single morning in July.

The problem for me, unfamiliar with sports halls, was finding the door. The command team had foreseen this and a snatch squad rescued me from the candidates' briefing. I was marched at the double to the other entrance and given my identity badge.

Inside, a hundred examiners were waiting to go over the top, backed up by simulated patients. Everywhere you looked, there was a gynaecologist. Our instructions boomed from the tannoy. "Do not start until the bell rings." I think that's what it said.

The candidates would come at us in two waves, the second held back until the first had broken our resistance. The hall was divided by screens into ten circuits of ten stations each. Mine was number B6 and my job was to stand beside a rubber pelvis while the candidates inspected its cervix.

My pelvis had seen better days. There had been supply line problems. Each of the identical circuits needed a pelvis. A vanload had arrived the previous afternoon but nobody on campus would sign for them so they had been taken back to a warehouse in the Midlands.

That was when the lecturers showed true Dunkirk spirit. All night they searched for replacements and, by golly, they found them. In the morning one lecturer was still there, looking pale. "Don't ask, Prof," she said.

As I waited, I breathed deeply and rechecked my computerised mark sheets. One false move with my HB pencil, one lozenge incorrectly filled, one anonymised 10-digit candidate number misread, and it was curtains for all of us.

Suddenly, the bell. We were off. One by one, candidates appeared. One by one they introduced themselves to the pelvis and asked its permission to proceed. I felt a growing urge to learn ventriloquism.

Aging rubber does not yield easily but the candidates were equal to the task. Each demonstrated the cervix and wrested back the speculum, eventually. Back on civvy street they were sweet and gentle but dammit, this was war.

## *Handing on the Gong*

Tonight there will be a little ceremony at our local medical society. As outgoing president I am required to unfasten my medal of office (a test of dexterity, as the catch tends to creep up under the back of the collar) and hang it round the neck of my successor. What he does with it then is up to him.

Doctors generally have little time for ceremonial or insignias. Most of us happily wore academic dress at graduation but otherwise pomp seems masonic and unnecessary. I rather like it, though. At the annual dinner of a medical royal college, for example, it is fun to ask visiting presidents to explain their traditional regalia. In some cases the tradition goes back all of 20 years.

Doctors also have little time for local medical societies. This is a pity. Medical networking nowadays is limited almost exclusively to people in your own specialty. Each of us relates more to the internet than to colleagues down the road or even down the corridor.

Most medical societies began in the 19th century, initially to discuss difficult cases. Then they began inviting out-of-town lecturers. Recently, as continuing professional development has moved into normal working hours, they have struggled to attract audiences. We tried subjects like genetically modified plants or medical aspects of medieval stained glass. They are fascinating but don't pull in the registrars.

Big names from outside medicine are prohibitively expensive, but distinguished medics are still willing, for expenses only, to fit journeys into fraught schedules and deliver talks that are often works of art. They know they will be addressing a tiny proportion of the local doctors, but that doesn't put them off, thank goodness.

Why bother continuing? Because it is enriching to feel that you are part of a learned profession rather than switching only between specialty silo and non-medical mode. Your colleagues become human beings, not names on a letterhead. And the meeting with the student presentations is truly inspirational.

For me, the scariest responsibility has been looking after the silk-lined box with the 19th century presidential medal. Inside the lid is a rather sentimental oath of office. My successor, a forward-thinking GP, may baulk at that. I'll find out tonight.

## *Just Call Me*

Like all consultants, I have a mobile phone. It never ceases to amaze me. Its batteries seem to last forever and no matter how many times it falls out of my top pocket when I bend over, it continues to work.

It does not take pictures, receive emails, open like a powder compact, sound like a frog, or play "Delilah" during meetings, but it does do texting. This means that my tutorial group can send me messages saying "U R L8. WHERE R U?" from deep within our medical school's labyrinthine teaching centre.

Our hospital, by contrast, has red notices in the corridors forbidding the use of mobiles "except medical emergency." I asked a midwife why. She said it was because mobiles were annoying. We agreed that in our experience they didn't stop drips or make monitors explode, but none the less the NHS prefers to summon doctors by bleep.

Bleeps are different from mobiles. Mobiles upset everybody within earshot, but bleeps only upset their owners. Bleeps are like babies—they make an insistent noise but cannot understand when you talk to them. I now leave mine in my sock drawer. (My bleep, that is.)

My mobile number is given out to just a few people and jealously guarded by the switchboard and my secretary. When I write it on the labour ward board I am gently chided. What if a patient sees it and copies it down?

Patients should know their place and stick to land lines. This is a challenge. In the past, you could rarely get through to a hospital, but nowadays calls are promptly connected—to recorded menus, music-on-hold, or voicemail—or surreptitiously rerouted to distant places, sometimes in another time zone.

What if we really want a patient to contact us? Even if she rings the right extension, it may be answered by a random passer by. We should do what the community midwives do, and give her our mobile number.

Generally we don't, fearing intrusion into our personal lives. So it's time for the NHS to start issuing us all with mobiles. As all calls are automatically logged it should be easy for the hospital trust to charge the appropriate primary care trust for our valuable time. It will mean having to carry two phones, but that should be no problem, unless we bend over.

## *Privates on Parade*

Regional theatre is thriving in England, especially in Yorkshire, but without much support from doctors, I'm afraid. At a concert or the opera my wife and I often bump into music-loving colleagues but in theatre bars we sip our dry white wine by ourselves. Still, it gives us a chance to look around.

Regional audiences are different from those in London's west end. Ours have hardly any tourists or star-struck fans, except when a celebrity vehicle is on tour.

In Britain, unlike in mainland Europe, theatregoers do not dress up, promenade, or socialise ostentatiously in the stalls. We are down to earth and stoical, and we try hard not to look middle class.

Our theatres keep saying they want to reach beyond their traditional audience base and we do our best to help. I wear my old trainers and we never speak aloud of Noel Coward. When the box office asks if we are unwaged we look embarrassed at having to say no. And if the programme warns about nudity we are careful not to nudge each other.

Frontal nudity these days involves only male actors. Farce has always involved someone losing his trousers but now, it seems, his underpants must drop as well. There is a characteristic noise that an audience makes when this happens—a sudden shriek of female hilarity. The effects of adrenalin on the chap in the spotlight mean that neither women nor men in the audience feel threatened.

Nevertheless it is distracting, particularly for an unsuspecting doctor in the front row. You look upwards with a fixed smile, trying to indicate that you are concentrating on the dialogue and the actor's subtle facial expressions. But the lights stay on, he jumps around a bit, and you begin to wish you were back in the fertility clinic. There at least you don't have to pay to get in.

Theatre reflects contemporary society, so perhaps it is no surprise that male actors are willing to accept humiliation while their female colleagues demand respect and stay dressed. I hope the boys catch up with them soon. Meanwhile, we aren't put off. We were part of a phlegmatic Sheffield audience for *The Romans in Britain* and we're off there again soon for a play entitled, ominously, *The Long and the Short and the Tall.*

## *Bring back post-nominals*

Dear Editor,

Catching up with my back numbers (I have a pile of unopened BMJs in the dining room) I was shocked to find in your issue of 4 April 1992 that letters like MB, MD, or FRCP will no longer appear after authors' names. You said: "The eagle-eyed will notice various small changes in this week's journal." Indeed we have, and may I be the first to protest.

Alert readers realised something was afoot on 4 October 1975, when you removed all full stops and commas from authors' qualifications. We stayed silent, feeling in those straitened times that the saving on ink was worth inadequate punctuation. That was our mistake. Emboldened, you lost no time in removing the letters themselves. This is a different matter entirely.

Using abbreviations to list one's achievements is a British tradition, still practised by Masters of Fox Hounds (MFH) and Commanders of the Order of the British Empire (CBE). Many years ago military decorations embellished your pages, and no editor would have dared to delete DSOs, MCs, or DFCs. My generation was just as proud of our hard-won academic credentials, but in today's BMJ the only place we can be MD FRCS FRCGP and TD (Territorial Decoration) is on the obituaries page.

Some will argue that you have struck a blow for egalitarianism by cocking a snook at the medical elite. What you have really done, I fear, is sideline universities, whose PhDs and MDs betoken academic excellence, and undermine the medical royal colleges, which have a hard enough job maintaining standards in today's jungle of incompetent quangos.

So please, stop hammering nails into the coffin of academic medicine. Bring back post-nominals to inspire the younger generation. If you don't like the old ones, you can invent new ones to represent today's medical hierarchy.

Young high-fliers could have a BOT (Been On Telly) while their seniors will trump this with FBOT (Finished Being On Telly). Doctors on local committees will be KTBW (Knows The Buzz Words) and those on national committees, KATBW (Knows All The Buzz Words). And for doctors who actually see patients, MB will be replaced by FA. (Fully Appraised. What did you think?)

Your humble and obedient servant,

## *Giving up on Getting Better*

The stillbirth rate in the United Kingdom has fallen steadily during my lifetime. This was not a by-product of prosperity: cars and foreign holidays do not save babies' lives. Things got better because we wanted them to. There was a consensus among professionals, politicians, and the public that we should work together to make pregnancy safer.

In 1998, however, the graph levelled off, and in 2002 the stillbirth rate increased for the first time in 50 years. Recent figures show the rise has been maintained. What is interesting is that we are pretending not to notice this historic change, let alone trying to understand what lies behind it.

Official statistics still say most stillbirths are "unexplained," but this is an old fashioned fudge. We know that over 50% of the deaths are associated with intrauterine growth restriction. The small babies who are at risk may be identified by ultrasound scans and timely intervention can deliver them alive.

We could try to save some of them but we choose not to. The reasons are not economic but political. Lay campaigners have managed to persuade us that pregnancy should be demedicalised. The NHS, intent on keeping people out of hospital, has been happy to agree. My antenatal clinic today is almost empty.

Pregnant women are now classified on arbitrary criteria as high risk or low risk. The former are carefully monitored. For the latter, the abdomen is checked by palpation, a technique unsupported by evidence. As a result, corrected singleton perinatal mortality is now higher among "low risk" than "high risk" women.

We do not mention this when women choose their antenatal care. Although we know that a hospital's stillbirth rate is inversely proportional to intervention and consultant availability, NHS patients are not allowed to book directly with an obstetrician. Instead, community midwifery is being overstretched.

Is it just that when figures are good, people give up on making them better? Not necessarily. When the risk of cot death was 1 in 500 a media campaign reduced it to 1 in 2000. Our current stillbirth rate of 1 in 200 could be tackled and the first step would be to give women the facts. But that would mean disturbing the new politically convenient consensus. Easier to keep quiet and let some babies die.

## *The History of Box-Ticking*

No one knows when or where the first human being ticked the first box. The word "tick" does not appear in the Bible. Archaeologists have found no traces of boxes—ticked, crossed, or otherwise—in Egyptian papyruses, French caves, or Asian temples. Someone has even proposed the highly implausible theory that in the past great civilisations flourished without questionnaires.

Aerial photography in Peru, however, has revealed regular rows of box like shapes covering an area of several square miles and headed by pre-Inca glyphs for the sun ("Yes"), the moon ("No"), and a cloud ("Don't know"). Yet none of these boxes appears to have been ticked, leading some to suggest that this is the first recorded example of a non-responder.

The modern questionnaire was developed in the 19th century by psychologists studying small children who could not read or write. By the end of the 20th century questionnaires were widely used in Britain to monitor the medical profession. Logical as this progression seems to us now, it was not without controversy.

Early in the 21st century there was a wave of early retirement among British medical teachers. They complained that no matter how inspiring their teaching, students always reacted by asking them to tick a box in a logbook. Older teachers grumbled that assessment of the infinitely subtle art of medicine had been reduced to computerised sudoku.

In 2012 the Third International Congress on Medical Box-Ticking achieved the remarkable feat of agreeing a single generic form for all medical questionnaires—psychosocial research, undergraduate and postgraduate training, peer review, and performance feedback from colleagues, patients, patients' relatives, and managers.

This proved to be box ticking's high-water mark. A backlash developed among lay people, who initially expressed discontent by ticking all the middle boxes, regardless of the questions. Resistance then crystallised into a global movement called "Stick Your Boxes" ("SYB"—or, in some countries, "SYBB"), demanding more free space for comments. Questionnaires slowly evolved into blank sheets and became extinct because nobody could be bothered to read them.

## *All Russian to Me*

My wife is learning Russian, apparently for fun. Subjunctives in Cyrillic, she says, are light relief from the bureaucracy of general practice. Our house is filling up with the works of Pushkin and books about Russian history. Vaguely interested, I found the country's troubled past hard to understand until I noticed the parallels with the NHS.

For example, two centuries ago the czar and the ruling class spoke French whereas the serfs spoke Russian. How on earth could two groups who had to coexist speak different languages? Then I remembered the NHS's managerial memos with nouns like "stakeholder," verbs like "drill down," and all those trendy abbreviations. Staff involved in patient care don't talk like that and have silent, serf-like contempt for those who do.

Then, during the communist era, Soviet policy was decreed by a leader in Moscow and applied, blanket fashion, across the country. Small town apparatchiks knew that disobedience meant death. Today, NHS middle managers believe their jobs (not their lives, admittedly) are on the line if they fail to implement the schemes of Downing Street advisers. Decisions come from large buildings in Leeds and London but are rarely announced. Instead, all trusts miraculously have the same cost cutting ideas at the same time. Only when the serfs go networking, perhaps at meetings of the Royal College of Serfs, do they realise what is happening.

When public announcements are made, they take the form of what used to be called "propaganda" and is now "spin". The Russian people would be told that the state was making more combine harvesters than ever before, and the books would be cooked to prove that nobody had to wait more than six weeks for a tractor. How nice it would be if the NHS, besides using similar techniques, went the whole hog and produced totalitarian artwork. Staff would be inspired by posters of square jawed doctors and nurses looking upwards, fists upraised, with guidelines unfurling behind them.

And finally, when the Soviet Union fell, the oligarchs took over. Young men became fabulously rich in mysterious ways and bought foreign football clubs. We serfs suspect that some people are doing very nicely out of the NHS. And if we find our premiership team playing PFI Moscow, our suspicions will deepen.

*I retired from my Chair in 2009 but continued doing consultancy work for the World Health Organisation until 2011*

# *"In and Out of Hospital"*
## *2007-2013*

### *Shy and Retiring*

It's never too early to start planning your retirement party. Don't assume someone else will do it for you. The NHS will acknowledge your forty years' service by deactivating your swipe cards, not by organising a booze-up. Alcohol and cigars are out, even though shortening your life would benefit the pension fund. And your contemporaries may well retire before you, so it's up to you.

Don't slip away quietly. Your workmates will hate you for wasting an excuse to jive or twist. Who knows, you may even enjoy the party yourself. But not if you try to organise it unaided. This is where we come in. Shyandretiring.com will take the strain, leaving you free to get tired and emotional or bitter and twisted, as you choose.

Our website is packed with fun ideas for a great leaving do. Our standard package (two speeches) and our premium package (no speeches) both include a surprise retiragram—your P45 presented by a stunning health secretary lookalike or a hunky guy wearing a car park attendant's uniform (but not for long).

What about a theme evening? With our "Pirates of the Caribbean" party you can walk the plank, prodded by a cutlass-wielding clinical director. At our "Sicilian" party a genuine former chief executive jumps out of the cake with a submachine gun. Or why not splash out on our deluxe package? Return to the boardroom where you were interviewed, trash it, then fly to Greece to renew your Hippocratic Oath.

Scared that nobody will turn up? Our friends at Rentacolleague.com provide past friends to reminisce with (you'll never know which of them is genuine) and fellow consultants whose names (let's face it) you've always been a bit vague about. They'll also include some heartwarming surprise guests. At last you'll meet the man with the hammer-drill who's been working next door to your consulting room for the past two years.

No need to worry about that farewell speech. We supply handouts for your guests to treasure forever, with titles ranging from "168 hours a week—we loved it!" to "21 reasons why the NHS is doomed." End your evening with our NHS karaoke, singing "I did it their way," and afterwards benefit from our FREE personal tutorial on how to behave when retired. Rule one: don't gloat.

## *Patients Keep Out*

The board is aware that despite our best efforts some patients are still managing to reach the hospital and see doctors. This is in flagrant contravention of trust policy, outlined below. Staff are reminded that caring for unauthorised patients may result in disciplinary action

*Referrals:* All letters must be directed to the NHS Referral Gateway, where they will be screened by a qualified individual within three working days before being returned to the GP as falling outside our guidelines. Thresholds for acceptance are regularly revised as part of the trust's award-winning PKO ("Patients Keep Out") initiative.

In line with NHS targets, under 1% of referral letters are now addressed to a named consultant. Nevertheless, 47% still begin "Dear Doctor," thus discriminating against non-medical employees. GPs will be targeted by our public relations consultants, Hay Trustus, to point out that only "Dear Trust," "Dear Referral Gateway," or "Dear Prioritisation Co-ordinator" are acceptable. From August, "Dear Doctor" letters will be returned unopened.

Informal communication between GPs and consultants remains a challenge. Spot checks are being stepped up on emails and telephone calls but there are reports of "accidental" meetings in supermarkets, at church, or at concerts unmonitored by CCTV. Staff must maintain a log of such meetings and sign an undertaking not to discuss patient care. Consultants married to GPs should consider their position.

*Website:* All NHS websites include only the names of board members and senior executives. Research has shown that doctors' names simply attract referrals, so these have been removed. It would in any case be prohibitively expensive for trusts to find out the names of their medical staff.

*On-site defences*: The PKO car-parking policy has worked well, but patients have begun arriving on foot. Every entrance is defended by a line of smokers on intravenous fluids with catheter bags prominently displayed. Pharmacy can advise on luminous additives.

Nevertheless, determined patients may get to a reception desk. Hay Trustus reports that these are generally staffed by helpful people who enjoy serving the public. An urgent programme of redundancies has therefore been put in place. Each receptionist will be replaced by a "POLITE NOTICE" stating that verbal abuse will not be tolerated. These are widely displayed by organisations run so badly that customers are driven to unacceptable behaviour. This will allow us to have patients removed by the police.

## *Confessions of a Collaborator*

Listen, I was just doing the regional specialist training committee a favour. They're good people. They care about trainees. I happened to be there when they asked for volunteers, that's all. I didn't even know what "MTAS" stood for.

Sure, I smelled a rat when shortlisting was postponed. Yes, I could have walked away when they said there were 500 candidates. But I felt committed. We all did. So we spent the best part of a week on line, scoring the answers to those dumb questions. It drove us crazy, but we met the deadline.

Afterwards we felt dirty. But by then, young doctors were coming for interview. We couldn't let them down. Hey, meeting them was a breath of fresh air. It restored our will to live. Too bad they have to wait so long for the results. We'll go back and find the ones we missed. We'll sort it out. That's what doctors do.

Colleagues are saying we should have boycotted it, taken a stand, caused chaos. They're calling us collaborators. That's rich, coming from a profession that's been collaborating en masse for 20 years. In the 1980s the government set out to take us over. We let them do it.

I can remember when the Hospital Consultants Committee took decisions. Did anyone start a protest march when the managers eased us out? No. And these days, when politicians reorganise general practice, do doctors write to the papers? No sir. We shrug and let them get on with it. We prefer seeing patients.

So when they set up new bodies to replace key functions of the royal colleges, who resisted? Not the colleges or faculties, all 27 of them with their 28 opinions. Certainly not the quango-loving doctors who jumped on the bandwagon. I heard them, you know, in trendy committees, patronising their clinical colleagues. It made me sick.

I could name names. But so could you. We all read them in the journals, those non-practising doctors being pompous about medical scandals. Or maybe we stopped reading and turned the page.

It had to end, and now it has. We turned on our own young. The public can't believe it. The politicians are scared. This is when people start shooting collaborators. Let's hope they shoot the right ones. They're spoilt for choice.

## *Going Public*

A television interview involves some heart searching. More so now than when I was a college spokesman. In that role you could reassure your colleagues (and yourself) that you were driven by duty. You received briefings and a line to take, and you could usually confine yourself to facts.

But when you're on your own, the phone call takes you by surprise. The questions are less research, more audition. "Are Britain's maternity services getting worse?" "Well, yes and no," you reply, "or to put it another way, no and yes." Finally the voice asks: "Would you be willing to talk to us?"

Would you? Do you trust the person behind the voice? She sounds concerned and well informed and her programme has a good reputation. The real question is, how deep is your despair? Services across the country are now controlled by national politicians who no longer listen to practising doctors. Let's go for it.

"We're in your area on Saturday," says the voice, "but in the morning we're interviewing a real person." Shared irony is a good sign. I ask if the interview will be over in time for me to get to the opera. The reply is not entirely reassuring.

Our managers, relaxed and helpful, say it's okay to film in the hospital. On Saturday afternoon, men with drills begin long awaited repairs to the lift. I feel a pang of conscience asking them to stop. The television crew decide my untidy bookshelves make a good background. "We like random," says the cameraman, removing my wall clock.

The interviewer already knows all the facts and figures. What she wants are opinions, succinctly expressed. Professors don't do succinct. She nudges me to be more outspoken, but I say I can't bring myself to frighten women viewers. Gently, she points out that this may be the only way to change things. We're both thinking the same: what a way to run a health service.

A final take in the ward. Beds are screened off, but the midwife and I sign a release allowing our images to be distributed "throughout the universe." Big in Ursa Minor, maybe. Will any of this be used? Will it make a difference? I suspect not. Anyway, I made it to the opera. The heroine died but, thank goodness, she wasn't pregnant.

## *Back from Basra*

When your son joins the Territorial Army it seems no big deal at first. Weekends on Salisbury Plain are healthy exercise for a lawyer. From time to time he helps to fire off a royal salute or invites you to a rather jolly mess dinner.

Then reality bites. Volunteers are wanted for a tour of duty "somewhere overseas." Not you, son, surely? Tell them you're an essential worker. Oh. OK. I suppose it's a matter of honour. That and no loss of salary, he replies. The government is desperate, after all.

The farewell, last September, was a cliché repeated down the centuries but no less affecting for that. Mum holding back tears, handshake from dad, laconic smile and a wave from the young man. Mum now says she thought she'd never see him again.

You keep checking for email. Communication with Iraq is fitful but you begin to notice a pattern. A brief, unexpected phone call just to say hello. Then silence for a few days. Finally, a short item on the evening news. A British soldier has been killed and the next of kin have been informed.

What does "being informed" entail, now that telegrams have been abolished? An army car waiting when you get home from work?

Mum sometimes thought she heard the doorbell in the night. Then, thank goodness, another email: "Day off, relaxing. Biggest danger is sunburn."

Here, the biggest danger is losing friends in hospital management. They tell us we can't afford more midwives because there's no money. When I remind the meeting that we can afford £3m (€4.4m; $5.9m) a day for the prime minister's war, everyone looks uncomfortable. Their silence implies: there's nothing we can do, so why mention it? My silence implies: that's democracy for you.

After six months the veteran returns, suntanned. He seems taller. Photos on his laptop show his comrades with camouflaged Land Rovers. And son in battledress with his number and blood group in big letters on the chest.

I feel smaller. Did I protest against the war? No, I left that to others. My father, wounded in 1944, and my son have done things I'll never achieve. My dad's generation set up the NHS only three years after coming home. My generation, combat free, can't even run it properly.

## *Doctor in the Booth*

It's five years since we've been in the recording studios, but little has changed. Some gizmos have been updated and the photo of the producer as a member of a long-haired pop group has gone, replaced by a picture of his contemporaries, the Beatles. Still, the elderly sofa and scattered musical instruments are comfortably familiar.

Can it really be more than three decades since our first show in the Edinburgh Fringe? This time we've decided to break with tradition and learn the songs before the dress rehearsal. Recording helps. Oddly enough, it's hard to memorise your own words. You have to work at forgetting the ones you deleted during the agony of composition.

Performing to a microphone generates a special kind of adrenalin. On stage, after the preliminary rush of anxiety all that matters is that the audience has a good time. Mistakes sometimes help. Alone in the recording booth, you need to get everything right for the friendly but fastidious team listening next door. You can't relax.

Your long-time collaborator (once a fellow houseman) plays his music immaculately and then it's up to you. You put the headphones on and your brain immediately ceases to function. Your colleague sellotapes the lyrics to the glass and mimes encouragingly. When you finish, a voice invites you to come out and listen to your efforts.

Sycophancy is not part of the producer's repertoire. After the second take he compliments you on no longer imitating a wounded boar and asks if you can try to avoid sounding like a man about to be hung in the morning. He suggests that you sing across the beat and you feel it would be uncool to ask what that means.

Modern technology, he says, can correct small errors in tempo but it has its limits. It cannot insert raw emotion. Goaded, you return to the booth and give it some welly. You wave your arms. You pout. You smile coquettishly at the microphone. You emerge drained and find the team next door chatting about football.

The songs are supposed to be funny. As the tapes play you watch surreptitiously, hoping for a smile, but everyone is concentrating on musical minutiae. Suddenly someone notices a joke and gets a fit of giggles. Bless him. There's still hope.

## *Forceps at Dawn*

In one of his early films David Niven was a doctor in an Alpine sanatorium. Barbara Stanwyck was his patient, a beautiful concert pianist dying from consumption. When she became distressed in the night he appeared immediately, hair immaculately parted, his face filled with debonair concern.

This scene from an otherwise forgettable movie often comes to mind as the phone beside my bed lets rip with its infernal ringing and vibrating. (At 3 am, why do the registrars call my mobile instead of my home number? I suppose I should take it as a sly compliment.)

You don't go to the labour ward in pyjamas. It will only amuse the midwives, frighten the patient, and disillusion the trainees, who will assume your valet has resigned. In fact you rarely need to rush. The more urgent the call, the more likely the registrars are to have sorted things out by the time you arrive. But you keep slip-on shoes ready and a shirt with cufflinks inserted. At traffic lights you do up your bow tie. Best to be legal.

After 25 years of this, your emotions are predictable. You start with self pity, particularly if it is raining and your up-and-over garage door empties itself down the back of your neck. You become sanctimonious as you drive past drunks emerging from nightclubs. If you are going to deal with a nasty complication you tense up, thinking of worst-case scenarios.

Usually, though, you are simply going to supervise a rotational forceps or breech delivery—things you did as a registrar without bothering the boss. You think dark thoughts about the epidemiologists who turned these procedures into rarities, and wonder what will happen when you and your ageing contemporaries retire.

You hurry past the smokers (always at the door, whatever the hour) and into what feels like the last reel of a western. "I know you're there. I'm coming to get you." For baby and professor, the stakes couldn't be higher. One false move and we're both in trouble. Too often, you ease the registrar aside.

As the birth ends you feel a sense of wonder, even after all these years. You drive home remembering the parents' faces and baby's name. A silly smile, yes. A little tear? Surely not. Dash it, you're supposed to be debonair.

## *Unfamiliar Territory*

As an academic you can become typecast. Your series of papers on, say, the left uterine artery leads to presentations at the European Uterine Society and the International Artery Association. Your talk at local medical meetings is "The left uterine artery: who needs it?" Your lecture for undergraduates is "The crazy world of the left uterine artery." Sooner or later you get bored and want to speak about something else.

Recently I've rediscovered the pleasure of lecturing on topics I know nothing about. As medical students we did this all the time, mugging up on new subjects and presenting them to the rest of our group. I still remember facts from talks I gave more than 30 years ago. On the receiving end, of course, you recall nothing.

These days it's easier with online library access. No need now for all that hard-won knowledge of the shelf layout in the basement. But the internet doesn't make things quicker. Once you have logged on to the Dictionary of National Biography, a couple of hours can disappear like magic. What an advance, though, to be able to waste time in the middle of the night and at weekends.

Admittedly, it takes a bit of nerve to lecture to women doctors on Elizabeth Garrett Anderson or to the Scout Association on Baden-Powell, but audiences are kind when they see you are enjoying yourself. My most challenging assignment so far has been a plenary address to radiotherapists near Vatican City. Steer clear of physics and religion, I decided.

By way of preparation I read the NHS Cancer Plan, unfamiliar territory to obstetricians. In our specialty we're used to the Department of Health trying to hide the fact that doctors take part in pregnancy care, and mentioning obstetricians last in the list of people involved with childbirth. I had assumed that all branches of medicine got the same treatment.

But here was an official document that seemed to value medicine's contribution. To my inexpert eye it looked as if practising doctors had been involved in planning the service. Crikey. What's special about cancer, I realised, is that everyone is against it, so the Department and the doctors are on the same side. Once someone discovers a cure, no doubt things will get back to normal.

## *Christmas Party Games*

Christmas will soon be upon us! Make sure your departmental party is one to remember with our medical updates to those traditional games.

*Musical cars*—Managers and consultants can play this one together. The managers begin by closing half the consultants' car park for essential maintenance. On 13 December they paint "Disabled Driver Only" on one of the 12 remaining spaces. With carols playing intermittently on the Tannoy, they paint one more space each day until Christmas Eve.

The winner is the consultant with the toughest 4x4.

*Strip poker*—This one's for the microbiologists. The aim is to keep a straight face for as long as possible while getting your male colleagues to strip. With the magic words *C difficile* you can easily get them to wear bow ties and shortsleeved shirts, even if they aren't paediatricians. Then, email them stern warnings about which body areas have the highest concentrations of skin commensals. If your poker face cracks, you lose.

*Beat the clock*—It's Christmas eve in accident and emergency. Several wards are closed for the holiday. Sister has just discovered a patient who needs admission. Players must find the on-call locum house officer before the clock strikes, or the trust will become bankrupt and the government will lose the next election. This game is really exciting. You will need a note from a cardiologist certifying that you are fit to play.

*Guess the guideline*—In a GP surgery, the computer has crashed. A newly married female solicitor wants the latest official advice on safe alcohol intake in pregnancy. Players have to keep talking until the bell rings. There is no right answer, so everybody wins.

*Metal puzzles*—A new twist to an old favourite. Players have to undertake a minor surgical procedure in the outpatient clinic. Each is given a sealed pack of instruments from the new central sterilising department somewhere in England. The winner is the first one to find a trochar and cannula that fit each other.

*Pin the blame on the donkey*—This time, players have to be MPs in marginal seats. Something bad has happened in or near the local hospital and the press are on the phone. The first to pin the blame on someone without needing any more information is the winner. Have fun!

## *We Never Talk Any More*

Our local theatre, the West Yorkshire Playhouse, is adjacent to one of the national offices of the Department of Health (DH). My only appearance onstage at the Playhouse, so far, has been to give a lunchtime talk to DH staff. One of them had organised a series of lectures in which consultants explained what our jobs involve.

It went reasonably well, as I recall, but it's hard to remember. It was a long time ago. In the 1990s direct contact between civil servants and doctors was a novel idea. Today it is unthinkable. Taking time out to understand what doctors do would be regarded as a distraction from the job of reforming the health service.

Communication between the NHS and doctors is now unidirectional. "Top down" messages have become public relations exercises. We receive flashy documents, sometimes fronted by a medical celebrity, featuring trite quotes and mawkish photographs. Doctors, who have no time for falseness, bin them.

Those who run our working lives feel that they know about medicine because they have been to a general practitioner, visited a hospital, or had a baby. Sometimes this, too, was a long time ago. If they want to catch up with modern practice they commission a survey. Or they speak to a medical member of a quango, who will see things as they do.

Genuine dialogue could give the great and good a reality check. It might help them recover the credibility they have lost by instructing general practitioners on when to open their surgeries, telling hospital doctors what to wear, announcing that hand-washing is a great new idea, and compelling trainees to write creative fiction in job applications.

Can we persuade the DH that there is intelligent life in the medical workforce? It's a tough assignment. You can talk to people only if they want to listen. We could start surreptitiously by persuading the cleaning contractors to leave copies of the BMJ in the coffee rooms.

Then, who knows? Someone might arrange some more lectures. Doctors could tread the boards at the Old Vic (also adjacent to a DH office). But civil servants will point out that all targets and innovations now come from Downing Street. No problem. There's a playhouse nearby which used to be called the Whitehall Theatre. It's fondly remembered as the home of British farce.

## *Resurrection in Rome*

Winter holidays used to be for the idle rich. Then they became the norm for junior doctors. Now even consultants (the least idle of hospital staff) sneak off for a week or so. But we feel guilty about it. With Christmas lasting longer every year, half term looming, and Easter following on, can we justify more rest and recreation?

My wife and I, raised as Scots presbyterians, avoid beaches or ski slopes and head for town, seeking somewhere stern and mind improving. This year it was Rome, which turned out to have everything we wanted: art galleries, museums, pouring rain, and a gale whipping up the Tiber.

Rome is refreshingly unselfconscious, with nothing left to prove. Or almost nothing. Her biggest monument is to a king who unified Italy in the 19th century. Leadership at last, it proclaims—no more squabbling and being pushed around by others. People dislike the huge memorial, but as British doctors we sympathised.

Western Christian art is everywhere. You can have too much of it. In gallery after gallery saints were sadistically martyred, babies were massacred, and Christ rolled his eyes in agony on the cross. We were familiar with the theology that justifies all this stuff, but it was never very convincing. We longed for some Orthodox icons to cheer us up a bit.

It was music, not pictures, that had attracted us. Our group, mainly senior citizens and Radio 3 listeners, walked to churches and palazzi to experience the delights of the Baroque. The local musicians, stocky men with shaven heads and designer stubble, nipped out for a smoke in the interval, and when they left, carrying violin cases and dressed in black, people got out of their way.

The climactic performance was Handel's *Resurrection*, with full orchestra and chorus. The soloists, including an angel, St John, and Satan, sang in Latin, but you got the gist without looking at the translation. Despite his wonderful bass voice, bags of personality, and appeals to the audience, Satan was never going to get a result.

"Strange," wrote Noel Coward, "how potent cheap music is." He didn't comment on expensive music, and Handel's power surprised me.

It made the Easter story seem almost logical. The triumph of goodness was inspiring, even to jaded doctors. And when we emerged the sun was shining.

## *The Royal College of Lay People*

We are pleased to announce a new royal college, the first for almost three months. The Royal College of Lay People (RCLP) aims to bring together all those who make decisions on health care in the United Kingdom. Opinion polls tell us that the public still believes that such matters should be left to doctors and that quangos are less trustworthy than medical colleges. The RCLP has been founded to correct these misperceptions and invites applications for the following faculties.

*Faculty of Campaigners*—Sitting on the pavement with a placard is all very well, but you can reshape the NHS more effectively by joining a committee. Preference will be given to those with anecdotes from the last century about substandard care received by them or a member of their extended family. Please be assured that no professional will challenge your views.

*Faculty of Health Economists*—It has been suggested that this faculty is not needed because all NHS professionals are now more cost conscious than care conscious. Vigilance is essential, however, as outbreaks of nambypamby rule bending continue to occur.

*Faculty of Chief Executives*—CEOs! Do you still feel accountable to your board, council, chairman, or president? The faculty will help you lose those outmoded inhibitions. You will be enabled to wield power ostentatiously or discreetly, as you prefer.

*Faculty of Media Editors*—With so many medical organisations now employing public relations experts, stereotypes are an endangered species. The faculty offers regular get togethers (with refreshments) where you can reassure one another that all consultants live in London, work in Harley Street, and spend their afternoons playing golf.

*Faculty of Statisticians*—Bored? Let us show you how stimulating it is to investigate the bleeding obvious. Projects for 2010 to 2020 will address unsolved questions such as "Are rich people healthier than poor people?" or "Do asylum seekers receive above average care?" The results may lead to decisive government action as early as 2025.

*Faculty of Politicians*—Attempts to form this faculty have been abandoned. During the pilot phase large numbers kept promising to turn up, but they all sent their apologies just before each meeting.

Stop press! Senior members of the medical profession are eligible to join the RCLP, provided that they have seen less than six patients in two years. Don't be shy. Coming out as a lay person is a liberating experience.

## *The Last Appraisal*

When I'm lecturing I often use the phrase "my wife, who is a GP." The all important comma after "wife" doesn't always come across clearly, so grammatically aware audiences are left with the impression that I have another wife who is not a GP. Or a harem of spouses in various specialties.

This name dropping is of course a pathetic attempt to increase my credibility. It says yes, I may be an academic in an ivory tower but hey, my other half lives in the real world. She knows exactly what to do when a butcher's assistant puts a blade through an artery or when an octogenarian wants to go to a family wedding in the Dominican Republic. She's seen it all.

At home we rarely talk shop and never mention names. This tacit agreement has spared her blow-by-blow accounts of university committees but sadly it has deprived me of many insights. I get occasional glimpses of the real world's challenges, from how to keep shoppers out of the health centre car park to how to keep terminally ill people out of hospital. And how to support their families? I don't ask.

This awesome range of skills is taken for granted. Whatever the health scare on the breakfast news, worried viewers are advised to go to their GP. When the government announces some new piece of social engineering, it is the GP who will have to make the decisions. As we get into our cars I feel relieved to be heading for the labour ward.

Thirty-something years on, along came appraisal. Days were spent anxiously filing records of attendance at courses and performance against targets set by people who have never practised medicine. She told me that appraiser and appraisee are paid handsomely to review these papers together. The first time, she returned happy and relieved. After the third year of the same stuff, she allowed herself some remarks about taxpayers' money.

Last month she retired. Today the practice held a farewell lunch. When I returned from work this evening the house seemed full of flowers, cards, and presents. There's a book in which scores of patients have left little messages. It's still too affecting to read it. Time, I think, for a small glass of wine. To tomorrow, and her first yoga class.

## *Are You Ready?*

Beyond Pakistan's northwestern frontier lies Tajikistan. Beautiful, mountainous, and poor, it is home to hospitable people of Persian descent. In the capital, Dushanbe, are shop names in Russian and, earlier this summer, a haze of dust blown there, people said, from Afghanistan.

Waiting for visas at the airport, we met men with guitar-shaped bags and London accents. They were members of Maroon Town, the first British band to tour Tajikistan. The name comes from a Jamaican community formed by runaway slaves, and this week's schedule included giving a master class in backbeat ska and playing at the British embassy.

Our own schedule, organised by the World Health Organization, included visiting a rural maternity hospital. On the way there we saw policemen stopping slow cars laden with household goods. Fast cars with darkened windows overtook us, heading north—Afghan produce, we guessed, heading to market.

Back in Dushanbe we realised that Maroon Town's embassy gig was for the Queen's official birthday. We phoned to ask whether visiting British doctors could drop by. Of course, my dear chap. Our Russian speaking colleague gave his apologies: Romania were playing Italy in Euro 2008, and he would be at the television till late.

The ambassador's residence is a small chateau up a suburban lane. The outside was decked with little flags, and inside were royal photos looking almost like holiday snaps. House and garden were filled with important people, most of whom, apparently, worked for international agencies. Over a Pimm's I learnt about the plight of refugee women from Afghanistan, fleeing domestic violence.

As Maroon Town swung into action we put down our drinks. "You're British," sang Lyn, the vocalist. "Do embarrassing dance moves." When the brass section played in close harmony I recalled Sidney Smith's comment that heaven is eating paté de foie gras to the sound of trumpets. Though of course all our nibbles were humanely reared.

The next night the band gave a concert beside the Opera Theatre. "Sponsored by the British Embassy," said the banner above the stage. Police loitered watchfully, and Lyn's personality filled the square. "Are you ready?" she grinned. The crowd roared back, waving and dancing. Tajikistan's civil war was over, and here was a multiracial band from Brixton rapping about peace. By Jove, I thought, I'm proud to be British.

## *Health Tectonics*

Always alert to innovation, today we introduce you to a new science that fuses medicine with geology. The academic discipline of health tectonics is just a few months old but already has a society and website and will soon have its own journal and a chair at one of our more dynamic universities. An inaugural world congress is planned for 2009.

Here's what it's about. Everyone is familiar with plate tectonics—the idea that Earth's crust consists of land masses that are still in motion—though that theory is only 40 years old. Before it people spoke of continental drift, a process by which all the continents, once united as Pangea, are slowly drifting apart.

With the healthcare sector now the size of a small planet, scientists have realised that it works the same way. Floating on health's molten core are enormous blocks such as politics, commerce, management, and the professions, each of which moves independently. Health tectonics is the study of these massive shifts.

Just as geological collisions produce mountain ranges and

earthquakes, the same happens in health care. Sixty years ago politics, crashing into medicine, formed the high peaks of the NHS. More recently, unexpected grinding of management on medicine resulted in the seismic shocks of MTAS.

Generally, however, health's tectonic plates are separating. Rifts have opened, and the process is accelerating. Attempts to stand on two plates at once lead to grotesque postures and risk of serious injury. Migration is still possible from, say, medicine to management but not in the opposite direction. And the professional plate has begun breaking up at an alarming rate.

Intercontinental communication used to be feasible by megaphone but now relies on cyber-messages. Giant packages of information are transmitted at 4.30 pm on Fridays. Scientists are concerned that force fields generated by these pulses of e-garbage may be increasing the speed of separation.

So, is health tectonics just another cause of gloom, like global warming? Hope comes from an unlikely source: planet healthcare's dead satellite, the private sector. We know it lacks the one element (teaching) essential for life, but it is held together by the unifying force of patient power. Could this primordial energy source exist within planet NHS? It seems like a crazy idea, but at next year's congress they're planning to think the unthinkable.

## *Alma-Ata No More*

Almaty, capital of Kazakhstan until 1998 and the country's largest city, is about seven hours from Heathrow: a meal, two in-flight movies, and a snack. It lies in a beautiful setting beside mountains on the country's southern border. Until 1993 it was called Alma-Ata, a Russian mistranslation meaning "father of apples."

Sitting there last week, I wondered whether the big sanatorium that housed our WHO meeting had been the scene of the Alma-Ata Declaration 30 years ago, something I remembered only vaguely but that has almost religious significance in the world of public health. A few minutes' googling disabused me.

In 1978 the first International Conference on Primary Health Care was held in a vast 3000 seat hall beside a specially built hotel. The representatives from 134 countries included Senator Edward Kennedy. The show was funded by the Soviet Union, keen to beat China onto the world stage. China stayed away.

The hotel is still there, the tallest building in Almaty. Primary care, however, has survived the fall of communism less well. Here, as in many post-Soviet countries, non-medical people use a familiar phrase when they grumble about rural health care: "You can say what you like about the communist era but …"

The Alma-Ata conference ("Health for all people of the world by the year 2000") was medicine's equivalent of the Woodstock festival, and its anniversary has inspired nostalgia among medical ex-hippies: "Yeah, man, there's been some, like, slippage. But, hey, we can still get there. Stay cool. Gather more data."

For us non-hippies it's hard to be cool. We ask ourselves why we go abroad with cash strapped organisations, offering sticking plaster to cover gaps in other people's healthcare systems. International aid budgets are laughably small, but non-governmental organisations have got used to them. In fact you suspect that they quite enjoy being short of money. Mother Teresa and all that.

The sanatorium, formerly a health farm for the party elite, has a magnificent inner dining room. Every mealtime each table has a notice with the name of an international organisation. The tables don't talk to one another, partly because of uncertainty about which language to use and partly because that's not what aid agencies do. Cooperation would smack of big business, which demands results. International aid, although it talks big, prefers to be a cottage industry.

## *Fireworks in Iran*

When you say you're going to Tehran in December, your colleagues look worried. This means someone else playing Santa at the Christmas party. And Iran has an image problem. No one actually says "axis of evil," but everyone thinks hostages, and some people just don't like the name. Why can't it still be called Persia?

My visa arrived in the nick of time after increasingly terse emails to and from WHO. As we landed at Imam Khomeini airport the stewardesses covered their hair. I expected hassle from the passport officer, but she almost smiled. Everyone, I found, had a gentle sense of humour under a veneer of caution. Veils are otherwise infrequent.

Anti-Western feeling was notable for its absence. The hospitals have an American feel to them, and doctors rely on standard US textbooks. Dollars (in cash) are the currency for visitors. Television has endless Hollywood movies. Yes, CNN was jammed, at least in my hotel, but there's still the radio, where the Voice of America competes successfully with the BBC.

Having missed the news from Baghdad of the press conference shoe attack, I was surprised to see a chuckling television reporter organising a shoe throwing competition in the street. One almost hit an elderly, burkha clad woman. The crew rushed over to apologise, saying they had mistaken her for President Bush. She laughed and laughed.

The three wise men came from these parts, but Iran's history of learning goes back long before that. These days the country's reorganised primary care system has to cope with a couple of million refugees from its eastern and western neighbours. The local obstetricians, all women, murmur unhappily about the fate awaiting Afghan baby girls once they are taken back home.

Near the end of my stay an explosion went off outside my window. My first thought was that this must be the latest manifestation of Western foreign policy. It turned out to be fireworks celebrating the Eid al Adha festival. Sipping orange juice and watching starbursts on the skyline, I felt as if I were back in Leeds, on call on millennium night.

It was snowing when I left for the airport, wary about returning to all the booze of our own religious festival. My medical host, a good Muslim, said she had just given in to her children's pleas for a Christmas tree. "Axis of evil," my foot.

## *A Sax and a Rose*

Funerals are a challenge to us bow tie wearers. Conventional neckwear is required, but you struggle to remember the Windsor knot. You can hardly sport a black tie in clinic, so you have to change on the way. In a train last week I persevered, peering at my reflection in the screen of my laptop.

It turned out that I needn't have bothered. This was a celebration, not a wake. Edinburgh's medical community turned out in force, in colourful ties and the occasional kilt, to honour the passing of Nancy Loudon, one of the country's best loved family planning doctors.

With canapés and champagne, the evening marked something more than a remarkable life. This was the end of an era. Nancy died aged 82. She was born six years after Marie Stopes opened Britain's first birth control clinic, in Holloway, London—as it happens, on 17 March.

Stopes (also from Edinburgh) and her US counterpart, Margaret Sanger, were trailblazers. They were followed by less eccentric but equally determined doctors who turned "birth control," with its undertone of eugenics, into "family planning." The current euphemism, "sexual and reproductive health," manages to be more explicit and vaguer at the same time.

We forget how tough those women had to be. They worked in slums and endured vehement criticism, even in Scotland. They responded with calm intelligence, not that that cuts much ice when religion is involved. One of Nancy's more memorable encounters was with a Mediterranean archbishop. Patience, dear: they've only just forgiven Galileo.

Times change. In the 1950s Nancy, an honours graduate, was made to quit obstetrics when she got engaged to a fellow trainee in the specialty. Years later she was in charge of the regional service and her husband, John, delivered my son and daughter.

Nancy had planned this celebration and thought music would cheer us up. Her granddaughter took to the stage with three other saxophonists from school.

As a finale the youngest member of the quartet played a solo. *"My love is like a red, red rose"* is hard to sing but comes across surprisingly well on sax. Our silence deepened as we heard the familiar, unsung words: "And I will come again, my love."

As we shook John's hand afterwards we noticed the red rose pinned to his lapel.

## *Clearing Out*

Retiring has its good side. The farewell party is fun, and the warm wishes of colleagues and patients are deeply touching. From now on, there will be no early morning hypertension as rush-hour cheats whizz past me in the bus lane.

The downside is clearing the office. It's like an archaeological dig. The Mesolithic has letters written with golfball typewriters. Look! Here's one from 1994, protesting against the health authority's decision to disband a committee providing specialist advice. How quaint.

Off they go for confidential shredding. Further down, though, is the Palaeolithic, with its nonbiodegradable lecture slides. Today's PowerPoint generation doesn't know how vital the medical illustration department once was to academic life.

Gosh, here's that slide from The Listener, the BBC's highbrow journal. (Yes, really—this was many years ago.) In 1980 it published the Reith lectures, "Unmasking Medicine," given by Ian Kennedy, then a young barrister. I made a slide of one of his subtitles: "We must become the masters of medicine, not its servants."

It seemed ridiculous. Medicine isn't a master-servant relationship, for heaven's sake. How wrong I was. Rarely has a mission statement been so stunningly fulfilled. The state is our master now, and Sir Ian has been loaded with honours by royal colleges anxious to associate themselves with it.

Some say that the profession brought this on itself by its overweening arrogance. Don't be so sure. I remember, on becoming a consultant in 1982, how uncomfortable I felt at being lifted onto a pedestal by the same public who took such delight in bringing us down in the 1990s.

Anyway, it's done now. The apparatus of central control covers everything from junior job applications to practice guidelines and appointments to the General Medical Council. We used to cite Germany in the 1930s or the Soviet Union as awful examples of how this can go wrong, but at least in those countries some doctors resisted. The British do things more subtly, and doctors seem to like it.

Discipline imposed by old fashioned consultants is now caricatured as a "climate of fear." Today's fear is not of the consultant's footstep but of the manager's email, as apparatchiks enforce targets set by the state. Doctors who once fought the system on behalf of patients are reduced to writing sad little articles. No wonder we're clearing out.

## *Health Risks of Volunteering*

The urge to do voluntary work overseas is strongest at the extremes of medical life. If, like me, you are an ageing academic, think carefully. Your health is precious, and there are several hazards that aren't mentioned on the Foreign Office website.

*Physical violence:* The Foreign Office advises you to be sensible and avoid high risk areas, but that isn't always possible. In South Kensington, for example, the desire to throttle someone can become overwhelming as you wait for hours in the visa section of the embassy. Whom to attack first? The couriers ahead of you with their bagfuls of passports? Or the football fans behind, with their obscenity-filled discussion of the upcoming away match?

*Hyperpyrexia:* If you're going somewhere cold you put on warm underwear, forgetting that you're not flying direct. Changing planes involves a sprint along heated walkways in woolly hat and quilted jacket. When you arrive at the gate, bathed in sweat, you are x rayed again and your water bottle is confiscated.

*Thromboembolism:* As a temporary adviser you will of course be travelling economy class. Remember how it was? Bolt upright at the back of the plane, watching a steward taking forever to dispense teensy weensy drinks in the distance. Next time (if you survive) tell your international sponsor that you don't care if adequate legroom means more expense and a bigger carbon footprint. In the humanitarian jungle, what counts is survival.

*Hypochondria:* Whatever the clock says, your bowel remains on Greenwich Mean Time. Alone in a hotel room with your laptop and a dicky wifi connection, you become aware of pains, paraesthesias, and pigmented lesions you never noticed before. So this is it. The NHS is thousands of miles away, and here you are, terminally ill. Will you make it to the end of the workshop? Or will there be some corner of a foreign seminar room that is forever England?

*Shame:* No matter where you go, everyone has heard about the sillier aspects of life in Britain. Don't ask your medical hosts if they've visited London. They will smile regretfully and explain that they tried for months to obtain a UK visitor's visa before deciding not to bother. Your few hours in that Kensington basement fall into perspective. What a paranoid and xenophobic nation we are. Shame won't kill you, but it's still a nasty feeling.

## *Norwegian Sea*

Like many landlubbers I enjoy BBC Radio 4's shipping forecast, with its exotically named sea areas. I assumed that beyond North Utsire you dropped off the edge, but recently my wife and I ventured across the 61st parallel, where the North Sea and the Meteorological Office stop. We wish we'd done it sooner.

Being of a certain age we sailed in more comfort than the Vikings, few of whom lived past 45. Not all tourists reach the Arctic by ship. Some go by motor caravan, others by Harley Davidson. At Nordkapp, mainland Europe's farthest and windiest point, the Hell's Angels had grey moustaches and goosepimply tattoos.

No one had told us about the Lofoten Islands, stunningly beautiful in the midnight sun. Long ago Gerhard Hansen had been a doctor there before returning to Bergen, discovering *Mycobacterium leprae,* and giving his name to the disease. Surprisingly Roald Amundsen was also a medical student before becoming an explorer and beating Scott to the South Pole.

But the original Norwegian hero was Fridtjof Nansen, the first man to cross Greenland on skis. World famous, he spent his later years helping victims of the Armenian genocide and Russian famine and paying ardent attention to Captain Scott's widow. You can read all this on the internet, but when you go round little local museums it becomes riveting.

Likewise, shipboard lectures are fascinating because of the location, however good the speakers. One, an ex-diplomat, commented movingly that beneath us lay thousands of merchant seamen from wartime convoys. When our geologist described what the melting polar ice will do to England we felt all the more gloomy because we had been taking photos of a glacier.

Our only duty was to be interested. Nobody was going to ask us to build our own Viking longhouse or draft a policy on Arctic mineral resources. This made me feel oddly guilty. Surely the considerable brainpower of all these retired people could be put to some use?

Richard Branson once had the same idea and started "The Elders," a group of statespersons that included Gro Harlem Brundtland (another Norwegian doctor). They're at the world's disposal but have received little attention. They don't carry a big enough stick. The only oldies the world really listens to are the mad dictators who refuse to sail into the sunset.

## *The NHS Film Unit*

When I heard that the British Film Institute has a mediatheque on tour showing old films about coal, I felt a rush of nostalgia. I grew up in a Scottish mining village where "NCB," the logo of the National Coal Board, had a much higher profile than the NHS. The local cinema didn't do social realism, however, and until recently I had never heard of the NCB Film Unit.

Its spiritual forerunner, the GPO (General Post Office) Film Unit, is better known because of its 1936 classic *Night Mail*, a documentary about the London to Glasgow postal train, with music by Benjamin Britten and verse by W H Auden. The GPO Film Unit was influenced by Soviet cinema, and its first director, John Grierson, was a socially conscious Scotsman in the tradition of Lord Reith, founder of the BBC.

The NCB Film Unit, apparently, was set up in 1953 by another Scot with a conscience—Donald Alexander, a Cambridge graduate who had been appalled at the effects of the Depression on the Welsh valleys. Despite the dangers of filming underground it produced over 900 films before it closed in 1984, the year of the miners' strike.

The NHS, two years younger than the NCB, failed to follow in its cinematic footsteps despite being, like the GPO and NCB in their day, the nation's biggest employer. You can see why. Grierson and Alexander set out to exalt working men. Doctors and nurses were nice middle class people who did not need propaganda to glorify or educate them.

Pity, but it's not too late. Both those units were created in times of austerity. Now that the NHS is the only surviving relic of Britain's socialist past, its faceless leaders should ensure that its heroic workforce is immortalised on DVD. *Brief Encounter* could celebrate the 5 minute appointment system, and a biopic about the endless succession of health secretaries could be called . . . well, *Inglorious Basterds* is too obvious, but perhaps Tarantino could be persuaded to do some pro bono directing.

The GPO Film Unit was subsumed into the Central Office of Information, which, its website says, "is the Government's centre of excellence for marketing and communications" and "is given annual ministerial targets to achieve." Say the word, minister. And if a Scots accent is still needed for voiceovers, I'm available.

## *Joking about Cerebral Palsy*

When you're an obstetrician cerebral palsy is never far from your thoughts. A brain damaged baby means years of suffering for patient and family and a field day for lawyers, though most cases have nothing to do with events in labour.

When you retire you try to put these things behind you, though the chance of a lawsuit will still be around for another twenty-five years. Invitations to meetings won't, however, and are hard to resist. Recently I spent two days in Dublin chairing a conference on cerebral palsy "from conception to birth and beyond."

At the start it looked like a tricky assignment. The front row was full of solicitors. After the first talk, each raised a hand to ask a penetrating question. I relaxed slightly when the speaker addressed them by their first names.

But the organisers had ensured that the programme would transcend legal issues. There were heart-rending videos of determined children trying to walk and then smiling, tired but triumphant. The patience of the physiotherapists was humbling. An orthopaedic surgeon explained how it took an entire day's operating to straighten the legs of one child (for a while) and hinted at negotiations with productivity conscious NHS managers.

Fintan O'Toole, drama critic of the *Irish Times*, told us about Christopher Nolan, who died earlier this year and who had produced world class literature using a rod strapped to his head and helped by his mother. For Nolan, like Christy Brown (author of *My Left Foot*) and the poet Davoren Hanna, breaking through the barrier of paralysis had been a liberation into language. O'Toole mused about the power of the Irish mammy.

Finally Francesca Martinez, a comedian from London (see BMJ 2002;325:342) was helped onto the platform. She has cerebral palsy and is very funny. When she found that one of the audience could not swim she patronised him mercilessly. "Are you . . . married? That's wonderful! How brave of your wife to marry a non-swimmer. Does she get respite care?" We were all laughing and thinking but mainly laughing.

After a career mired in the statistics of preventive care, I was overwhelmed at the one-to-one dedication of so many people to patients who had no hope of cure. I wish that video clips, literary intellectuals, and feisty comedians had been around years ago when I was being trained. Still, better late than never.

## *The Shame of Obstetrics*

I rarely admitted to being an obstetrician before I retired. People get embarrassed when they can't pronounce your occupation. Cabbies taking me to the royal college would ask me to explain the difference between obstetrics and gynaecology, and their opinion of the specialty would depend on how successful their family's reproductive history had been. That applies to everyone, of course, not just taxi drivers.

I was not alone in being shy. My younger colleagues called themselves fetal medicine specialists. The classified section of the Leeds phone book now goes directly from "Nursing homes" to "Off licences." Take a look at your own local hospital website: if "obstetrics" appears, it's in the minority.

Most of my contact with my old specialty nowadays is on visits abroad, mainly to countries where Russian or Arabic is spoken. It is like stepping back in time. Colleagues there are confident, assertive, and not at all ashamed of their job title. They proudly correct any interpreter who mistranslates "obstetrician."

If the big surprise eastwards is that obstetricians are comfortable in their skins, the difference in the other direction is that in all Western countries except ours women can choose the person who will deliver their baby. Websites in the United States and Australia advise on how to select an obstetrician. "Interview three before making your choice," suggests one.

Its UK version doesn't even consider the question. "You may be put under the care of a hospital obstetrician," it says, but only if you have an abnormal history. Maternity services here are excluded from "choose and book" arrangements, and in any case "choice" in the NHS means choosing between hospitals, as if that is what matters. Choosing our clinician is not an option for any of us—or for our GP.

Because few GPs do their own antenatal clinics, the only option for a pregnant woman is midwifery care. The idea was that this would reduce intervention in labour, but it has not worked. In today's risk averse climate only two thirds of first-time mothers have a normal delivery. For most of the rest, their baby will be delivered by a stranger, anxiously summoned during labour.

I try to avoid explaining this in detail to my audiences abroad. After all, they've invited a teacher from Britain because they believe we do things better here.

## *An Avalanche of Apple Pie*

A colleague recently calculated that, as lead for obstetrics in his hospital, he had received 3825 pages of advice, guidelines, and reports about maternity care from various bodies. I should point out, in case anyone from top management is listening, that "recently" means a year or two ago. Rest assured that he is on target, and his total must be well over 5000 by now.

I was reminded of this last month at a meeting where a midwife's presentation included an impressive montage of current documents. These days the covers are glossy and colourful, but the titles remain traditional, with words like "towards" and, in our specialty, "delivering." The National Institute for Health and Clinical Excellence guideline on normal childbirth for healthy women is 332 pages long. What about unhealthy women? Don't ask.

How nostalgic it is to remember my days on working parties that produced this kind of stuff. How carefully we crafted our bullet points, exhorting doctors to be nice to patients, improve their handwriting, and be kind to small furry animals. And how sad that both my grandmothers passed away before they had the chance to read our thoughts on sucking eggs in the new millennium.

Hospital doctors are largely protected from this avalanche of motherhood and apple pie by their clinical directors. Last year I was asked to give a talk about being open when mistakes are made. Luckily, after preparing it I checked with Google. "Being Open," I discovered, was a major NHS initiative, cascaded in 2005 to many levels of bureaucracy and even more quangos but not to consultants like me. (It is now being relaunched with "webinars," as I'm sure you know.)

With a general election looming, our apple pie industry is under siege. There is talk of culling quangos, which means a possible reduction in the size or even (brace yourselves) the number of guidelines. People are saying that nobody reads them and that services might actually improve if working parties were disbanded and their members did some work for a change.

There's still time to fight back. Tell your parliamentary candidates that staff, trained for a decade to follow instructions, cannot suddenly be asked to think for themselves. No return to the 20th century. The BMA must take a stand against the threat, even though, deep down, we know it will never happen.

## *The Black Knights*

I never met Sir James Black, who died last month aged 85, but I used to worry that I might. Not that I move in Nobel prizewinning circles, but we ageing Scottish doctors tend to hang out in the same places from time to time.

What worried me was that I might have a senior moment and congratulate him on the Black report, a public health document written thirty years ago by a completely different Scotsman, Sir Douglas Black, who died in 2002 aged 89 (BMJ 2002;325:661). I've always been prone to such gaffes, muddling up friends who share similar faces, ages, sexes, and orders of chivalry.

With the Blacks it wasn't just the name and the knighthoods. Both were graduates of St Andrews, and both came from archetypal Scottish backgrounds. James, born in a mining village, was the son of an engineer, and Douglas, born in Shetland, was the son of a minister. They also shared an aversion to political correctness and would no doubt scorn the labels "left" and "right" that people love to apply, particularly this month.

James worked in big pharma, the bête noire of lefties everywhere, and invented two drugs that became world best sellers. His *Daily Telegraph* obituary said that "no man on earth earned more for the international pharmaceutical industry." He made little money himself, however, and his Nobel prize horrified him. He was afraid it might persuade him that he had something important to say.

Douglas did have something important to say but fell foul of right wingers. A lifelong NHS supporter, in 1977 he was commissioned by a Labour government to report on social class differences in health. Then there was a general election. Only 260 copies of the Black report were printed, and the new government, under Margaret Thatcher, disowned it.

How quickly we forget. Last month we Brits affected amused disbelief at the way the Americans fought over President Obama's health proposals. How can the United States tolerate disparities such as a fourfold difference in maternal mortality between African American women and white women?

As Douglas might have reminded us, the United Kingdom has similar discrepancies. For example, maternal mortality among black African women in the UK is six times that among white women. But independent thinkers like the Blacks are out of fashion. As we endure another election campaign, I look back with envy at the slugfest surrounding the US health bill. There, unlike here, you could see some substance underneath the spin.

## *Marie Lloyd's Bruises*

I've just watched a one woman play about Marie Lloyd, the music hall entertainer. She was born in 1870 in London's east end, and her real name was Victoria Wood. Coached by her father, she made a stunning debut aged 14, when she silenced audiences by flirting with the men. Two years later she was earning the huge sum of £100 a week.

For a modern audience her story is uncomfortable as well as inspiring. It is disturbing to realise that the sex appeal of adolescent girls was being exploited long before the era of the pop video. On the other hand, Marie clearly had a unique talent—her sense of pitch was praised by George Bernard Shaw—and she later used her success to fight the theatre owners who paid peanuts to her fellow performers.

The gynaecologist in me wondered why this sexy woman had had only one child. I think I can guess the answer, having recently written a paper that involved typing "criminal abortion" into the online BMJ archive. (The many articles before 1914 are a revelation.) Knowing the euphemisms used for coitus interruptus in the railway age added piquancy to the innocent lyric "Oh Mr Porter, what shall I do? I wanted to go to Birmingham but they're taking me on to Crewe."

But the real discomfort came when we learnt that Lloyd's third husband used to beat her up. Here was one of the most liberated women in the British empire being struck repeatedly by a former jockey. "Please, not on me face! You can't hide them bruises, can you, girls?" This line, which would have bonded her to a Victorian audience, is met with uneasy silence today.

The more we study marital brutality the more confused we become. It is now called "intimate partner violence" by academics who study women and worry about nomenclature. Its original name, "wife beating," placed the blame squarely on the perpetrator. If there is ever to be a cure, it will involve men talking to men.

The play, *Marie,* written by Steve Trafford and starring Elizabeth Mansfield, is full of music. It is a wonderful example of the fact that you can learn more from two hours in the theatre than from a month in the library. In the dark nobody sees your tears.

## *Doctors of Mirth*

A sense of humour was never the leading prerequisite for a medical career, but now it has slipped off the list completely. Interviews for medical school have become earnest, scripted affairs, and the days of hospital revues are long gone. Soon postgraduate centres will have notices like those at airports, warning that if you make a joke you will be arrested.

Doctors used to enjoy a bit of fun, but you have to go back a long way to find written evidence. In the 19th century the Harveian Society of Edinburgh regularly awarded the degree of Doctor Hilaritatis (doctor of mirth). One recipient, who rose to achieve a knighthood and presidency of a royal college, continued to write and perform comic songs well into old age. It says so in the BMJ archive, though his stern Victorian face, on page 935 in April 1900, shows no hint of mischief (BMJ 1900;i:935-7).

Today, if you search for the word "humour" on bmj.com, almost all the results are from the obituaries. While we're still alive we want to be seen as deeply serious people. Part of the reason is that doctors have not yet adjusted to living with the NHS and its unforgiving quangos. In the countries of the former Soviet Union, where they have longer experience of oppressive bureaucracy, doctors have evolved a delightful ability to make subversive wisecracks while keeping straight faces. Underground humour is essential for living under regimes that really do arrest comedians.

The other reason is the mood of the times. In most professions the cavaliers have been silenced by the puritans, for the time being at least. It is now a falsehood universally acknowledged that all laughter must cause offence to somebody, so authority figures are scared of betraying any trace of levity. The result is that comedy has been hijacked by young people who set out to be offensive. They seem to do very well out it.

Some of us are fighting back. Next month my musician friend Walter and I are returning to the Edinburgh Fringe. Our first show, in 1974, included a ward round by a brass band, but these days we avoid medical allusions. We've decided to list our entertainment under "musicals" rather than "comedy," mainly to do justice to Walter's compositions but also to avoid attracting punters in search of sex and swearing.

## *Just a Song at Twilight*

Like me, the Edinburgh International Festival was born in 1947 as a result of the second world war. My parents met during the Allied invasion of Italy. The festival was part of the effort to replace pan-European carnage with something better. Its organiser, Rudolf Bing, had fled Germany in 1934 and helped to found Glyndebourne Festival Opera—now, ironically, perceived as quintessentially English.

Edinburgh still has an international feel during its annual cultural jamboree, though nowadays aesthetes are outnumbered by fans of alternative theatre. Last month there were over 2500 fringe shows, and the streets were full of backpackers, clutching maps as they dashed from venue to venue.

All of which means profit to the canny locals. The city's academic institutions hire out their premises to entrepreneurs. The university graduation hall hosts stand-up comedians. The Royal College of Surgeons squeezes actors from across the world into its lecture theatres, but its teaching suite for minimal access surgery remains off limits, at least for now.

College fellows who wish to perform must pay the going rate. It's worth it, because the symposium hall's acoustics are ideal for cabaret—and indeed for classics. When we arrived, a huge, piano shaped package was being manhandled up the stairs. Within 90 minutes it had been unwrapped, played, encored, and whisked off to its next concert. Follow that, boys.

Since our days as junior doctors in Edinburgh we've returned to play the fringe festival a dozen times. It's hard to explain why, but, dash it, a hobby shouldn't need explaining. Some people climb mountains, some restore steam engines, and some write songs. Because they're there, OK?

Songwriters are roped together in pairs, like mountaineers. The composer is the creative artist (where on earth does a new tune come from?), but lyric writing is also a tricky craft—part emotion, part crossword puzzle. Without a deadline we would never get the job finished, and without an audience we would never know whether the thing worked.

For a song to have international appeal it should be wistful or downright miserable. Proper operas have tragic tenors and suicidal sopranos. After a lifetime in medicine we've had quite enough sadness, thanks, but perhaps our jokes are holding us back. Without them, who knows? We might be sitting on the lawn at Glyndebourne letting others do the work.

## *Who Needs Press Releases?*

Every morning I receive an emailed list of stories that are making the news in women's health. Clicking on links brings up the printed pages, but I rarely bother. Once you've read the précis you could write the headline yourself.

I used to be media spokesman for a royal college, hence the daily updates. It was exciting to be on the front line, facing salvos of questions whenever a story broke. Sometimes a platoon of us would be dispatched to various television studios to reassure the nation simultaneously on different channels.

Our role was to provide soundbites of common sense in response to the latest claims from campaigners, politicians, or researchers. Friday was our busy day, when the weekly medical journals appeared. Unfortunately for us, newsrooms had advance knowledge of what was to be published, and we didn't.

Responding to reporters used to mean dashing to the library and phoning them back. Today, with the internet, it can still be difficult to unearth the peer reviewed version of a breakthrough if the media have picked it up from a paper in an obscure journal—or, rather, from the accompanying press release.

Medical editors claim they have no control over what appears in the lay press, but a glance at my daily email shows non-random clustering of stories. As I learnt from my time on the front line, few reporters read medical journals. They rely on tip-offs in the form of press releases and then phone their contacts.

As editor of a specialist journal myself, I've thought of playing this game. Why not raise our profile by hyping one of this month's papers? Or maybe start a global scare, leaving it to today's spokespersons to calm things down? I don't, but I can't prevent others from doing so. For universities and their press officers, media attention is an indicator of success.

Who benefits from press releases? Not the doctors who have to explain each false hope or needless scare to worried patients. And few scientists welcome the stress of talking to camera about their work. The beneficiaries are journalists, who of course say that openness is good. If so, why not let the rest of us in on the conversation and publish the press releases alongside the papers? The archive could make interesting reading.

*Footnotes*

- *Editor's note: The BMJ has been publishing its press releases online since 1998.*

## *How Many Miles to Bethlehem?*

The closest I've got to Bethlehem was a medical workshop in Beirut last month. Or was it earlier, at a conference in Damascus or Amman? Distances in the Middle East can be deceptive. Are we talking geography, politics, or psychology?

As the crow flies from Jerusalem, Beirut is 145 miles (230 km) northwards and Amman is 44 miles to the east. On a map of England, if Oxford is Jerusalem, then Beirut, Damascus, and Amman are Leeds, Hull, and Welwyn Garden City.

What different images these names conjure. Beirut still suggests violence, despite the beauty of its corniche and the American University's clock tower, rebuilt after the 1991 bombing. Damascus reminds Christians of Paul's conversion, though it long predates the

New Testament. And Bethlehem, especially in December, is an icon of sentimentality, evoking images of shepherds bathed in starlight.

Today Mary and Joseph would have a tough time reaching that stable, let alone fleeing to Egypt. Nazareth is in Israel, or the "Occupied Territories," as it was called during our workshop. Whatever name I use I must brace myself for emails. Bethlehem is only six miles south of Jerusalem, but miles are irrelevant because the town is in Palestine (or, if you prefer, the West Bank), and there is a wall between them.

Our workshop was organised by the World Health Organization through its tactfully named Eastern Mediterranean Regional Office. I learnt that WHO does not provide estimates for maternal mortality in the West Bank (or Palestine Northern Governorates), which has its own maternal mortality survey initiated by the United Nations Relief and Works Agency and run by the Ministry of Health.

In 2009 the maternal mortality rate in Bethlehem, based on four deaths, was around 60 per 100,000 births. In Israel in 2008, according to WHO, the rate was seven per 100,000. You or I might think a way could be found to allow pregnant women prompt access to Israel's world class medical facilities, but not even the United Nations Human Rights Council, which regularly discussed this problem, has worked out how to do this.

Until recently women gave birth in cars at checkpoints and sometimes died. No maternal deaths at checkpoints were reported in 2009. This may be because of an initiative by Palestine to establish its own hospitals or because families have stopped trying to take women to Israel for help. Either way, women are still dying. It makes you weep.

## *Bombs and Tunnels*

Visiting Vietnam in 2011 produces mixed feelings if you were a student in the 1960s. The "American war," as of course the Vietnamese people call it, was beginning when I entered medical school and ending when I graduated. The British prime minister had resisted US pressure to send troops (those were the days, eh?) but did not denounce America's epic struggle to save the world from communism.

As our cruise ship approached HaiPhong I felt more than my usual guilt at being a tourist in a developing country. HaiPhong and Da Nang were names I had last heard in news bulletins filled with casualty figures. US student demonstrations had helped stop the killing, but it never occurred to me to join Vanessa Redgrave and other lefties protesting outside the US embassy in London.

Vietnam had seemed a small country, but now it has 87 million people, most of them too young to remember the war. The nation is used to fighting. It expelled its Chinese overlords a thousand years ago and did not take kindly to French colonialism in the 19th century. Independence from France was the main goal of Ho Chi Minh, whose little body is still on display in a huge Soviet-style mausoleum in Hanoi.

After the Japanese left in 1946 the United Kingdom and the US could have supported Vietnamese self-determination. Instead they helped the French to return. Ho turned to Moscow, and the stage was set for decades of appalling carnage in Vietnam and Cambodia. Northern Vietnam is dotted with war cemeteries, but the country is surprisingly low on bitterness.

The south has a guerrilla theme park with a grisly display of man traps. Visitors can enter a hidden tunnel, now somewhat enlarged. I lasted three metres before retreating and lingering beside mannequins showing how improvised explosive devices were made from undetonated US bombs. For me, it seems, the horrors of war are preferable to a touch of claustrophobia.

Today the Communist Party is in charge, but the country is socialist in name only. Nobody speaks French or Russian any more. Capitalism and the internet are everywhere. Education is expensive, and there is no free healthcare for the poor. It feels as if the US won. They might have done so without all those expensive bombs if they'd listened to Vanessa.

## *Come Back, Mr Chips*

Invited recently to give a talk on "the role of men," I felt I had plenty to say. Men make up only a quarter of the NHS workforce. Gender politics are deterring almost all male medical students from a career in obstetrics. Television commercials are filled with feckless male stereotypes. For a lecture, though, I needed some facts that were up to date.

Firstly, let's consider men's role in reproduction. Last September, the European Science Foundation reported that a fifth of men have abnormally low sperm counts. The Foundation linked the decline, and a quadrupling of testicular cancer in Scandinavia, to environmental factors. Furthermore, testosterone concentrations in US men have fallen substantially in the past 20 years, even taking obesity into account.

This was news to me. If such worrying changes were affecting women they would be all over the media. Scientists are recommending urgent research, but it is not clear if anyone is listening, perhaps because the experts calling for help are men. We need more female andrologists.

What about broader issues? Fortunately, Social Trends, that treasure trove of national statistics, is now on the web. I was pleased that the gap in pay between the sexes has disappeared among people under 30 but unhappy that, compared with 10 years ago, men older than 25 are more likely to be living alone—and if they are older than 75, much more likely.

But the trend that really upset me was in education. I knew, of course, that girls do better than boys at school, but the difference in percentage points between girls and boys who passed two or more A levels has increased from 2 in 1990-1 to 12 in 2005-6. The reason is not hard to find. Male teachers are leaving in droves. The number of male secondary school teachers in UK state schools fell from more than 150 000 in 1981 to fewer than 100 000 in 2006.

Does this matter? Doctors seem comfortable with medicine becoming, eventually, an all female profession. I think teaching is different, especially in a country where 2.8 million children are being raised by lone mothers. Surely boys need male role models outside the worlds of sport and computer games.

Putting this and more into my PowerPoint presentation, I braced myself for a hostile reaction. "Serves men right," has become a familiar response. But when I finished speaking, the faces in the small room were thoughtful, regardless of sex.

## *No News is Good News*

When the latest report on maternal mortality in the United Kingdom was published three months ago, there was a small flurry of press interest, focused on a rise in deaths from sepsis (BJOG 2011;118:s1). The press interest quickly faded because no one was to blame: most of the infections had been acquired in the community. Had the infections arisen in hospital all hell would have broken loose.

Scapegoats, individual or institutional, are essential nowadays for triggering action in the health and social services. Heads roll, public inquiries are convened, and very occasionally care improves. There is a better way, exemplified by a news story tucked away in the report.

In the UK the Confidential Enquiries into Maternal Deaths divide causes of death into those that result from pregnancy directly or indirectly. For 20 years the leading direct cause of maternal mortality has been thromboembolism: since 1985 it has killed 272 women. The inquiry soon found that the main risk factors were caesarean section and obesity.

In the early 1990s the idea of guidelines was still controversial, but in 1995 the Royal College of Obstetricians and Gynaecologists issued recommendations on anticoagulant prophylaxis during surgery. These recommendations were swiftly implemented, and deaths from thromboembolism after caesarean section fell considerably.

Purists carped that the observation of a fall in deaths was not randomised or controlled, but to everyone else the lesson seemed clear. Deaths from thromboembolism in the antenatal period and after vaginal delivery continued to rise, however, and in 2004 the college produced a new guideline to tackle these deaths. The results finally appeared three months ago. Deaths from thromboembolism have fallen substantially, from 41 in 2003–5 to 18 in 2006–8.

Saving the lives of 20 women is not a big story when nobody, least of all the women themselves, knows who they are. If the media had noticed, they would have asked why it took so long. The answer, unattractive to politicians and bureaucrats alike, is that you need time to get things right. This is why clinicians are so sceptical about instant guidance produced in reaction to shrill headlines.

My long involvement with the confidential inquiries gained me no academic brownie points, but it was the most rewarding aspect of my medical career. Today the inquiry's future is under review. I hope it survives. It convinced me that guidelines are a good thing, and if it can do that, it can do anything.

*Footnotes*

- *Competing interests: JOD was a national assessor in obstetrics to the Confidential Enquiries into Maternal Deaths from 1994 to 2011.*

## *Father of the Bride*

Our daughter got married at the end of May. The date was decided long before William and Kate announced their own plans, and we were lucky that the royal couple chose April. I was able to sit in front of the television, hankie at the ready, picking up hints on how a bride's father should behave. Calm, supportive, dignified, and immaculate: check.

I suspect, however, that Mr Middleton did not have to tie the ribbons onto his car himself. This may have been easy in the era before aerodynamics, but today designers have removed anything that protrudes and might impale a pedestrian. String and ingenuity are required, and a dad's calm and immaculateness are tested.

When patients used to tell me how worried they were about impending matrimony I would reassure them that weddings in real life (unlike soap operas) always make everyone happy. My advice was correct but based on flimsy evidence. I was remembering a distant occasion, organised by our parents, when my bride and I simply had to turn up, look pretty, change our clothes, and leave after the first dance.

Things are different now, at least for us non-royals. The average age at time of marriage has crept above thirty, and responsibility for planning the day tends to rest with the couple themselves. This is a giant leap forward. We parents simply have to turn up and look mature. It is a rare opportunity to meet charming thirty-somethings en masse, and the experience is overwhelming. We feel like extras in a Richard Curtis film.

These days the venue can be secular, and there are no restrictions on the sex of the bridesmaids—or "bridesmates." The marriage register still has to be filled in by hand, but it is unusual for the registrar to have to write two different addresses. He manages to make the ceremony special. Did I do that for each consultation during my career? I doubt it. The photographer's technical ability, like a surgeon's, is taken for granted, but unlike a surgeon he must remain affable throughout the procedure.

The younger generation revealed unexpected skills, fashioning headwear out of table napkins and making speeches that were moving but not mawkish. We oldies danced a bit and then slipped away to swap tales of our most recent hospital visits. And the bride? She was beautiful.

## *When I'm 64*

Last weekend, the 1971 medical graduates met in Edinburgh. We've had reunions before but this one was special. With most of us retired, for the first time in our lives we felt relaxed. The hospital and medical school have moved to the suburbs, so we could admire the new site and reminisce among the luxury apartments that have replaced the old one.

But the real thrill was the rebirth of our student band, the Unbelievable Brass, complete with trumpets, trombones, sousaphone, rhythm section, and contingent of non-medical players. We drew heavily on Herb Alpert and the Tijuana Brass, who were big in the 1960s. What style we brought to those student parties and posh balls. Man, we were cheap.

Forty years on, an out of town rehearsal seemed a good idea. Village halls today are equipped with sound systems, spotlights, immaculate toilets, and almost enough parking for our rather nice cars. Our pianist, now director of music in a cathedral, brought the scores, reprinted on his computer. Concentration was intense as the jaunty syncopations re-emerged, occasionally juddering to a halt when the repeat marks were missing.

I loved that first run-through. After decades in medical politics and academia, it was bliss to be part of a gathering with no subtext. All that mattered was the music—and the logistics. Shifting a drum kit doesn't get any easier. My role was to play maracas, do introductions, and sing a little: mainly Beatles classics, added to our repertoire when they first appeared.

We were scheduled to perform after dinner in a historic library. When the university heard about this, their emails became tense. Evidently they had heard about bands from the swinging '60s. How loudly would we be playing? I shall treasure our reply, written by the sousaphone player, now professor of musical acoustics in the department of physics and astronomy.

Our playlist includes Lennon and McCartney's *When I'm 64.* Coincidentally the gig was two days after my 64th birthday. As a student vocalist I never really thought about the deeper meaning of the lyrics, but I think I expected still to be working. Of the boys in the band, it is the doctors and schoolteachers who have retired, beaten down by bureaucracy. Bit of a waste, maybe, but at least we have time for maraca practice.

## *Upcoming Conferences*

Hi! We're sending you this email because you recently attended a conference on <FILL IN SPECIALTY> and we think you'll want to know about future meetings tailored to your personal needs as a senior <FILL IN SPECIALIST>. Book now to enhance your professional development at early bird rates.

*Expert witness update*—Learn how to make yourself attractive to lawyers, avoid sarcastic remarks from the bench, and fit in some clinical work between your visits to chambers. Next year the form of words required on page one of your reports will change again and you risk professional and financial ruin by getting it wrong. "These two days have changed my life": (delegate at last summer's update). Only £750 inclusive of claret.

*Health service reform breakfast*—Make the voice of <FILL IN SPECIALTY> heard in the corridors of power. Senior politicians and lobby groups have been invited to this round table discussion chaired by the chief executive of a leading think tank. Please submit your question on the attached form, stating dietary requirements. Time and venue: 7 30-8 30 am in central London. £400 with reductions available for the unwaged.

*Managing difficult people*—Is your progress toward foundation trust status being slowed down by "stick in the mud" colleagues? Here's a rare opportunity to learn new ways of persuading them to face reality. Human resources specialists from Palermo and Moscow will be visiting the United Kingdom to share their unrivalled expertise in gaining the cooperation of stubborn individualists. Location to be confirmed. Souvenir umbrella provided.

*Medical entrepreneurs' motivational event (MEME)*—Clinicians like you will soon be in sole charge of the NHS budget. Using it in innovative ways could bring recognition and honours. Learn from the experience of inspirational people in other disciplines, including global business, the media, and sport. Network with like minded doctors, and see what the competition is up to. Hosted by a leading television news reader, the annual MEME evening always sells out quickly. Register now, as space in the Albert Hall is limited. Cost: £550 a head or £6000 for a table of 10.

*Preparing for retirement*—In today's financial climate, it is never too early to put your pension arrangements into the hands of an expert advisor. Let us nurture your future while you enjoy complete peace of mind and devote yourself completely to the care of the poor and the sick.

*Practice timeshare*—Turn your well earned holiday into much needed income for you and your colleagues. Gain valuable experience of the acute management of sunstroke or skiing injuries. Representatives of <FILL IN SPECIALTY> in picturesque resorts are coming soon to a luxury hotel near you.

## *Christmas Lecture*

In my first interview for an academic post they asked me why I wanted to be a university lecturer. I said something like, "Well, I like lecturing," and quickly realised it was the wrong answer. Nobody trusts a smart alec, especially one who enjoys public speaking.

At least my reply was honest, though nowadays that may be hard to believe. Back in the 1970s all you needed for a talk was a set of multicoloured felt tip pens. You had fun preparing customised overheads and the audience had a good time watching you attempt to project them the right way up. You were in complete control of the visual aids and could decide whether the top, middle, or bottom of the isosceles trapezium should be in focus.

In those days the recipe for a good lecture was a prolonged power cut and that has become more true as technology has moved on. Today there are microphones, but they are in front of the speaker and not to the rear, where he or she is usually facing. There is a computerised projection system but nobody knows how to switch it on. The climax of the meeting is the breathless arrival of the secretary who knows the password.

A gulf has opened between the generations. Medical students, facing a technical hitch during their presentation, simply frown, tap the laptop and sort it out. Lecturers of my age generate audience participation as we move the cursor slowly around searching for the icon for full screen, which is in a different place on each postgraduate centre's system.

Like everyone else, speakers are now enmeshed in red tape. Weeks beforehand we have to complete an online form giving our aim, our five learning objectives, an abstract of 200 words (they will be counted by computer), a brief biography (I write a new one each time), and a statement on whether we shall require medical assistance to reach the podium.

But in December the rules are suspended. Next week I'm giving a Christmas lecture and all I have to do is turn up. This loosening of the bureaucratic straitjacket is unnerving. What style should I choose—scientific, nostalgic, provocative, funny (best avoided), or motivational (too expensive)? Or do they just want me for my white beard? Anyway at Christmas, who's listening?

## *Saving Charlotte Bronte*

With Dickens' 200th birthday only days away, Britain's love affair with 19th century novelists continues. The Brontë sisters have another film out, and it is only two years since Elizabeth Gaskell's work was last on television. What impresses me is how productive they all were in their short lives.

Emily and Anne Brontë died in their 20s, and Gaskell and Dickens in their 50s, but the death that still grieves me, as a Yorkshire obstetrician, is that of Charlotte Brontë. Newly married and pregnant at 38, she soon began vomiting. Her friend and biographer Mrs Gaskell later wrote that "a wren would have starved on what she ate during those last six weeks."

Today her hyperemesis would be treated with a routine drip, but sometimes cure can be elusive, particularly if the patient resents the pregnancy. When I was a student, before the Abortion Act of 1967, our textbooks pointed out that hyperemesis can lead to liver failure and it may be necessary to terminate the pregnancy.

This, I assumed, was not an option for Miss Brontë—sorry, Mrs Nicholls—in 1854. Recently, however, I was invited to write a review of the history of abortion. I was surprised when my online searches of the BMJ and the Lancet revealed that criminal abortion was available then in England's industrial cities. That and infanticide, as the millponds testified.

I wondered if Mrs Gaskell knew. She wrote about Manchester's slums but she was married to a Unitarian minister. Had she heard what women resorted to, long before contraception? Did she sympathise?

Coincidentally, another invitation arrived soon afterwards, to speak to the Gaskell Society. It meets in Knutsford (the real life Cranford of Gaskell's novel of the same name) in a Methodist chapel. I felt hesitant about raising this question but it was answered matter of factly, and I was sent a photocopy from Gaskell's collected letters: "How I wish I had known!" Gaskell wrote. "I do fancy that if I had come, I could have induced her,—even though they had all felt angry with me at first,—to do what was so absolutely necessary, for her very life. Poor poor creature!"

But nobody had told Mrs Gaskell about Brontë's sickness. Charlotte was a parson's daughter, and in her poignant final letters she seems to accept God's will. Could her friend have persuaded her? If she had, would we ever have known?

## *The Late Show*

Comedians are living longer these days. In the past century few reached their 70s, and one or two famously died onstage aged around 60. Comedy, like medicine, benefits from the authority that comes with age, but it is a hard life and these days its practitioners tend to ease up as they get older. Even Dame Edna Everage, now 78, is hanging up her frock.

All the more remarkable, then, is that Britain's most successful comic, Ken Dodd, is still touring at the age of 84. He recently filled a 1500 seat theatre in Leeds, and tickets were scarce. Venues used to print their brochures with "Sold Out" over his picture, and a woman behind me said that she had been trying for years to see him perform.

We knew what we were in for. He came on at 7 pm and was scheduled to finish at midnight. Neither of his supporting acts was very long. During the interval, at 9.30 pm, the audience swapped reminiscences ("Last time he went on till . . .") and then filed back with a determined air. We would see this through.

He was wonderful. His troublesome cough soon disappeared. There were fresh stories, silly images, sharp observations, songs, and cheerful self deprecation. The show, with its costume changes and two man band, was carefully structured. What a joy to hear five hours of jokes with no swearing. (His comment on modern stand ups: "I blame the parents. They learn that language at home, you know.")

He still does his ventriloquist act. Near the end he and Dicky Mint shared a quiet conversation under a single spotlight. People stood up to take photos, suddenly aware that this was living history.

Indeed it was. In the 1950s he had played the Leeds Empire ("None of you remember it." . . . "Oh yes we do!") where a woman at the top of the bill advised him, "Always leave them with a tearful earful." Tonight it came naturally. Another famous contemporary had died, and Doddy, pointing out that we really were watching the last of the red nosed comics, sang "Absent Friends."

As we emerged, a coach was waiting to take an elderly group home, 60 miles away; tired but happy, no doubt. A man with no agenda except generating laughter is worth a long bus trip, even after midnight. And it's nice to see a professional your own age; a pleasure that you can't get on the National Health.

## *Never a Cross Word*

Medical crossword enthusiasts can take heart. Last year the BMJ, under pressure from the Action on Crosswords for Doctors Campaign (ACDC), set up a committee to consider the pros and cons of a weekly puzzle. Its report, after many hours of silent deliberation and Biro clicking, is almost ready. A draft (partly in pencil) has been leaked and, in the interests of openness, here is a summary.

*For:* A crossword creates a strong sense of community among its devotees. In recent years the medical profession has become fragmented into groups defined by specialty, age, and preferred social networking site. These groups never meet and rarely communicate with one another. A BMJ crossword will restore a shared sense of purpose across the profession.

*Against:* To complete a crossword, you need to be able to spell. Having gathered much of its evidence via Twitter, the committee became concerned that this might be an insurmountable barrier and commissioned a survey which, surprisingly, suggested otherwise. Although young doctors have lost the ability to punctuate or use uppercase letters, they have benefited from regular subliminal exposure to spellcheckers, albeit American.

*Options:* The committee spent much time discussing whether the proposed crossword should be simple or cryptic. A simple crossword, with clues like "Carer rarely glimpsed at the bedside nowadays (5)" (Answer: "N_R_E"), is inclusive but unsatisfying; a cryptic one might be criticised for being elitist. A possible compromise, the BMJ sudoku, was rejected as too reminiscent of medical school and royal college examinations.

*Political bias:* The committee prefers a cryptic crossword but is aware that the clues can reveal unconscious bias—social, geographical, or political. For example, a satisfactory anagram clue for "Andrew Lansley" would be "Adrenals newly rearranged for health secretary". An unacceptably aggressive one would be "Politician is ensnared wally in trouble." If possible, anagrams should be avoided, says the committee, because they present no challenge to internet users.

*Future action:* Perhaps the most entertaining section of the report is appendix 3, which gives hundreds of examples of acceptable British medical clues, such as "Eardrum operation, not Wallace's (8)." These are likely to keep the ACDC quiet for some time because the answers are in appendix 4, which won't be published until next year. But be warned, BMJ, you can't stall us forever.

## *A Golden Age*

A trip to the National Railway Museum in York always produces a frisson but last month was special. Coinciding with the jubilee celebrations was Railfest 2012, billed as Britain's biggest ever gathering of rail record breakers. Historic locomotives large and small awaited informed homage from the nation's trainspotters.

Yes, we were all wearing anoraks (in fairness, it was an outdoor exhibition) and yes, sales of dry white wine were outstripped by a beer called Flying Scotsman, but the crowds were not limited to grey bearded geeks. There were youths too young to remember steam hauled summer holidays, and there were wives trying hard to look interested.

Nobody was writing down numbers. We knew them by heart and, besides, all the engines had names. *Princess Elizabeth* was there, appropriately, and so was the curvaceously streamlined *Duchess of Hamilton*. I wonder whether those actual ladies, back in the 1930s, enjoyed sharing their names with such clanking monsters. Perhaps this came under the heading of noblesse oblige.

The tradition of naming engines continues. A few days previously an engine had been named by (but, somewhat unchivalrously, not after) a glamorous television personality, and when we arrived the loudspeakers were announcing a naming ceremony in the red zone.

We hastened past City of Truro, chugging around with carriages full of trippers, and joined the throng around the dais.

The VIPs, with identity badges on yellow lanyards, seemed surprised to see us all. Behind them, a curtain covered the nameplate of a gleaming electric freight loco. What impressed me about the platform party was that they were all engineers, including the president of their professional organisation (the second woman to hold the post).

When a hospital or health centre is opened, it is usually by a politician or maybe a royal. You're unlikely to have a speech from a doctor saying how proud they are to be a medic, or to hear the president of a royal college reverently listing illustrious predecessors to approving nods from the audience.

What a revelation to see a profession glorying in its past, upbeat about its future, and able to make public speeches without sanctimonious buzz words. Finally the engine was named: IMechE Railway Division. Catchy, eh? As we left, a dad was photographing his son beside Hogwarts Castle. It was a steam engine, and it was magic.

## *Anybody Else For Warfarin?*

Another long haul flight in economy class, another pulmonary embolus. More than a decade after I experienced my first one, it was déjà vu. Fourteen horrible hours crammed in the back of a plane, several weeks of foolish denial that my leg was swollen, a few days of increasing breathlessness, and, finally, lifesaving intervention from colleagues who were unfazed when my symptoms hijacked our editorial meeting.

After my first episode, I had taken warfarin for several years because there was no evidence to indicate whether it was better to keep taking the tablets and risk a bleed, or stop taking them and risk a recurrence. Then my well informed general practitioner emailed me some new studies that concluded it was safer to stop if the event had a transient cause. Against my instincts, I did so, and sure enough I was fine—at least for the few years that equated to the original studies' follow-up period.

Now I'm a lifelong client of the warfarin clinic. It is wonderfully efficient. "There are new alternatives," said the very experienced associate specialist in charge, "but we should probably stick to what we know best." You bet. I had had enough of evidence based advances. All of this was a year and a half ago; it takes that long to be able to write about it. No matter how fit I feel, those regular visits to the clinic act like a medieval memento mori, as I sit anonymously in a little queue of older people, waiting for someone to call my name.

Until recently the clinic was in an old house surrounded by trees. It had a relaxing atmosphere and was, of course, doomed. After the health authority decided to close it they sent someone to ask patients if they would be inconvenienced; she looked pleased when I reassured her I wouldn't be. Eyes on her clipboard, she asked me my sex and then (lowering her voice) my sexual orientation. "At my age," I murmured confidentially, "it's hard to remember."

Her questionnaire had a free text section and she noted my comment about the therapeutic effect of buildings. There's little evidence for that effect, though. I expect I shall grow to love the clinic's new home: a modern health centre with a vast waiting area full of young women and noisy kids. It's all rather nostalgic for a retired obstetrician. The phlebotomists are as efficient as ever, only these days they need louder voices.

## *All Together Now*

Doctors who graduate together have a lasting bond. Or rather they used to have, when classes were smaller. Today, half of the United Kingdom's medical schools have annual intakes of 250 or more (some many more), and even the most sociable of students must find it hard to know more than a few of their contemporaries.

Mass gatherings become rare as the course progresses, but last month the Leeds third year students came together for their professionalism ceremony. Initiated last year, it celebrates the time when things start to get serious. Fripperies like biochemistry are past, and from now on students will spend time with patients, who will regard them as doctors.

At the ceremony some of the men had already adapted and were bare below the elbows under their academic gowns. The students read the Declaration of Geneva in unison. Not the Hippocratic Oath, which among other things would have involved promising to "keep myself far from . . . all seduction and especially from the pleasures of love with women or men, be they free or slaves." The preoccupations of oath writing committees change over the years, and today's version includes a detailed list of prejudices that must be eschewed.

The occasion was a moving welcome to their vocation. It made me wonder why medicine, unlike the Olympics, has no closing ceremony. Soldiers at the end of a campaign stand on parade and listen to a morale-boosting speech of thanks. Doctors, by contrast, creep away one by one, like the musicians in the last movement of Haydn's Farewell Symphony.

But we still enjoy getting together. Last month, as well as robing up for the students, I attended a couple of reunions of older doctors, many of them retired. At one, there were wry stories about how the NHS had marked their departure—a proforma email from human resources, with the name misspelled. For one person, the only official acknowledgment of a lifetime of service had been the deactivation of his car park pass.

The second reunion was a group of specialists who had met every year for decades and who now realised just how much those get togethers had sustained them through some difficult times. They worried that younger professionals now lack this support system. When the going gets tough, folks, you need more than Facebook friends.

## *Talented Oldsters*

Near my former office is a blue plaque commemorating the Braggs, father and son. In 1913, William Bragg, professor of physics at Leeds, built a spectrometer after his student son Lawrence had a flash of insight into the nature of x rays. Together, "working furiously all through the summer," they founded the science of x ray spectroscopy.

Two years later they won the Nobel prize. Lawrence was twenty-five and remains the youngest ever laureate, though four other physicists have won at the age of thirty-one. Albert Einstein, who received his prize at thirty-three, reportedly once said, "a person who has not made his great contribution to science before the age of thirty will never do so."

If he said that, he was wrong. William Bragg had been an inspiring teacher, but his research career did not begin until he was over forty. And the stereotype of youthful brilliance has changed. The average age of those who win a physics Nobel prize is now sixty-six and the big ideas no longer come early. A recent analysis in *Proceedings of the National Academy of Sciences* concluded that "great achievement by age 40 occurs in only 19% of cases."

Medicine is no different. Frederick Banting, discoverer of insulin, was 32 when he won in 1923 but John Gurdon, the 2012 prize winner, is 79. The mean age of those who make major discoveries in medical science, according to the analysis, is 50. This seems to apply not only to laureates like Robert Edwards, the pioneer of in vitro fertilisation who was 53 when the first test tube baby was born, but also to others like Ian Donald, who was aged 48 when his seminal paper on ultrasound was published.

Nevertheless, doctors still tend to regard research as a youthful phase, like puberty, that we pass through on our way to becoming well rounded practitioners. Listening to students or trainees talking about their work is a stimulating experience, but few established doctors have the chance to do so now that the orbits of consultants and trainees rarely coincide.

In recent years NHS research has been transformed from a cottage industry into a vibrant organisation, the National Institute for Health Research, which, as I just discovered at their annual trainees meeting, nurtures talented youngsters. What about talented oldsters, I wonder? Are there medical William Braggs who missed out but want a research life after forty? Without their Lawrence-like registrars, is there a way to engage them?

## *Retirement: the Four Year Itch*

Retirement is one of those sensitive topics, like politics and religion, to be avoided when talking to doctors who are still working. It risks provoking a diatribe on the new NHS pension arrangements, their children's university tuition fees, and, for comparison, bankers' bonuses. We of the boomer generation have learnt to keep our mouths shut and our heads down.

If it's any comfort, young doctors, let me reassure you that retirement is rather a disappointment. Yes, there is the occasional luxury cruise, but it doesn't last long. Yes, there is the bus pass, but unless you retire to central London it will not change your life. And yes, there are Harley-Davidsons, but you're still too sensible to buy one. This is a tough truth to come to terms with, believe me.

Retirement is a process, not an event, and adjusting takes time. At first you feel disoriented, but you soon get used to your new routine. It takes much longer for the bitterness to fade. You keep remembering those years before retirement when, out of tune with the target driven NHS, you were seen as a misery-guts for predicting disaster. Hearing your thoughts now being echoed by Robert Francis doesn't help.

Eventually anger gives way to smugness. Your former colleagues' tales of their computerised voice recognition dictating equipment make you thank heaven that you are well out of it. But at around four years, doubt sets in. Deep down, you still care. Did you give up too readily?

After all, Church of England clergy retire at 70 and Supreme Court judges at 75. Sepp Blatter and Bernie Ecclestone are still running world football and Formula One racing at 77 and 82 respectively, and every week on BBC Radio 2, Brian Matthew is presenting Sounds of the Sixties at the age of 84.

But hey, you say, my work was tougher than theirs. What about all those nocturnal dashes to the labour ward? Then you see our current prime minister, exempt from the European Working Time Directive, making decisions at 3 am that are almost as important as yours were, and you remember his predecessor Winston Churchill winning his last general election at 76.

It's an unpleasant phase, this four-year itch, but I'm sure it'll pass. Telling you about it has helped. In fact, I think it's already wearing off.

## *A Granddad Writes*

Most of my friends are grandparents, and they all say how enjoyable it is. For a retired obstetrician, however, the final run-up to grandparenthood is a bit fraught. After decades of being called to difficult labours, one becomes too aware of the risks. Statistically, I kept telling myself, things should be OK.

Indeed they were, and once the reassuring text and photo arrived from a distant delivery room overlooking Big Ben, I settled down to write about the rigours of experiencing pregnancy at third hand. But hold on: I've already written on "My grandchild's birth," years ago when my daughter was at school (BMJ 1988;297:1208). It was an attempt to predict the future. But how did it stack up against reality?

Not very well, I'm afraid. For example, I failed to forecast the communication revolution. Today the website Mumsnet is the source of all information on pregnancy and beyond. Phone calls to an obstetric parent are for quality control purposes only.

And I failed to predict the short postnatal stay for healthy women. My daughter was happy to go home after a few hours, but I've never liked the idea. Now, I see, an entrepreneur is planning a private retreat for new mothers who are willing and able to pay upwards of £2000 for the three days of rest they once got on the NHS.

Of course, my article was not really about the future. It was about the 1980s, when midwives were struggling to escape dominance by obstetricians, and labour wards were run by junior doctors who had little chance of becoming consultants. It all seems a very long time ago, and it did not take supernatural powers to see that the system could not continue.

But the degree of change in 25 years is still surprising. How did I fail to foresee the gender shift in my own specialty? The influx of women obstetricians has removed the main barrier between doctors and midwives—the undercurrent of militant feminism that used to make our relationship so difficult.

I'm sure that in another 25 years people will again look back in disbelief. Separate royal colleges for midwives and obstetricians? Really? What won't change, though, is the joy of a new life, helped into the world by midwives who, my daughter tells me, were wonderful.

## *Contraception in Copenhagen*

The first thing you notice in Copenhagen is that people are slim. Then you notice the bikes, parked in vast numbers both in the city and beside rural railway stations throughout Denmark. How delightful it must be to live in a flat country where cyclists have the right of way.

The Danish empire once stretched from Greenland to southern England. A thousand years later the Danes seem relaxed about having let it go, but I think it's a shame that these amiable people lost the battle of Hastings. I blame their snobbish cousins from Normandy for landing us with a class system that the English still have no wish to dismantle.

We were in Copenhagen for a global conference on contraception. Fertility control used to be my main interest before I got involved in trying to reduce maternal mortality. The meeting reminded me how closely related these topics are, despite their wide disparity in financial support from pharmaceutical firms.

A conference should leave you with a memorable message or image, and this one had both. Well used to hand wringing about maternal death in Africa, I was surprised when a Kenyan speaker said that some sub-Saharan countries still have 19th century British or French antiabortion legislation inherited from colonial times. She estimated that more than five million African women undergo unsafe abortion every year, and 30 000 die as a result.

The image was from Europe: an astonishing graph of fertility in Romania, beginning in the communist era when contraception was restricted. In 1966 abortion was also outlawed and fertility increased, but only briefly because women resorted to illegal abortion. In 1989 the law was relaxed, and the number of legal abortions rose sharply, and then it fell almost as rapidly because women were at last able to use modern contraceptives.

What was fascinating about the "Romanian experiment" was how little the national fertility rate changed. What was chilling was the rise in maternal mortality from abortion as women risked death to limit family size. In the 1980s the overall direct maternal mortality rate peaked at 147 per 100 000 births before falling to fewer than 20 per 100,000 in recent years.

Yes, said the speaker, the graph has been published. Back home I found the paper in the *Journal of Family Planning and Reproductive Health Care*, which I had missed in January. It had been a long journey to discover what was lying on my desk.

## *The Fight for Good Writing*

As a journal editor, I'm part of an ageing rearguard defending the English language. The job has changed over the years. Online editing is done at home, on a train, or even (heaven help me) on holiday, and most papers now come from outside the UK. Just how pedantic should I be?

The best English no longer comes from Britain or even Ireland. Scandinavia is reliable but not quite as good as China, where authors use commercial language services (though sadly, not for their revisions). But even professional editors have irritating little quirks. Instead of "and" they write "as well as," and "therefore" becomes "as such."

French English can tantalise you with phrases that aren't quite right but cannot be improved, though eventually you learn that "even if" means "although." Americans always use "exam" for "examination." Nobody from any country uses the word "but." Instead they begin every second sentence with "however."

Many languages have no definite or indefinite article, and I sympathise with authors who insert "the" or "a" in all the wrong places and omit them from all the right places. Some British doctors have this problem, and their senior coauthors are too polite to correct them. Or perhaps they feel that's my job. Or maybe they just don't care.

It has long been unfashionable in Britain to worry about grammar but things may be changing. Civil servants are once again being urged to use plain English. Their style manual, *Gower's Complete Plain Words*, written in 1954 and reissued in 1973, is still in print, though one Amazon reviewer advises, "Don't buy this book unless you have a very strong foundation in grammar and punctuation." That should narrow the UK market.

I bought my copy forty years ago after my first BMJ article had been ruthlessly subedited. I also invested in *Thorne's Better Medical Writing*, written by Stephen Lock, previous editor of the BMJ. Appendix B, "Words to avoid," is an education in itself. Appendix C, "Pseud's corner," includes "holistic" and "parameter." Today "iconic" could join them.

Stupidly, I gave away my Thorne, but I've just replaced it with a second hand copy from the library of one of our leading universities. They had evidently decided to get rid of it. That says it all.

## *Flying a Desk*

A hospital chief executive once sadly remarked to me, "Very few doctors can think at my level." I remember trying to ignore the gesture his hand was making, rising as he said "my level." This was in the 1980s, when the idea that a hospital secretary was higher than a consultant was mildly irritating. Today it is a given, and doctors are being encouraged to aspire to becoming a chief executive.

That ambition never crossed my mind, perhaps because I grew up in the wrong era. My favourite childhood reading was Richmal Crompton's Just William books, about a boy who kept subverting authority, and in the 1950s we had war heroes like Douglas Bader, an ace pilot despite being a double amputee, who had scant respect for bureaucracy.

In *Reach for the Sky*, the film of Bader's life story, he turns down an administrative post because he hates the prospect of "flying a desk." The phrase was common in the air force, where the distance between senior staff and the real workers could be measured on an altimeter. I first came across it at an impressionable age, and it stuck in my mind.

The film reinforced the idea that rebels were in the right and had all the fun. What a pity we kids had no movies called, say, *Managing Difficult People*, about the unsung heroes who keep an organisation running. Or *Nottingham's Greatest Sheriff*, about a man who rose to the challenge of administering a medieval city while under fire from reprobates who kept shooting arrows through his windows. Today's youngsters are similarly imprinted. International corporations are now Hollywood's rent-a-villains.

In medicine, undergraduate teaching may have moved from being pathology centred to patient centred, but it is no closer to the business school. Postgraduate education focuses on how to follow guidelines, not how to write them. And as consultants become more and more specialised, they are less and less likely to think at the level of a chief executive.

The idea of doctors running hospitals seems more fanciful than ever, but what about our professional organisations? They too have become businesses, and bit by bit chief executives are taking over the controls. Presidents come and go but the chief executive is always there. You need to put in hundreds of hours before you can fly a desk safely, and doctors just don't have the time.

***

*In October 2013 the BMJ was substantially reorganised and a new team of younger columnists took over. And not before time, some might say!*

# *Index*